Traumatization and Its Aftermath

A Systemic Approach to Understanding and
Treating Trauma Disorders

Antonieta Contreras

Routledge
Taylor & Francis Group

NEW YORK AND LONDON

Designed cover image: © Jos Diaz Contreras

First published 2024
by Routledge
605 Third Avenue, New York, NY 10158

and by Routledge
4 Park Square, Milton Park, Abingdon, Oxon, OX14 4RN

Routledge is an imprint of the Taylor & Francis Group, an informa business

Library of Congress Cataloging-in-Publication Data
Names: Contreras, Antonieta, author.
Title: Traumatization and its aftermath : a systemic approach to
understanding and treating trauma disorders / Antonieta Contreras.
Description: New York, NY : Routledge, 2024. |
Includes bibliographical references and index.
Identifiers: LCCN 2023016441 (print) | LCCN 2023016442 (ebook) |
ISBN 9781032457659 (hardback) | ISBN 9781032457635 (paperback) |
ISBN 9781003382478 (ebook)
Subjects: LCSH: Post-traumatic stress disorder.
Classification: LCC RC552.P67 C6678 2024 (print) | LCC RC552.P67 (ebook) |
DDC 616.85/21—dc23/eng/20230527
LC record available at https://lccn.loc.gov/2023016441
LC ebook record available at https://lccn.loc.gov/2023016442

ISBN: 9781032457659 (hbk)
ISBN: 9781032457635 (pbk) ✔
ISBN: 9781003382478 (ebk)

DOI: 10.4324/9781003382478

Typeset in Goudy
by codeMantra

Traumatization and Its Aftermath

Traumatization and Its Aftermath delves deep into the complexities of traumatization and is a practical, comprehensive guide to understanding and overcoming the impacts of adverse circumstances.

In these pages, readers will gain valuable insights into trauma's diverse forms and the importance of understanding traumatization on an individual level. This book answers questions including "Why don't some people heal as easily as others?" "Why do some people experience trauma after 'seemingly insignificant' incidents?" and "Why does overdiagnosis fail so many people?" Readers can also find criteria for evaluating their own trauma, information on how to heal from a trauma disorder, and better ways for treating complex trauma.

Traumatization and Its Aftermath guides readers through each element of the personalized struggle for survival and offers compassionate and patient explanations on how to shorten this struggle—and even prevent it. Packed with detailed resources and accessible storytelling, this book is a must read for clinicians and anyone looking to better understand the mind, body, and natural ability to heal.

Antonieta Contreras, a former banker originally educated as a mathematician, is a Gestalt and trauma-trained psychotherapist with a practice in New York. She has spent a decade as a consultant, supervisor, and faculty at the Institute of Contemporary Psychotherapies (ICP). She lectures on sexual trauma at New York University and oversees consultation of various EMDR groups.

"Antonieta Contreras has written a book that offers both clients and clinicians a clear view of trauma's effects on the neurobiological domains of trauma as well as a roadmap for treatment. *Traumatization and Its Aftermath* switches the clinical focus from resolving traumatic events to understanding, assessing and restoring the nervous system to optimal states. To illuminate her points, Ms. Contreras provides a composite case study travelling backwards from a traumatizing experience that tipped the neurobiological scales to the familial and societal antecedents that stressed the system. Written in an easy, conversational tone that belies the complexity of the information it conveys, this book is as readable as it is comprehensive. Both clients and clinicians will want it on their shelves."

Lana Epstein, LCSW, *senior trainer for the Sensorimotor Psychotherapy Institute, and EMDRIA-approved consultant in EMDR*

"Antonieta Contreras has written one of the most comprehensive books on all things trauma. Remarkably knowledgeable about the trauma field, past and present, I would be hard-pressed to see what she left out. An excellent teacher, Contreras makes difficult concepts come alive and readily accessible. She clearly differentiates trauma and traumatization, identifying the threat to safety as underlying all traumatization. Her systemic view is of great value and rarely so well-articulated, delineating how traumatization impacts various expressions of the nervous system, including emotional, regulatory, cognitive/perceptual, and identity. Throughout this book, Contreras narrates the story of 'Michaela,' a fictionalized yet very believable survivor of complex trauma. She shows the reader that what may at first glance appear to be a single traumatic event is often embedded in years of multiple, interacting factors, including personal, familial, epigenetic, and societal. While this book was initially conceived as a self-help guide, it evolved into a wonderful resource for survivors of trauma, and for beginning and seasoned trauma therapists alike. While I place myself in the latter group, I learned a lot, particularly how to think more clearly and complexly about what we mean by traumatization and its aftermath. While this book is more about the nature of traumatization than its healing, Contreras's final chapter introduces a fascinating sequential treatment model worthy of close consideration. Go out and buy this book. You, and your patients if you are a therapist, will be glad you did."

Ken Benau, PhD, *independent psychologist and author of* Shame, Pride, and Relational Trauma: Concepts and Psychotherapy

To my children
My daughter, my light!
My son, my drive!

To those that have inspired me to learn

To those that motivated me to grow

To those that forced me to fight and become

And to you!
The reason I wrote this book

Contents

Figures

Tables

Abbreviations

ACE   Adverse Childhood Experiences
ADHD   Attention Deficit Hyperactivity Disorder
AFS   Attachment Failure Syndrome
AGTS   Aggregated Trauma Syndrome
ANS   Autonomic Nervous System
APA   American Psychiatric Association
APa   American Psychological Association
ASD   Acute Stress Disorder
BPD   Borderline Personality Disorder
C-PTSD   Complex PTSD
CBT   Cognitive Behavioral Therapy
CDC   Centers for Disease Control and Prevention
DID   Dissociative Identity Disorder
DNA   Deoxyribonucleic Acid
DSM   Diagnostic and Statistical Manual of Mental Disorders
DTD   Developmental Trauma Disorder
DV   Domestic Violence
DVC   Dorsal Vagal Complex
EMDR   Eye Movement Desensitization and Reprocessing
FTI   Fisher Temperament Inventory
HPA   Hypothalamus-Pituitary-Adrenal Axis
HPD   Histrionic Personality Disorder
ICD   International Statistical Classification of Diseases and
          Related Health Problems
IFS   Internal Family Systems
IPAR
Theory   Interpersonal Acceptance-Rejection Theory
ITT   Intergenerational Transmission of Trauma
LAM   Latin American

MDTT	Multi-Dimensional Dynamic Trauma Treatment
NS	Nervous System
NPD	Narcissistic Personality Disorder
OCD	Obsessive Compulsive Disorder
PAG	Periaqueductal Gray
PD	Personality Disorder
PFC	Prefrontal Cortex
PSNS	Parasympathetic Nervous System
PTSD	Posttraumatic Stress Disorder
PVT	Polyvagal Theory
SAd	Systemic Adversity
SAM	Sympathetic-Adreno-Medullar Axis
SNS	Sympathetic Nervous System
SPS	Strange Situation Procedure
SSP	Strange Situation Procedure
TA	Traumatizing Agents
UTI	Urinary Tract Infection
VVC	Ventral Vagal Complex
WHO	World Health Organization

About the Author

Antonieta Contreras, a former banker originally educated as a mathematician, is a trauma psychotherapist who graduated with a Master's in Social Work from NYU. After forming her clinical skills as a gestalt therapist and training at agencies with highly traumatized people, she received a specialization in Trauma Studies from the Institute of Contemporary Psychotherapies (ICP) and in Human Sexuality from NYU School of Medicine. She maintains a private practice where she combines different trauma modalities as well as the contemplative techniques that she learned from studying within Buddhist traditions. She has been a consultant, supervisor, and faculty at ICP, where she spent the last seven years building and teaching the curriculum of a postgraduate program to train clinicians in becoming trauma therapists. She also lectures on sexual trauma at NYU, runs EMDR groups toward certification, frequently interacts with followers who seek out her answers about traumatization online, and has given talks in hospitals, agencies, and universities to create awareness about trauma.

Preface

The word 'trauma' was so foreign to me that I don't remember considering it as a possibility when I was first diagnosed with Major Depressive Disorder. I was one of those people who thought their life could not have been better. A blessed person with a beautiful life. I had no relationship to this word 'trauma,' or to mental illness of any kind. To my ears, the word 'trauma' meant experiencing horrible things, things that you can't recover from. I'd had my share of hardships, but I was someone who fought to the end and never stayed down for long.

But then, one day, all my energy went away. Suddenly everything I did made me tired. The route from my bed to the door was a marathon. Easy things felt difficult, and things I used to enjoy seemed pointless. Nights were agonizingly long. Even when my marriage, my life, and my health were crumbling, I carried myself with the attitude that everything was OK. I'm fine, I would say. Don't worry, it's just a phase, it will pass. I told myself I'd conquer this just like everything else, just like I'd done with all the other cuts and bruises I'd ever had. But I suddenly felt that I went from being a force of nature to becoming a puddle on the floor.

My system had been protecting me for years, but it couldn't handle more weight. Even though I wanted to keep fighting, my system couldn't, and I reached a point where I could either accept I was not well or risk of becoming a resident of a very dark place. So I had to force myself to accept help. Through the healing process, I started to learn about the psyche and about traumatization. After a career in finance, I took on a second life as a trauma clinician. The book you're about to read isn't about me but includes the learning I accumulated in my quest to understand what was happening to my system.

My healing journey was long, in part because I didn't know what was needed to get better. It did give me the opportunity, though, to see the magnitude of what 'trauma' means for each individual and for those that have to interact with a traumatized person. I learned that even though trauma has extraordinarily important implications for so many facets of life and society, it's not well studied or understood. There is a desperate need to know more about it, a need to ease some of the anxiety of not knowing what's going on, a need to know who to go to after spending years in therapy with almost no results (or after getting worse with no trauma-focused treatments), a need to find out, specifically, how deep the wound is. The questions far outnumber the answers, but asking is the first step.

In my effort to go deeper and deeper, I went into teaching the neurobiology of trauma for several years while maintaining a full-time practice. It wasn't until the imposed isolation of the COVID-19 pandemic that I saw the opportunity to make information about trauma available more broadly. By chance, I happened upon Quora, an online platform where people ask questions of all sorts, answered by whoever feels engaged with the subject. The Quora community is vast, and participants come from every corner of the world with a wide range of backgrounds and experiences. There is an active presence of therapists and college professors on the platform, which enticed me to respond to questions there and to connect with seekers who I could help.

Even though I first saw Quora as a chance to give back, I actually ended up learning a lot from it. The questions/answers posted are so interesting in their reflection of what's going on in the collective brain in real-time—from common understanding, deep insights, and actual life experiences, to widespread misinformation. After responding to hundreds of questions, it became clear to me that many people have doubts about the validity of trauma and traumatization. Questions about whether individuals are traumatized or not seemed to consume and debilitate people on the site. Anxieties over whether therapists are doing the right thing are pervasive. It's not uncommon to see people reporting that their treatment is making them feel worse. The questions came not only from those who suffer from trauma issues but also from clinicians who have not yet trained on the subject.

It's clear that there is a deep and widespread need to understand more about what traumatization means and how it operates in the brain. Since I had spent several years researching everything related to traumatization, I've felt motivated to respond to the range of questions about trauma that people have been asking: What symptoms do you need to have to qualify for complex PTSD? What happens if trauma is not resolved? How do you know if a child is traumatized? How does childhood trauma affect a person's development and sense of self? and many many more.

When I first thought of writing a book, I imagined a self-help book of answers to the most common questions. But increasingly I saw similarities between the Quora confusion and the conversations I was having with my students and supervisees. At every education level, from novice to professional, there were huge holes in understanding the trauma phenomena. While anyone with curiosity about the subject of trauma can learn something from this book, I wrote it with the following audiences in mind:

- Therapists looking to become trauma-focused clinicians
- Clinicians looking for reference books on trauma
- Traumatized individuals in treatment
- Individuals who can't afford therapy, but feel that they might be traumatized, suffering from a disorder or an emotional wound (as you'll see, there's a big difference), and what to do in these cases.

In my years of seeing clients, I have been humbled by the power of this information to change long-held narratives, daily outlooks, and entire lives. I wrote this book with them in mind. Though one book on trauma can only cover so much (and even less now with the furious pace of new research on the subject), I've attempted the most comprehensive study I know how. Although the book is necessarily incomplete, my hope in writing is that it will reach the person who needs it today. If you have more questions, you can always find me on Quora. If you're struggling with traumatization right now, know that I've been there. Sometimes a bit of new information can be the start of an unexpected journey.

Okay, let's go.

Introduction

Trauma became the household term it is today based on the suffering of soldiers and victimized women—or so the legend goes. This is partly true if we consider how the studies of symptoms began, but in terms of widespread trauma treatment, a more recent event forced a mainstream shift in the therapeutic arena. The events of September 11th of 2001 and the introduction of the threat of terrorism into the popular imagination made a large number of therapists realize that they didn't have the tools or understanding to treat the level of distress that Americans were experiencing. Nothing is more 'effective' at activating our survival circuits—the ones at the core of the traumatization process—than terror. After 9/11, large groups of clinicians with previous knowledge of crisis, grief, and bereavement came together to offer the services so urgently needed. But it soon became clear that the attack was going to have repercussions long after the initial shock even for those that had not lost anyone. Treating traumatized individuals became a bigger priority, and the interest on training programs focusing specifically on trauma treatment grew exponentially.

I was lucky enough to train at—and eventually help run—a program that made a significant contribution to defining trauma treatment. After graduating from their program, I joined their mission to expand the understanding of psychological trauma among professionals by reaching out to the clinical community. I devoted time to going to clinics, hospitals, and agencies to give talks about how being exposed to events that could jeopardize peoples' lives affected individuals' mental health. After the Q&A sessions, it became evident that many clinicians were not aware of the fundamental principles of how the nervous system affects the psyche; the foundational change in trauma studies and treatment hadn't reached most people in the field. For example, trauma treatment's basic premises that (1) the recounting of traumatic memories may be counterproductive, and (2) unhealthy patterns of behavior are a consequence of the activity of the nervous system (including

DOI: 10.4324/9781003382478-1

resistance to treatment) were too new to be adapted easily. Expecting professionals to unlearn the basis of their formation was challenging and was going
to take time, a delay that always accompanies paradigm shifts.

At the same time as I was giving the talks, the concept of trauma was gaining
popularity. But the general public was becoming acquainted with frameworks
that were already outdated, like using fight or flight descriptions from the
1920s that new findings had rendered incomplete. Being up to date on the
latest neurobiological findings is essential to making treatments more effective. I hope that by including them in this book, more people can adapt and
understand the extent of the paradigm shift.

When the list of the main reasons why one could become traumatized was
expanded to include abuse and neglect during childhood, the idea that there
were also 'small traumas' was easily adapted to the previous conceptualization
of emotional suffering and became the standard. This changed the way trauma
was spoken about; the word trauma then became even more widely used to
refer to *the event*, but it was also used to name overwhelming stress, shock,
reactions, consequences, a 'disorder,' emotional struggles, or even being scared.
When 'trauma' became so freely used, a multitude of individuals began to see
themselves as traumatized. Suddenly, a large number of clinicians had to shift
from working with 'the transference' to working with emotional dysregulation
and treat their clients as trauma patients even without having a clear understanding of what traumatization implied or what its treatment required. The
need for more tools to understand and effectively intervene with traumatized
individuals, as well as the need to differentiate who was traumatized and who
wasn't, continued to grow. It's now clear that traumatization is a strenuous
process that the nervous system undergoes during periods of perceived lack of
safety, and that the process can be stopped at various points. This book includes
explanations of both extremes and what's in between, examining in-depth how
'life-threatening' is less literal for our psyche than it is to our intellect.

I was so excited to be part of the new conceptualization of mental health
that it first drove me to learn neurobiology so that I could deepen my understanding of the fundamental role of brain activity in emotional reactions
and cognitive distortions. I eventually became a Board Certified Neurofeedback clinician, which helped me translate the previous psychological concepts into neurobiological terms. I even went through a four-year program
that studied Buddhist principles under a neuroscientific lens. My passion for
neurobiology is culminating in this book, which intends to make clear dis-
tinctions among all the misperceptions surrounding such complicated phenomena, de-pathologize some of the natural occurrences that have been seen
as deficiencies, and shed light on symptoms that have been left outside of

the conversation. I also want to clarify many of the uses of the word and elements of the trauma phenomena to help you know to what extent you have been a 'victim' of the misinformation, or if, instead, you need a more focused treatment for your traumatized system. My wish is that you can expand your understanding of the term trauma and notice when you might be referring to the whole phenomena without specificity, or when you are correctly identifying the emotional struggle of feeling at risk. Hopefully, by the time you've finished this book, you'll be able to differentiate between the origin of distress, what happens to the system when it goes through the struggle for survival, and if there are consequences.

Additionally, I want to clarify two things. First, that traumatization—an essential part of the trauma phenomena—involves several different unconscious and involuntary mechanisms. Second, that involuntary mechanisms can become volitional if we develop an awareness of what they are and how they operate. One simple way to put it is to break down the trauma phenomena into three essential parts: the traumatic event, the individual who experiences it, and the relationship between those two. That relationship between the individual and the event is as unique as each one of us. And it's how we relate to the event that makes the difference between whether the result after a traumatic experience is enduring damage or not. Many times, that relationship is not chosen but established. It's established by living on auto-pilot (without our active mental participation) or by the influence of whatever surrounds us (the media, the family/society values, popular schemas/beliefs, misinformation, etc.). The widespread belief that the level of traumatization depends strictly on the level of danger of the event is incomplete. The reason people differ on whether they become traumatized or not depends on something that I call 'traumatizing agents': factors that accentuate and prolong survival responses that end up causing dysfunction. To introduce you to this idea, one or two traumatizing agents are included in each of the first nine chapters.

The word 'individual' reflects how each one of us is truly distinct, with unique and subjective experiences. This subjectivity plays a very important role in traumatization. Each one of us can have different experiences from the same occurrence. The same event can be devastating for some while uneventful for others. This is why not all soldiers develop Posttraumatic Stress Disorder (PTSD) after being in a war zone, why some people seem oblivious to the perils of a pandemic, and why someone can develop severe symptoms from encountering mice in their home. In mental health, nothing is absolute. Our brain has more connections among its neurons than stars in the Universe, and the number of possible combinations among them is infinite. It's therefore critical that the treatment of traumatized individuals includes the individuals' specific characteristics, level of resilience, circumstances, and history. This is the reason I am a therapist and focus on trauma work 1:1. That's also why it's so crucial to understand the relationship individuals develop with their occurrences instead of assuming traumatization just because similar circumstances traumatized others.

The text is structured into three main parts: Part I is about traumatization (why and how it occurs); Part II examines its aftermath, describing the whys and hows of when the injury goes deeper and deeper (and why it is possible to stop it); Part III is about healing and why a systemic approach can be the best option for recovering. Part I sets the theoretical premises for Part II, as Part II explains how layers of traumatization become trauma disorders, and how we can diagnose or assess them.

In Part II, I'll introduce Michaela and her family. They will be integral to the 'case' that will show how traumatization happens to ordinary people (as opposed to people in high-risk professions and circumstances). You'll be able to follow a thread of the different layers involved in the development of trauma disorders as you hear Michaela's voice. You'll see how she and her brothers were affected differently even though they were raised by the same traumatized mother.

Through this book, I focus on the reasons people develop trauma disorders (the whys) and the ways in which those trauma disorders unfold (the whats) rather than talking about the causes (the horrible events). This is why most chapters begin with questions. I want to provide answers that serve as a foundation from which the trauma-focus modalities can find a base. Many modalities give us techniques and tell us how to apply them but we may need to know why and when we need these modalities, and how to make them fit every client's individuality to increase their effectiveness.

To create the foundation I'm proposing, this is what each chapter will help you understand about traumatization:

1. Chapter One introduces you to the nuances of the trauma phenomena through a survey of the many concepts and constructs that fall under it. By the end of the chapter, you'll have learned to differentiate when something is 'traumatic' from what is 'traumatizing' in order to facilitate the discovery of who is traumatized—and who is not. I will also introduce you to the different trauma disorders someone can develop, so your vocabulary can expand beyond 'trauma' and 'PTSD.'
2. In Chapter Two, you'll learn about the basics of neurobiology and trauma. I'll explain that trauma disorders unfold from the set of processes called survival mechanisms that are prompted to operate when we are in

danger. The chapter includes descriptions of our brain's characteristics that can hurt but also heal our nervous system. The chapter ends with a description of danger and threat, two important external traumatizing agents (elements that contribute to amplifying the activation of the survival circuits, and therefore, the alterations in the functioning of the nervous system).

3. In Chapter Three, I will go deeper into traumatization, a process that is best understood by deconstructing it. I'll review, one by one, how preventive and protective mechanisms get activated when we encounter danger. I'll also explain what tools are available for diagnosing a trauma disorder, including how the misinformation of pop-psychology can have a negative influence on the industry and our psyche.

4. Chapter Four expands on the systemic cost of traumatization. Here you'll learn about each of the affected areas of the person's internal system. I call them 'trauma domains' to emphasize the systemic nature of the alterations suffered during the struggle for survival. Healing a trauma disorder goes beyond processing traumatic memories; trauma treatment needs to attend to all the domains affected. This chapter breaks down how the domains function in ordinary conditions and contrasts that with how they become modified. There are nine domains; the first five are part of Chapter Four: emotions, dysregulation, memory, cognition and perception, and self. The other four are incorporated in the chapters where their importance is more relevant.

5. Chapter Five starts with the narration of a date-rape by the book's protagonist: Michaela. Her case will illustrate three key processes: (1) How PTSD unfolds after an identifiable event? (2) How PTSD evolves into dysfunction? (3) How to diagnose PTSD using the diagnosis manual with an expanded view of its criteria? This chapter also expands on the traumatizing agent shame (and related self-conscious emotions).

6. Chapter Six covers prolonged traumatization. Using the allostatic model for maintaining internal equilibrium, you'll learn how a complex presentation of PTSD can evolve when the destabilization of the system happens gradually, not all at once. I expand on stress as the main internal traumatizing agent at this level of complexity, and on abuse as the external traumatizing agent that affects adult relationships. Michaela talks about her romances in this section to illustrate how the system can suffer alterations due to mental undermining and gaslighting without anyone noticing. I offer the available diagnostic tools and a method to be able to identify the symptoms that can reflect this type of complication.

7. Chapter Seven covers the type of disorder that can unfold when traumatization occurs during the years when the brain is still forming (Developmental Trauma Disorder). The anatomy of brain development is clearly

described as a preamble to being able to understand how deep the effect of these occurrences can be. Neglect and adversity are the external traumatizing agents covered in this chapter. In this chapter, I include a bio-psycho-social model to assist in conceptualizing this level of damage.

8. Chapter Eight talks about the most important findings of attachment theory and expands on it to explain the reason why failing to attach to the 'mother' at birth (and even in the uterus) can have devastating consequences. You'll see how that specific wound is so severe that, even without a clear life threat, it could be the origin of a trauma syndrome on its own. This book compassionately includes everyone's struggles and how they affect others instead of finding who to blame. Michaela's mother's traumatization history is used to explain the effect that it has on her children, not as an accusation but as the conceptualization of how a traumatized individual can affect those around them if they don't find resolution for their emotional struggles. Rejection is presented as an external traumatizing agent and 'rejection sensitivity' as internal that potentially increases the damage of a failed attachment. Adversity adds to attachment issues causing disorganization in the attachment and fostering several impairments.

9. In Chapter Nine, the greatest complexity in the trauma phenomena occurs when it is not only the individual who is traumatized but when the traumatization occurs to a whole group of people. The external traumatizing factor in this chapter is systemic adversity, which includes the transmission of trauma from previous generations, and anger/hatred are described as the internal traumatizing agents that increase the damage. The chapter proposes a classification for this type of injury as 'aggregated trauma.'

10. The last chapter presents a systemic approach to resolving traumatization and healing trauma disorders. The chapter introduces healing agents and the idea of shifting from 'survival mode' to 'living mode.' The chapter includes a new model to treat traumatization and its aftermath using a multidimensional dynamic methodology that assists in the journey to repossess one's life.

Throughout this book, you'll find many ways of seeing that *the diagnosis of a trauma disorder is not a death sentence*; there are many ways to heal instead of accepting it as fate. While you'll see the various ways your own biology participates in making you 'sick,' you'll also learn that it has all the elements to move into healing. As you navigate this book, remember that our brain prefers health over disease—and that our mind is the most powerful known entity in the Universe.

Part I
Traumatization

why do you always come back

to the mountain to the biggest up there, there is

why does it feel so good to you

teetering until the light passes

shouting until the dark comes

climbing upwards arms open into the crimson sky

why do you go inside yourself

and find only I

how old is that

how long have you gone to such great lengths and found only this

—Matt Kagen

Let me start by making clear, upfront, that 'trauma' is about *evading death*. Trauma as psychological phenomena is highly correlated with our hardwired survival circuits. If we confront something that can jeopardize our existence—if our brain assumes that we could die—our innate need to survive takes over the will. That's where the '*struggle for survival*' starts, an internal struggle that deserves more attention than the origin of the distress. While the initial cause of the struggle may dissipate, the effects can stay active as a prolonged process that hurts our system and our lives. The process that stays active is called *traumatization* and it is the main subject of this book.

DOI: 10.4324/9781003382478-2

Traumatization is an arduous activity undergone mainly by the body during the period when one feels threatened and the whole system—ruled by the autonomic nervous system (ANS)—works at keeping the individual afloat. Since the evaluation of risk is as subjective as each person's perception, the length of the struggle can be short, or it can last 'forever.' What does it depend on? Well, *to resolve traumatization our brain needs to be convinced that we are safe*. Safety is key when we talk about trauma. But safety is not literal. Feeling unsafe—whether or not you actually are—is what makes it so difficult to live and heal after the overwhelming experience of being shocked or exposed to 'extreme' danger.

In Part I of three, 'Traumatization,' you'll gain an understanding of the scope of the trauma phenomena and everything involved during the struggle for survival—and why it can either end up as an anecdote you tell your children or as lifelong suffering that won't stop with you.

One
The Meaning of Trauma

Is trauma a cause or an effect?

What's the relationship between trauma and traumatization?

Is traumatized the same as PTSD?

Trauma, as it's studied today, is such a complex concept that calling it 'the trauma phenomena'—one that encompasses a wide range of clearly differentiated observable components, from cause to effect—seems appropriate; phenomena, in psychology, has been defined as the fundamental "process that has theoretically deduced antecedents and consequences and thereby helps explain human cognitions, feelings, and behaviors" (Iso-Ahola, 2017). To make it easier to handle and understand, it's helpful to separate the antecedents (cause) from the consequences (effects) and to further subdivide 'the cause' into external and internal originators. Before we get that granular, however, there are some basic misinterpretations to review and solve.

The term is so widely used that there is plenty of confusion about what exactly it refers to when someone mentions the word 'trauma.' Let's imagine this scenario: you are part of a family of 8 and everyone refers to each one of you by the same name, the name of your father: Bob. Can you see how it could become confusing? Imagine asking: "Who's there?" "Bob!" "Who's not coming?" "Bob!" "Who has a fever?" "Bob!" "Whose gift is this?" "Bob's!" You may never see each family member as distinct and the name Bob would lose all meaning and hierarchy. A similar confusion happens with the way we are using the term trauma, leading to misconceptions about what belongs to the phenomena or not, their level of importance, and the severity of the manifestations. This book aims to bring clarity to this confusion by integrating as many of the explanations as possible about why exposure to taxing adversity, constant threat, or shock makes us suffer from mild to extreme

DOI: 10.4324/9781003382478-3

and from a moment to a lifetime. Clarity is a goal on its own, but here we also have a more ambitious aim: to show how *understanding* traumatization can lead to *resolving* traumatization, stopping the dysfunction from becoming habitual, and ameliorating its consequences.

What Does 'Trauma' Mean?

> Trauma as causal is what puts us at risk, trauma as the effect of that experience is what makes us unwell. Trauma as phenomena is every mental occurrence in between.

It might be hard to believe that the trauma phenomena are a relatively new subject in psychology and psychiatry. Even though societally we've become more used to the term 'trauma' than ever, during previous decades, there was a strong reluctance to go deep into the repercussions of traumatization. Since it places active responsibility on whatever causes it—whether that's a person or an institution—it has proven challenging to openly admit the extent of the damage caused by subjecting someone to threatening situations. On top of that, paradigm shifts always find resistance, and the new perspective on mental health that uses a neurobiology-based lens asks for profound changes in the way we should think about, treat, process, and mitigate the consequences of psychological struggles.

Therefore, before we embark on finding the meaning of trauma, I want you to consider the following: *concepts (and constructs) are not fixed*. Most definitions we talk about in psychology are speculations, theories, and propositions. Definitions come and go. Terms change meaning. Statements and theories are discredited. You may have followed the conversation and controversy about the Diagnostic and Statistical Manual of Mental Disorders (DSM); international conferences have been held for years now with the purpose of debunking the use of diagnostic labels to categorize mental health, calling them unscientific (Ghaemi, 2018) and exposing the negative impact that diagnoses have on one's self-perception and psyche.

As new discoveries are reached, words and notions shift; psychiatry changes the name and criteria of mental disorders every few years. Psychotherapy too is constantly transforming as new schools of thought add modalities for treatment. Why? Well, because it's impossible to dissect the mind in the ways that science dissects organs, and therefore, it's not as easy to find answers; we still lack a definite conclusion on what alleviates emotional struggles. The mind and the brain are part of the system that governs our mental health and we are just starting to understand that the mind and brain are not the same.

So, I encourage you to accept the notion that many of the concepts about mental health you may have been hanging onto and treasuring as the ultimate reality (including a diagnosis that someone may have given you) may have evolved, changed, or even disappeared. If you allow your curiosity to help remove some of your preconceptions, I can assure you that you will learn much more about mental health and if traumatization plays a role in yours.

WHAT TRAUMA IS AND ISN'T

Not a week goes by without having to explain to someone that being upset is not the same as trauma and that having negative/disturbing emotions or dreams doesn't necessarily mean the person is traumatized. People obsess over trauma with thoughts like, "How do I overcome the trauma of working long hours?" or "How can I get past the trauma of being yelled at?" Keep in mind the following distinction: being emotionally hurt is common, while enduring long-lasting damage from being emotionally overwhelmed after

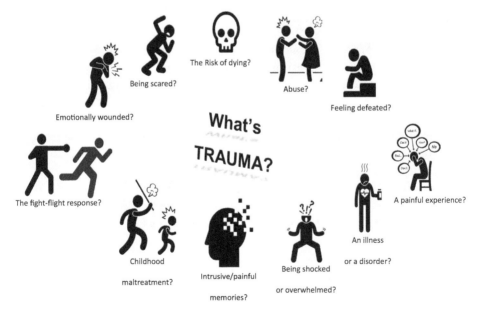

Figure 1.1 What's trauma?

threat is not. Figure 1.1 shows several different options of what people may question what trauma is.

Trauma always refers to the effects of the activation of the innate survival circuits that are designed to protect the individual from the possibility of dying after a severe reaction to a threatening occurrence. Trauma, in the strictest sense of the construct, is connected to severity—severity in the precipitating event, in the reaction, and in its aftermath. This is important. For trauma to be a thing in anyone's life, the person has to have been exposed to a severe event or circumstance that pushed their brain to use exaggerated measures to guarantee survival, causing severe consequences to their system.

TRAUMA = Severity in the exposure + severe reaction + severity in the aftermath

'Severity in the exposure' means that the nature of the event experienced was such that it makes one feel at risk of losing one's life—or something as valuable as life—and includes intensity, frequency, or constancy. A 'severe reaction' means that the person feels so shocked or afraid that their system needs to activate extreme measures. 'Severity in the aftermath' means serious alterations during the activation that cause a large set of symptoms that become an emotional disorder, bringing dysfunction to one's life. The severity of the event alone is not enough to call it trauma.

If we observe Figure 1.1 again, the answer to "what's trauma" would be "all of the above" (and more) but not any of them alone. Saying that someone has trauma implies long-lasting damage; long-lasting damage means overall dysregulation of the autonomic nervous system (ANS)—the part of the nervous system that automatically regulates involuntary physiologic processes—and alterations in almost every task connected to it. Dysregulation is the stamp of being traumatized. What does that look like? Dysregulation means losing the capacity to modulate and control your emotional responses. Dysregulation is an extreme physiological issue, not only equivalent to losing one's temper occasionally. When traumatized, the system radically loses internal balance and the ANS shifts its functioning to live controlled by the survival circuits, perceiving everything as threatening and everyone as a possible aggressor. At that point, the system has shifted gears into 'survival mode.' The interventions to mend our emotional upheavals, while necessary, are not the same as those needed to heal a nervous system in survival mode that has lost coordination and connection with impartiality or with an objective assessment of reality. Therefore, it's good to remember that *one doesn't need to heal if one is not ill.*

Think about hitting your leg in the corner of a chair. You'll experience pain, and you'll maybe develop a bruise, but you won't necessarily be damaged or suffer from leg dysfunction on an ongoing basis (unless, of course, the impact damaged your nerves, bones, or muscles severely).

Using the previous example, try to recognize the effect of using the term 'blow' to refer to hitting your leg versus using the word 'trauma.' Similarly, using 'emotional blow' to refer to events that are not necessarily traumatic makes it much easier to parse through the nuances of the experience. Verbalized, it sounds like "How do I overcome the effects of the emotional blows I suffered in childhood?" or "How can I get past the emotional blow of being betrayed?" versus the vagueness of referring to those events as childhood or relational trauma. Read them out loud and notice how your body responds differently.

Why does this matter? For starters, our personal narrative and the perception of who we are impact our mental health more than we could imagine. The stories we tell ourselves inform our emotional responses, and they can actually become mental realities (Lehne et al., 2015). If you call hitting your leg 'trauma,' you'll most probably start limping. If you call it a 'blow,' you'll probably continue walking as usual. Someone who says they have "a lot of trauma" regardless of what happened to them is already shifting their expectations to a defeating outcome even if the adverse circumstances didn't defeat them, or were inconsequential in terms of life threat. A trauma disorder unfolds from the severe stress that crushes one's hopes, defined by an extremeness that goes beyond tolerable. By clearing up the distinction between an emotional wound, traumatic, traumatizing, and traumatized, we can find out the extent of the damage that the occurrences have left on us, whether they were unbearable, or if they reached the intolerance point.

THE TERM TRAUMA: INJURIES, WOUNDS, AND THE LIMITS OF THE DICTIONARY

The word 'trauma' is used in several languages to mean the same thing—perhaps as it comes from the exact same word in Greek that means 'injury' or 'wound.' The medical community in the West adopted the word in the 1600s to refer to physical injuries but when it comes to 'psychological trauma,' the injury has been neglected as the main focus. The many different concepts applied to the term 'psychological trauma' lack congruency between themselves, whether in dictionaries, psychological texts, articles, or books on the subject. Of course, we also don't have a complete agreement on the definition of many words and concepts like stress, emotion, and plenty of others that we use all the time when we talk about mental health.

Trauma's infancy as a psychological concept may explain why the term is used as a noun *and* as an adjective, as well as indistinctly used to name an object *and* a subject. It's common to find the term used interchangeably to name a traumatic event, adversity, a disturbing memory, the result of those events, and the processes in between. Sometimes in the same sentence! But traumatic (the adjective about the event), traumatizing (the adverb), traumatization (the verb), traumatized (the adjective about the subject), and trauma—the injury (the noun)—are not the same thing and to use them interchangeably shortchanges the range of human experience. This differentiation matters and you'll see why through the book.

THE TRAUMA PARADIGM: HYSTERIA, SHELL-SHOCK, AND TAKING RESPONSIBILITY

The trauma phenomena have been studied clinically on three different occasions and twice abandoned. The first time it was studied under the name 'hysteria' (during the 1880s), and half a century later as 'shell-shock' (during WWI and WWII). Each time, the symptoms intrigued medical doctors, but effective treatment was lacking. Today we're in the third wave of trauma studies in what is its greatest paradigm shift: looking at traumatization through the Posttraumatic Stress Disorder (PTSD) diagnosis. When studies were first abandoned, psychological trauma was too connected to incest and misogyny, which could have contributed to the decline in interest. During the world wars, well, addressing traumatization meant confronting the consequences of sending citizens to put their 'lives at risk'; concepts like courage, patriotism, and loyalty opposed the conversation. It's obvious that both of these types of happenings meant that few wanted to acknowledge the damage—or be made responsible for the deep distress inflicted on others. Studying and understanding traumatization necessitate accepting the psychological damage of war, sexual misconduct, domestic violence, and poverty as well as the impact that maltreatment, rejection, punishment, or neglect have on people in general and on children's development in particular. In this third exploration of the effects of traumatization, some findings have made it evident that there is psychological damage from sexism, racism, oppression, and other social and institutionalized practices that impact members of society for generations. There is still resistance, but there is the need to face the emotional crisis societies are going through—due in part to ignoring traumatization's aftermath—as well as facing the bold fact that we can contribute to the deterioration of our health if we don't participate in resolving traumatization internally.

BEFORE AND AFTER PTSD: THE RISE OF TRAUMA STUDIES

It took hundreds of years for the word trauma to be first applied in reference to emotional injuries. William James mentioned it when explaining that a 'psychic injury' was caused by emotional shock—and that its memory (repressed and remaining unhealed) became an internal injury, *especially to the brain*, potentially resulting in a behavioral disorder of organic origin where "certain reminiscences of the shock fall into the subliminal consciousness" (James, 1894). If left there, James observed, this injury became permanent 'psychic traumata.' James was already talking about the physiological injury and its consequences, an observation that is confirmed by all the recent neuroscientific findings. Almost 100 years later, the first serious attempt to 'officially' recognize that there were specific psychological consequences to having been exposed to shocking events happened when the American Psychiatric Association (APA, 1980) introduced the PTSD diagnosis in the DSM-III to validate the extreme strain soldiers experienced in Vietnam as well as their subsequent emotional dysfunction.

Before PTSD, during the creation of psychological studies, it was assumed that most 'abnormal' behavior was mostly genetically based or shortcomings based on a lack of character. It has taken significant time and effort to shift the paradigm and understand that shock/stress not only *strains* our nervous system but *destabilizes it*. We now know that if our system is destabilized, our emotional health becomes affected; cognition and perception change, which, in turn, affects our behavior.

In the 1980s, the debate was about whether PTSD was a disorder or only a process. The first explanations of PTSD, before we knew better, were focused on the physiological response mostly explained by the fight/flight reactions and some people never updated their definition. It was later understood that those survival mechanisms were only the first two of several—identified as peritraumatic (they happen before we become traumatized). Only in the following years did the trauma studies start including broader consequences besides affected memories.

Almost a decade after PTSD appeared, Judith Herman realized that having just one diagnosis (PTSD) was not enough to do justice to traumatization beyond a single event; prolonged exposure to extreme stress (such as domestic violence or torture) needed to be brought in as part of the phenomena, and she called it 'complex PTSD.' Since Herman opened up the space for the evolution of trauma studies, thousands of research articles have appeared, most of them building on PTSD as a foundation—since it's the only criteria accepted by the medical community. The studies and explanations have become extremely profound, detailed, and technical, naming every single structure of the brain that gets activated during traumatization or affected after. Since the consequences of traumatization are so extensive, it has even been found that exposure to traumatic circumstances can have different types of manifestations and that traumatic circumstances can be of a different nature than we once thought. The new findings and the way we conceptualize the phenomena have moved away from the simplistic PTSD diagnosis into a more expansive conceptualization. We now have a better grasp of the construct that enables us to see that *when one goes through an experience where physical or mental integrity is compromised, the system can get injured, and the psyche wounded, with lasting consequences.*

TRAUMA IS NOTHING AND EVERYTHING: A PREVIEW OF THE SYSTEMIC APPROACH TO DECONSTRUCTING THE TRAUMA PHENOMENA

The debate about trauma has often centered around the *event* (the 'cause'). The many definitions that emerged covered a wide range of possibilities, differing from each other depending on how much weight they place on the experience versus the response, and between the shock and the pain. Only a few highlighted the damage—or its duration. When those definitions were written, it was more evident 'what' shocked people and 'how' they responded but not 'why' they faced an enduring problem yet. Therefore, definitions explained 'trauma' as emotional distress, emotional wound, memories, events, adverse circumstances, physical responses, and emotional reactions. Each has been used to explain 'trauma' and they all have made their way to mainstream vocabulary. Figure 1.2 shows several of the different uses of the term, clarifying their significance.

As you can appreciate, all the options are extremely different in nature. I'm going to use what happened to a client—Jon—to separate the components of the term in one case and show you how to differentiate them:

Emotional Distress/Overwhelm Only applies when distress comes from severe risk or threat		Adverse Circumstances Not all adversity is traumatic or traumatizing
Emotional Wounds If not related to danger should not be included	**USES OF THE TERM TRAUMA**	A Physiological Response Refer to responses like fight/flight but the response is not all
Traumatic Memories Memories from traumatic events are just one consequence		Emotional Reactions Agitation, sweat, pounding heart, etc. are normal reactions to shock
Traumatic Events Events are just the cause but not the effect		Sequela (Disorder) Symptoms that indicate alterations and the survival mode

Figure 1.2 Uses of the term trauma

Jon, as a kid, hardly escaped when his father threw a heavy object toward him after finding he had done something 'unacceptable.' His shock grew when he felt the strength of his father's hands slapping his face and head repeatedly (traumatic event). Jon kept a clear image of the incident (traumatic memory), experienced it as a horrible moment where he felt scared of his father and completely unsafe (experience), felt overwhelmed with distress and the shaking of his body (reaction), and wanted to escape him forever (response). After hearing him recount this, I asked if he felt defeated (a clear marker of traumatization). Many people would believe he did, and he said his wife has always assumed he got traumatized on that occasion, but he shared that even when he felt totally and completely hurt and unloved at that moment (distress), he did not stay feeling like that for long. He reflected that because his father seemed different the day after, reconnected, apologized, and helped him feel safe and cared for by him, eventually he 'recovered.' Still, every time he remembers it, he quivers (emotional wound). The aggression is unforgettable (painful memory) and may be unforgivable—(conceptually)—but naturally, our bodies try to heal instead of staying in shock. Even when some memories and ill feelings linger, or we casually refer to those memories as trauma, nobody should be assigned the label of PTSD for such occurrences. The individual may remember an event for the rest of his life, but that doesn't mean they'll be inevitably harmed (disorder) from that event. Jon is a successful individual with a strong family. And he has loved his father dearly for the last 30 years.

Regardless of how the term is used, we need consensus. The definitions of trauma in the literature present a somewhat disjunct image of what the phenomena could be; it may be because we have not considered trauma as systemic phenomena. Traumatization can only be truly understood if we dig deep into each and every aspect of the way our mind works in unison with our nervous system (and the nervous system of the people we interact with); we may not be used to that type of perspective. That may be why the term is used loosely and the definitions are quite different from each other. Under further investigation, we could notice that many of the definitions focus only on a segment of the phenomena. We can think of them as slices. Have you seen one of those cheesecakes you can buy that are already partitioned and the slices have different toppings? Some slices have strawberries, others caramel, chocolate-chips, etc. At the deli, it's easier to get only one slice, just as a clinician, a researcher, or a blogger will choose one angle. If you give different people one of the slices and ask them to describe the cheesecake, each one of them would give you a different description because they may have never acknowledged the other slices or thought of the cheesecake as a whole.

TAKING THE SUFFERING OF TRAUMATIZED PEOPLE SERIOUSLY

Nowadays, studies about traumatization are more abundant and profound, and we are starting to assimilate that traumatization has more devastating consequences on our health and the health of our society than we thought. That's why the risk of going backward should not be ignored. If we use 'trauma' with the alarmist and dismissive tone people used for 'hysteria' or 'shell-shock,' or apply it to almost all emotionally charged situations, we could lose some of the progress we have achieved. Hysteria was misused to name 'sexually needy' and uncontrollable women, while shell-shock was made equivalent to cowardice; trauma now is becoming equivalent to being a victim of hurt from hundreds of types of actions (parenting practices, criticism, disrespect, etc.). With overgeneralization, one runs the risk of misunderstanding the message of those suffering the serious cost of living traumatized, which could take the conversation (or the therapeutic intervention) down the incorrect path. Here's how: if one interprets 'trauma' as being hurt, the event that hurt us, the hurtful memories after, or the resulting symptoms of being hurt, it would be easy to argue that everyone 'has trauma' in one way or another. And if 'everyone' has trauma, no one would be held accountable, people will not receive the right attention and treatment, and the funding to investigate something everyone seems to experience will be cut off. One of my nightmares is imagining that we reach a point where being traumatized is seen as inevitably part of life, or that trauma was only a fad—both of which would make trauma studies and research lose importance yet again and would set us back in our understanding of what mental health depends on.

Those that suffer from a trauma disorder only wish to be taken seriously in the pain of feeling that, for them, nothing seems to work. For many, suffering all sorts of psychological and interpersonal issues becomes the confirmation of their inadequacy—an idea that could be relieved once they understand their biology. That's why the paradigm shift brought about by neuroscience needs an even wider reach. Many of the concepts about mental health— such as the one that says that if there is no health, then there is illness— need to be reviewed. They have contributed to debilitating one's mental stability, deteriorating self-concept, and diminishing one's sense of agency. If someone receives a diagnosis such as PTSD just because they experienced something shocking, and PTSD is considered a mental illness, the message is that the person is mentally ill, defective, or broken—all very defeating concepts, and defeat alone is more significant to deteriorate our health than many 'traumatic' events. Believing one suffers a mental illness is so debilitating that it has the potential to make the person dysfunctional; the diagnosis becomes the 'relationship' with the experience and with oneself. If we were to consider a more systemic approach, the name of a diagnosis like PTSD should be taken only as an indication that there is a disruption in optimal functioning at a systemic level instead of making one feel mentally unwell with no control over one's mind or fate. Once the severity of the damage is assessed, the interventions to bring the system back to regular functioning could target the specific alterations suffered, giving hope and agency to the person. Finding the right balance between over-pathologizing and normalizing the level of damage is key to serving those that have been afflicted after a traumatic situation.

Personalizing Trauma

I worked in a mental health clinic in Harlem, NY. The books I had read about trauma had prepared me to recognize that most of my clients there had experienced immense levels of shock, traumatic stress, adversity, and misfortunes. Still, I didn't have the tools to diagnose or help them. Something that deeply intrigued me was why someone that had her kid killed in her arms was functional, while someone else was unable to tolerate the 'trauma' of not speaking English and lost emotional control every time she was addressed in English.

Learning about how the patients' constant stress from adversity impacts their health, how to intervene, and whether it's possible to relieve some of their suffering and dysfunction, made me (and many clinicians) eager to answer *what's the key element(s) that affects someone so extremely while not others?* Most clinicians facing traumatized clients are also puzzled when finding that some interventions are useful for some while detrimental for others. My thesis here is that traumatization is not only systemic (affecting the person's internal psychological and biological systems) but also that each one of us establishes a different relationship to the experienced traumatic incidents. That's the reason it becomes necessary to make trauma *about the person and not the event* and the rationale behind the consensus that the PTSD diagnosis falls short.

A VISUAL REPRESENTATION OF THE PROCESSES OF TRAUMA: CAUSE, EFFECT, AND WHAT HAPPENS IN BETWEEN

We can conceptualize 'trauma' as the relationship between a person, an event, and a result. Let me explain the phenomena visually: Figure 1.3 shows the elements that play a role.

First, a healthy person gets exposed to something that is objectively scary on its own like lightning (*traumatic*). When lightning strikes in a space that jeopardizes the person (*traumatizing*), it is then considered a *traumatic event*. The person is severely shocked and scared which activates the survival circuits (*traumatization starts*) and causes the person to react to the possibility of being killed by a lightning strike. A series of processes begin in the shocked person's nervous system (*traumatization*) depending on the anticipation of

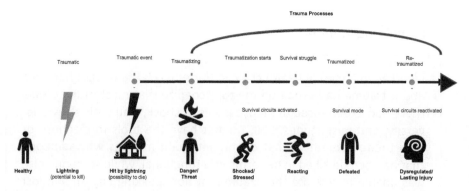

Figure 1.3 Trauma processes

the consequences of the threat. As long as the person continues feeling in danger, their system will continue using the processes that alter the regular functioning of the system (*struggle for survival*). Part of this struggle includes the effort to be safe like running away or calling the fire department; if the effort to be safe doesn't resolve—the house is burning—the person may feel *defeated*, which the brain interprets as the need to continue using the protective processes in a lasting manner shifting into survival mode (*traumatized*), manifesting symptoms that disrupt their life and enjoyment. The person's ANS is now dysregulated, and the possibility of retraumatization will be always there. Let's go over each process in detail.

ASSESSING 'TRAUMATIC': A NOT-SO-SIMPLE TASK

When PTSD appeared in 1980 in the DSM, events were considered traumatic when they were "outside the range of usual human experience" and caused the same "significant symptoms of distress in almost everyone" (APA, 1980). Today, the latest version of the manual (the DSM-5-TR) considers an event traumatic when it could mean "death, threatened death, actual or threatened serious injury, or actual or threatened sexual violence." The latest definition is more inclusive but it is still not close to reflecting the subjective ways humans experience extreme stress and fear and respond to danger and threats. Hopefully, the criterion continues to progress until it's accepted that the events that should be considered 'traumatic' are many more than what's listed. The conceptualization of 'traumatic' in this text goes beyond events that result in PTSD since all trauma syndromes are equally important and because what threatens one person is different from what threatens others. Hence, 'traumatic' in this book is related to *the potential* of being killed or irremediably injured (physically, psychologically, socially, and even financially). Traumatic is whatever action, event, or circumstance **has the potential** *to jeopardize one's life or physical/mental/social unity*. An appraisal that depends on the subjectivity of each one of us.

A breakup may not be traumatic per se but it has the potential to damage someone's stability and put the person's future at risk *if* the relationship is considered vital (think of an ill person that is cared for by the spouse). However, if the relationship was inconsequential, a breakup isn't traumatic.

Some events are considered traumatic by default because they jeopardize everyone who is caught in them, such as car crashes, being in war zones, or having major surgeries. Those situations endanger people's lives and therefore are traumatic in their own right. Many other situations may not be intrinsically dangerous for everyone but can be perceived as such by specific people. For example, a baby may consider a 'long' absence of the mother as life-threatening, but the eight-year-old kid used to see mom going to work every day may not.

TRAUMATIZING OR NOT? DANGER AND PERCEPTION'S ROLE IN TRAUMATIZATION

An event only starts to be 'traumatizing' at a specific point: when we become personally affected by it—whether in actuality or perceptually. As shown in Figure 1.3, lightning is traumatic because it is known for its potential to kill and destroy, but it's not until it hits the 'healthy' person in the figure (or the place they inhabit) that we can say that lightning is traumatizing. Perception plays a role here. Many people may enjoy seeing lightning while just a few may find it life-threatening; for the ones who fear it, their system starts the process of protecting them every time they hear lightning, especially if they or someone they know were harmed by it, even if it's not even near the place where the person is standing. For someone that has a specific phobia for lightning, their system could react even when watching lightning in a movie.

Given our subjective perception and the way our experiences inform our nervous system and emotions, almost every event has the potential to be traumatizing if it causes a reaction that exceeds our capacity to stay emotionally stable, leads our system to not bounce back to normal functioning, and if it makes us feel incapable of feeling safe. It's the person's subjective perception of danger that makes an incident traumatizing or not.

Almost all mental phenomena move in a continuum. There are extreme cases, there are cases that break the rule, and they are cases that are so mild that may be ignored. I will try to mention the extremes when important, but if I don't, keep in mind that a range is always implicit. For instance, if the person feels at risk by an event that is not threatening to others, that person could still develop a trauma disorder, but also, just because a traumatic event leads to a traumatizing experience, it does not mean that the person who experienced it is *traumatized*. We'll see now how the outcome depends on our perception of risk and of what we fear.

DANGER/THREAT AS TRAUMATIZING AGENTS: INTRODUCING THE ELEMENTS THAT EXACERBATE TRAUMATIZATION

Since trauma is about survival, it's correlated with danger and with being or feeling threatened, lacking safety, or being at risk. There is danger out there, and there has always been. That's why we are equipped with a system designed to help us overcome dangerous situations. From natural disasters to threatening people, our system is prompt to be alert, looking for ways to minimize the possibility of being killed by something or someone. Hence, *danger and threat* (externally) and *fear* (internally) are the initiators of the hardwired protections for survival. Therefore, I include them as part of the traumatizing agents (which I will define soon). Unfortunately, the survival processes' design is such that if not managed well, it can end up hurting us. Remember dysregulation? The effects will become clear as you keep reading.

TRAUMATIZED: THE LONG-LASTING INJURY

Traumatized is another way of saying that someone suffers from a trauma disorder. Many people use the term synonymously with scared or shocked, but the dictionary definition of traumatized includes the word 'lasting.' Being traumatized is the end result of a failed struggle for survival: the system is not able to find a resolution to the confronted danger (doesn't feel safe) and it gets altered to the extreme of destabilizing the person's life. The processes that get activated during the struggle have the potential to rewire the brain for the worse as soon as one feels defeated and stops trying to recover safety. That's what being traumatized is: *operating under a new program, a maladaptive one that keeps the body anticipating danger in a very subjective way, malfunctioning, with a lack of internal equilibrium, and focused on survival.* One way to look at the traumatized self is to understand that it is taking on *a deficient and ineffective way to use the energy of the brain to avoid death in real-time,* even once there is no longer the possibility of dying. Therefore, the dysregulation does not really relate to how dangerous the event was, but how much one feared it and how much (or little) one could recover trust in overcoming it. That's how personal becoming traumatized is. In the next section, we'll see how 'traumatized' goes beyond the initial binary of traumatized or not into a spectrum based on different factors.

THE RISKS OF OVER-DIAGNOSING TRAUMATIZATION

Time is an important factor when talking about trauma phenomena. PTSD and a lot of its research include the moment of shock when the responses of the nervous system get activated. Time is also implicit in the DSM-5 criteria for PTSD since it doesn't apply unless the individual has experienced the symptoms for at least 30 days (or six months with 'delayed expression'). Still, it is not easy to find research on what happens during the days between the shock and meeting the criteria for PTSD. Actually, the APA resolves it by creating another disorder, called Acute Stress Disorder (ASD) with almost identical criteria to PTSD but with a duration of the disturbances lasting only three days to one month after exposure to the traumatic event. This means that the APA is missing addressing the fact that PTSD is not something that happens 'automatically' after a shocking event, but that it develops only when the system fails to recoup. Therefore, ASD is, in fact, pathologizing the body's effort to recover from the shock. That shows that the body's need to recuperate is hardly addressed and understood. Calling those 30 days a 'disorder' or even 'trauma' is like calling bleeding after a cut an infection. These arbitrary 30 days mark the period where the body goes into an effort to reestablish regular operation. Without recovering, the body would keep the score. As you can appreciate, there is a tendency to pathologize the natural processes our system goes through, because as part of a system, our body needs to perform many tasks before it can go back to baseline.

Before we move into learning how trauma disorders develop, let me remind you that traumatization can be prevented early in the process, or resolved at any point during the struggle if the one encountering or experiencing the traumatic event intervenes and regains confidence. Being traumatized is not the unavoidable consequence of going through traumatization or experiencing a traumatic event. Once one becomes traumatized, healing will be needed after—or at the same time—the fears and survival activation get resolved. Figure 1.4 shows the timeline.

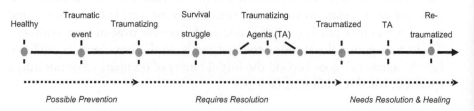

Figure 1.4 Prevention, resolution, or healing timeline

Developing a Trauma Disorder (or Not)

> Kim Jong Min has a song that talks about how strong people build air-planes, while others (weak) build parachutes. It is a great image for making sense of traumatization. Traumatized individuals are normally less energetic, creative, or motivated not because they are weak, but because their brains are too busy trying to survive, so yes—they spend a lot of time 'making parachutes' because they feel in free fall and are concerned about crashing into the ground.

Let's look at when traumatized people spend time 'making parachutes' on a spectrum. On the one side, there is a mild version of PTSD where symptoms go away by themselves within a year (approximately) after a single traumatic event; on the other extreme, there is a large set of alterations, severe distress, and massive dysfunction (emotional and psychical) due to a complex accumulation of traumatic situations (one's own or from others), traumatic stress, chronic traumatization, and constant/prolonged traumatizing circumstances that kept pushing the limits of the nervous system to a point of complete despair. The worse the traumatization suffered by a person, the more the fear of 'crashing into the ground' becomes a reality. Besides PTSD, the severity of the manifestations changes according to the several trauma syndromes that can develop, which depend on contributing factors like when in life the traumatization occurs and what type of circumstances originated the symptoms—including social context.

It's worth mentioning that the continuum doesn't necessarily move as a smooth progression. It is not uncommon to meet people that are able to endure long-term traumatic stress (stress resulting from a constant or prolonged feeling of threat) with just a few mild symptoms that shift to a sudden manifestation of a severe syndrome after a relatively small traumatic occurrence. One single experience can overload a system that held on for a long time.

THE TRAUMA SYNDROMES: PTSD, C-PTSD, DTD, AND MORE

Most of the manifestations after traumatization unfolds depend on the reaction that set the survival mechanisms in action, and the age when they occurred. The consequences could be distinguished between a trauma disorder caused by a single event to more complex syndromes due to prolonged repeated traumatic and adverse circumstances, the traumatization carried by those that raised the child, the environment they grew up in, the accumulation of all of them, or any combination.

The most commonly found name for a trauma disorder that falls beyond PTSD is C-PTSD (or complex PTSD). It has gained so much recognition that even though it did not make it into the revision of the DSM-5, the ICD (International Statistical Classification of Diseases and Related Health Problems) is including it in its latest version (ICD-11) to be a billable disorder. 'Developmental Trauma' is also increasingly becoming part of our vocabulary, as well as 'Attachment Trauma' and 'Intergenerational Trauma,' but they suffer from the same issue of referring to the circumstances and the consequences interchangeably.

I've written a chapter on each of the syndromes that I see as encompassing the most clearly distinguishable characteristics. I've also added 'Aggregated Trauma' to name a syndrome that aims to include many variations of the damaging effects of some social practices. On the spectrum, aggregated traumatization is where the contributing factors reach their peak in terms of severity and level of dysfunction.

Although we know from all the research that only a minority of survivors develop a long-standing disorder like PTSD (Bryant et al., 2017), it is still not well researched why or how this happens, or the reason some people suffer from symptoms for a very long time while others don't. The concept that attempts to explain it is resilience (the capacity to bounce back from adversity and restore equilibrium), but we don't know enough about how it interacts with the survival circuits, or why some people have a lot and some have almost none. My thesis is that it has to do with (a) the extent of the resources (internal and external) people count on, and (b) the relationship the person establishes with the traumatizing experience. When a person notices those two factors and how they affect them, resilience begins to build up. In the next chapter, I will further explore this relationship with the event while I expand the idea that traumatizing agents decrease our resilience and worsen our symptoms, interrupting the key resolution of the struggle we saw in Figure 1.3.

CONTRIBUTING FACTOR: AGE AND TIME

Traumatization can happen at any time in life. Nobody is immune to it. It can happen in the crib or at the nursing home, but the point in life when it happens contributes to the type of symptoms and the severity of the damage. Traumatization has a different effect on a nervous system that is immature (underdeveloped) than on a mature one, and has also a different effect if it happens on a system that had already suffered alterations previously. Therefore, we can observe differences between three main categories (that I cover extensively later on):

- Complex Traumatization (diagnosed as C-PTSD): a prolonged period or recurrent exposure to traumatic situations at any age.
- Developmental Traumatization (diagnosed under DTD): traumatization while the brain is still forming.
- Attachment Traumatization: a wound suffered at birth or during the lactation period when attachment fails to form. Sometimes included to refer to prolonged or constant ruptures occurring in infancy. (Some authors call it Relational Trauma but Developmental and Complex traumas are also relational, and therefore, I avoid the term.)

CONTRIBUTING FACTOR: SOCIAL CONTEXT

Many sociocultural factors can affect an individual's reaction to traumatic experiences. In communities exposed to constant threats, the diagnosis of PTSD is never enough—it is always accompanied by other clinical symptoms and psychosocial difficulties, relationship problems, identity challenges, and existential hardship (Gailiene, 2015). Depending on the social context, the spectrum goes from the traumatization suffered by one individual to the traumatization of a whole society. The most frequently used constructs are as follows:

- Intergenerational Trauma: refers to traumatization sequela that is passed to family members.
- Cultural Trauma: used to refer to extreme forms of social abuse and discrimination that keep communities in a state of defeat and dishonor.
- Historical Trauma: refers to the consequences of the cumulative emotional harm of a generation of individuals that share identity characteristics and experienced social discrimination or oppression throughout history.

CONTRIBUTING FACTOR: MAGNITUDE AND AGGREGATION

One question I hear often is whether a person can suffer from several traumas. Traumatization is systemic, which means that the entire system—its organs and functions—gets affected, and once it is affected and it is already traumatized, more exposure to risk prolongs the survival mode and worsens or adds symptoms and dysfunction. Since it's common to equate trauma with memories, people assume that having new traumatic memories means more trauma; in that sense, someone could feel that more exposure to events that jeopardize their integrity puts them more on edge than fewer events. The disruption that memories create is a symptom and the more traumatic memories, the more possibility to experience flashbacks or nightmares, and more acute hyper-vigilance since there will be more triggers for survival. Even then, the person may not be traumatized yet; flashbacks are only one criterion among seven to meet the PTSD diagnosis. For those which system has shifted the focus to survival (operating in survival mode), they get more easily startled, anxious, fearful, and reactive, because the need to survive seems higher and less probable, and therefore, more traumatic events will cause the dysregulation to continue escalating. A trauma disorder can grow as an infection grows. When an invasive object (virus, bacteria) reproduces to the point of damaging the cells in our body, signs and symptoms of an illness appear. In the same way, when there is more exposure to threats (objective or subjective), the survival mechanisms continue damaging organs, altering functions, and modifying behavior. Many other disarrays can follow.

Someone that functions in survival mode already is more likely to experience shock, and symptoms of PTSD would be much more obvious and difficult to treat. As the disorder gets worse, resilience diminishes, perception becomes more distorted, regulation becomes harder to achieve, and hyper-vigilance will disrupt every interaction. More traumatization blocks the possibility of resolving the origin of the struggle. Let's now move into understanding the neurobiology of traumatization and how the brain works to keep us alive.

References

American Psychiatric Association (APA). (1980). *Diagnostic and statistical manual of mental disorders* (3rd ed.). Washington, DC: American Psychiatric Association.

Bryant, R. A., Creamer, M., O'Donnell, M., Forbes, D., McFarlane, A. C., Silove, D., & Hadzi-Pavlovic, D. (2017). Acute and chronic posttraumatic stress symptoms in the emergence of posttraumatic stress disorder: A network analysis. *JAMA psychiatry*, 74(2), 135–142. https://doi.org/10.1001/jamapsychiatry.2016.3470

Gailiene, D. (2015). *Lithuanian faces after transition: Psychological consequences of cultural trauma* (pp. 234–248). Vilnius: Eugrimas.

Ghaemi, S. N. (2018). After the failure of DSM: Clinical research on psychiatric diagnosis. *World Psychiatry: Official Journal of the World Psychiatric Association* (WPA), 17(3), 301–302. https://doi.org/10.1002/wps.20563

Iso-Ahola, S. E. (2017). Reproducibility in psychological science: When do psychological phenomena exist? *Frontiers in Psychology*, 8, 879. https://doi.org/10.3389/fpsyg.2017.00879

James, W. (1894). Review of Breuer and Freud's 'Über den psychischen Mechanismus hysterischer Phänomene'. *Psychological Review*, 1, 199.

Lehne, M., Engel, P., Rohrmeier, M., Menninghaus, W., Jacobs, A. M., & Koelsch, S. (2015). Reading a suspenseful literary text activates brain areas related to social cognition and predictive inference. *PLoS One*. https://doi.org/10.1371/journal.pone.0124550

Two
The Science of Trauma

Why does our own system attack our mental health?

What's the relationship between your brain and your wellbeing?

What are the brain's characteristics that can help us avoid traumatization?

Survival is a primordial need hardwired in our brain from birth, and maybe even from before we come out of the womb. It's so important that it could be considered the brain's main task: doing whatever it takes to keep us alive. When I say "whatever it takes," I mean it: the brain prefers to work deficiently ('hurting' us) than to stop working. The brain has a bias toward survival so strong that it rather turn a person into a zombie than allow their biological system (the group of organs that work together to carry out the tasks that keep one alive) to completely cease. That's why this book covers the science of the trauma phenomena, mainly to explain what parts of our neurobiology connect *living* and *surviving* (and disconnect us from enjoying).

It was not until the 1970s that the discoveries of the relationship between the brain and the mind started to bear fruit; neuroscience and advances in neuroimaging have allowed mental health professionals to realize that understanding the brain adds perspective to existing therapeutic modalities, complementing them. We wouldn't have an understanding of the trauma phenomena—or psychology for that matter—without exploring the brain. By reviewing our tendency toward survival, the way the brain works, and the agents that make traumatization last, this chapter will help you connect the dots.

DOI: 10.4324/9781003382478-4

Survival as an Internal Traumatizing Agent

A few years ago, a very close relative of mine fell down the stairs and was taken unconscious to the closest hospital. I rushed to be there. Nobody else had arrived yet, so the doctor approached me and explained that she had a cerebral hemorrhage and that he had to open her head urgently to extract the damage because her risk of dying was high. It seemed likely that he would have to remove part of the cerebral cortex, which horrified me. When he saw my reaction, he tried to comfort me by saying "Don't worry! People can continue living with only a third of their brain." He was serious. That's how I imagine the brain would try to comfort us after letting our system operate in survival mode: "Don't worry! You can continue living with only a third of your mental health."

What's survival? In essence, something we all, eventually, fail at, right? On a more serious note, survival is defined as the state of continuing to live or exist. Some people consider it an instinct and many scholars include it under the construct of self-preservation. Survival is primal across all beings, while self-preservation develops as we humans become more aware of our individuality. Why is survival so important? Probably because we are part of an ecosystem that needs equilibrium, and each one of our existences is part of that effort.

ADAPTATION: SOMETIMES IT HURTS BEFORE IT HELPS

In order to survive, we have to adapt; adaptation is the process by which our system becomes better suited to its environment. Many of our processes and functions follow that principle. At a very basic level, we have reflexes that act without volition and some of them are involved in protecting us; coughing, sneezing, and blinking are examples of simple protective reflexes. We also count on more complicated processes that make sure we stay alive; they could be automatic, like the stress response, or volitional, like the capacity to reflect for decision-making. Through our evolution, we have survived for thousands of years by finding all sorts of ways to defend ourselves when threatened, by memorizing our discoveries, and by absorbing and sharing the information others have learned or discovered.

In biological terms, most of our hardwired survival circuits are ruled by the autonomic nervous system (ANS). The ANS is responsible partially for what happens in the aftermath of a traumatic incident that leaves us in a state of confusion and pain, and even with a damaged functioning—but its intention is not to harm us. It actually wants to either help us get rid of the threat or to numb the pain for us to be able to tolerate extreme hurt. Emotionally, however, becoming numb or disconnected as an adaptation has the potential to hurt our system and our relationships because it goes against the way we engage and enjoy life. As disease is a natural consequence of our design, adaptation is a basic function that doesn't consider health, just survival. Trauma disorders are the product of the maladaptation resulting from that design.

SURVIVING: A BALANCING ACT

In order to survive, every system, organ, and cell in our body is designed to work with and among each other's systems, organs, and cells to maintain an internal balance. When the conditions are not ideal, but instead, jeopardize our survival, the brain will make the necessary adjustments to keep us alive, modifying cells, organs, and system functions. *Survival is, in essence, a balancing act.* For humans, to survive is not related only to avoiding who is going to kill us, but also to feeling safe, which includes finding someone to trust, and ways to be seen, heard, understood, accepted, and cared for. If we fail to have those essential needs met, we feel insecure, vulnerable, defenseless, and alone. The irony is that not even 'mothers' are equipped to help their children meet all those needs well. We are a very delicate species, and also, a complicated one. It's not uncommon to find parents (or relatives, friends, etc.) that are judgmental, demanding, insensitive, critical, and neglectful, not to mention those that are aggressive, abusive, cruel, and punitive. For many individuals, it's harder to survive in the family home than in the jungle.

HOW DOES OUR SYSTEM CARE FOR OUR SURVIVAL?

The easiest place for our system to be is at optimal functioning, which means having internal harmony and equilibrium. Although each organ has specific jobs, they are all dependent on each other's good functioning. The nervous system is in charge of the collaboration among various organs. It counts on the ANS to do many of the automatic processes that don't need our volition, cognition, or even our awareness. Its big boss is the hypothalamus, a brain structure in charge of regulating homeostasis (internal equilibrium). The brain monitors changes in the body's energy state and sends signals to the hypothalamus, which follows by modulating the activity of the ANS as a response to maintaining the system in balance. The ANS exercises control over the activity of most tissues and organs in our system since it enervates the muscles of most organs and glands (including the heart).

Even when the ANS conveys autonomy in its name and works optimally on its own, that doesn't mean that we are powerless over how it functions. It has been demonstrated that we can alter our physiology and our most basic functions at will with the use of our thoughts, concentration, attention, awareness, and determination. For example, our thoughts are correlated with the way our heart oscillates; if we are stressed or experience negative thoughts, the heart rhythm pattern becomes erratic and disordered, but if we calm down or shift to a positive state, the heart regulates its rhythm and its variability (Grossmann et al., 2016). Self-regulation, a skill used in healing, is based on this premise.

To achieve regulation, we need to understand the ANS's two branches: the sympathetic and the parasympathetic which work as a team to regulate and balance our system's activity. The ANS responds by either (a) *stimulating* body processes through the *sympathetic* division after receiving information about what's going on in the body or the environment, or (b) *inhibiting* the body processes if that's what is needed to maintain stability and harmony through the *parasympathetic* division.

The sympathetic nervous system (SNS) is in charge of putting us in action. It is also responsible for the famous fight-flight response to prepare the system for protection and to help us get out of dangerous situations. In most descriptions of the SNS, its connection to the fight or flight response is invariably mentioned and it's not uncommon to see this highlighted as its main task. This makes it seem as if the SNS is only activated when we need to fight or flee but the SNS is always active, during wakefulness, and even in our sleep, to keep our organs operating.

The other branch of the ANS—the parasympathetic nervous system (PSNS)—does its part in maintaining stability by conserving energy, slowing the heart rate, and increasing activity in some glands and organs like relaxing sphincter muscles in the gastrointestinal tract. It's also behind some protective actions that lower our vital signs to help us overcome threats. Besides the protections activated when one is at risk, it also participates in the regular emotional states from depression to contentment. When the PSNS becomes over-activated, it could disconnect our awareness from pain, physically and emotionally (known clinically as dissociation) by numbing our body or detaching from our emotional responses and/or our memories.

The SNS and PSNS have complementary functions and normally work by compensating for each other's activation. When you hear "the nervous system is dysregulated" (Behel, 2021), it means that the SNS and PSNS have stopped balancing each other out. Standard published work on the ANS covers the sympathetic and parasympathetic as the common understanding of its division. Stephen Porges questioned this theory when he found that the vagus nerve, a complex network of more than 100,000 fibers and a main component of the PSNS (carries 75% of all parasympathetic fibers), includes two different responses depending on the part of the vagus that innervates the organs. The vagus nerve mainly carries sent signals from the organs to the brain to let it know their states. It also plays an important role in detecting internal activity through interoception; its fibers go beyond the brainstem connecting to a brain neural network that interprets internal changes, anticipates physiological needs, and sends instructions to fulfill them. The vagus explains, for example, how traumatization stays in the body as memorized pain, fear, and emotional reactivity. The Polyvagal Theory (PVT) expands its relevance in trauma studies.

THE PVT'S CONTRIBUTION TO OUR UNDERSTANDING OF SURVIVING

The PVT was proposed in 1994 by Stephen Porges. It added understanding to the ways the ANS—informed by the vagus nerve—protects us from threats. With this theory (Porges, 2009), Porges challenged the previous understanding of the way the ANS activates defense mechanisms and defines it as a system of three circuits instead of two, proposing that newer circuits inhibit older ones and that the ANS is hierarchical instead of antagonistic.

Porges emphasizes the ANS's value to attachment theory pointing to the correlation between facial expressions and prosody during caregiver and infant interactions. It further explains that evolved species like ours (and other mammals too), instead of seeing others as predators, can feel protected and safe by connecting. The theory proposes social-engagement, mobilization, and immobilization as a model for survival instead of the fight/flight/fawn model previously used. PVT also provides us with a divergent view of the relationship between the principal branches of the ANS and the vagus nerve itself. It differentiates brainstem areas that regulate the organs situated above the diaphragm from those regulating organs below the diaphragm. The differentiation is based on how the ventral part of the vagus is myelinated, while the dorsal stayed unmyelinated. Myelinated means covered by myeline similar to how cables are covered by rubber.

Ventral

This branch, unique to mammals, is responsible for the parasympathetic action of lowering heart rate, engaging and regulating muscles in the face and head, pairing social functions of engagement with bodily sensation, and states of safety and connection, including staying calm, engaged, attentive, interested, ready, and joyful. It affects body functioning above the diaphragm and serves the social-engagement system. It has the very important characteristic of being able to turn off fight-flight protective mechanisms to regulate extreme defenses with calming and soothing effects. It is also responsible for lowering heart rate after stress.

Dorsal

This branch engages with the immobilization response in reaction to life-threatening circumstances, and is more primitive, slower, and less organized. It starts in the skull near the jugular opening. It is common in all vertebrates and it's unmyelinated. It affects body functioning below the diaphragm (the gut) and is involved in heart, lung, and digestive issues. It can send the system into immobility or dissociation, including feeling paralyzed, numb, or 'not here' using a more abrupt break.

Both the dorsal vagal complex (DVC) and the ventral vagal complex (VVC) exert inhibition on the SNS (Schwartz, 2013).

THE IMPORTANCE OF INTERNAL HARMONY

The ANS branches are always working on keeping the system balanced (this is true whether or not we adhere to the PVT or a more traditional view). That balance has a name—it's called homeostasis. Homeostasis theory defines it as the tendency toward a relatively stable equilibrium between interdependent elements, especially as maintained by physiological processes. Many nervous system processes are designed to preserve this internal equilibrium, keeping the levels of chemicals and operation between organs 'the same' and 'still' regardless of the changes it needs to make in daily life. Almost every movement or action we perform carries a homeostatic process, including homeostatic feelings connected to emotions that influence many other processes, actions, and behaviors as adaptation tools (Damasio & Carvalho, 2013) that can displace or disrupt some part of our non-stop balancing act. Maintaining a stable condition for optimal functioning depends on many variables such as body temperature or fluid compensation. The body doesn't like wild fluctuations because it operates optimally if it keeps a steady state; for example, if we have exercised, homeostasis will take care of producing sweat to keep the body cool, getting rid of excess body heat, and protecting itself from overheating.

Maintaining internal equilibrium is also related to the amount of energy that the brain consumes to operate, and how it allocates it. To maintain balance and be effective, the brain anticipates most occurrences in order to start assigning energy to a task before it's even required (Barrett & Simmons, 2015). In the presence of stress or aversive stimuli, the brain anticipates the activation of the stress response system, the complex range of mechanisms involving the endocrine, nervous, and immune systems that will require huge amounts of unexpected, non-habitual processes. This presents a big challenge to homeostatic activity and puts it at risk. The mechanisms used to confront traumatic events disrupt homeostasis in multiple areas of the brain, areas that are recruited to respond to the threat, affecting feedback mechanisms and the corresponding body areas. If homeostasis succeeds in its goal of maintaining effective functioning, life continues, but if it fails, disaster, dysfunction, illness, or even death proceeds. We will learn more about how survival mode is connected to losing homeostasis later.

TEMPORARY NUMBING PAIN, LONG-TERM DISCONNECTION

The number of chemicals intervening in traumatization is so large that it could take a whole section to describe them. Hence, I'll only share the information about stress hormones and analgesics because they are extremely important to why we get traumatized and why some of the symptoms feel so foreign from our routines. We respond to stressful events by initiating the stress response that includes the release of glucocorticoids from the adrenal cortex (Steckler et al., 2016). Activation of the stress response causes several physiological changes that facilitate our chance of survival where two major components are involved:

- The sympathetic-adreno-medullar (SAM) axis secretes noradrenaline and norepinephrine and provides a rapid physiological adaptation to the stressor with fast and short-lasting responses like alertness and vigilance.
- The hypothalamus-pituitary-adrenal (HPA) axis secretes glucocorticoids (mainly cortisol) and is slow. Its three main components are the hypothalamus, the pituitary gland, and the adrenal glands.

This is relevant for trauma studies because when stress is extreme, our blood gets flooded with hormones (epinephrine, etc.) and analgesics (endogenous opioids, cannabinoids, etc.) that will make changes in the relocation of energy to (a) make parts of our body stronger or (b) reduce activation in some organs. Their importance will be more evident once we talk about dissociation.

Brain under the Trauma Lens

Remember my dear relative with cerebral hemorrhage? During her convalescence, she didn't even remember the most important information, like the names of her children. When she tried to answer questions, she responded with something completely unrelated but was aware that the words coming out of her mouth were not the ones she intended to say (aphasia). Her 'cables' were 'wet' and 'crossed.' Many other of her functions had been altered as well, and it was amazing to see how she recovered them one by one. I got a firsthand look at brain functionality through her healing process. Even when her functionality came back, her behavior was not the same. She now had no problem asking people to leave her alone after a lifetime of being the most social and polite person ever; she became preoccupied with things that she never gave importance to. There were other small changes in how she dealt with emotions that surprised everyone that knew her before. If you've ever experienced something similar with a friend or relative, perhaps you've also observed how the brain is responsible for many subtleties of our behavior, emotions, and perception, and how our delicate brain heals itself. (Well, sometimes! I'll tell you later how my mom's never healed). In this section, we will see specific brain characteristics in charge of our actions before and after experiencing terror, as well as why this matters.

From the beginning of psychiatry, psychological disorders were studied based on assumptions and interpretations more than on the understanding of how the brain, emotional responses, and behavior interact. But neuroscience has made so much progress that now we have the capacity to observe brain activity in real-time, opening a world of knowledge that explains many facts that we could not even have guessed. Let's learn some of those new discoveries.

THE HUMAN BRAIN: A PREDICTION MACHINE

There are thousands of papers describing which parts of the brain intervene in each process of the trauma phenomena, but the most interesting findings are those bringing light to systemic healing, seeing the brain as the coordinator of the activity of our system and subsystems. For example, it was recently postulated that our brain is a hierarchical 'prediction machine' working on reducing our uncertainty about the environment (Badcock et al., 2019). This confirmation adds depth and possibilities to our understanding of the brain's characteristics that could be a great asset in resolving traumatization; it directs our attention to perception, which is an essential component of how we engage with the world, assessing our experiences either correctly or incorrectly. Perception should always be considered when talking about traumatized individuals because perception becomes affected in such a way that it starts to fail at predicting outcomes correctly. The brain of a traumatized individual will predict negative outcomes, will see danger everywhere, will anticipate failure, will intertwine present experiences with previous ones, and will see more changes oriented toward needing to survive a threatening world. These distortions also affect emotional responses. Our emotions are also reactions to brain predictions, and traumatization transforms both the predictions and the reactions. To achieve the optimal regulation of all our systems, our brain processes, integrates, and coordinates the information it receives from the senses to then make decisions that will perform the needed tasks. Besides managing our physiological operations (breathing, digesting, etc.), the brain is in charge of all we feel, all we experience, and everything we think we are.

THE BRAIN: AN OPTIMIZATION APPARATUS

Allow me to say that even with the power and sophistication the brain has, it is not that 'smart.' I like calling it an efficient but mindless 'apparatus.' I use the word apparatus because the brain is really like a machine with specific programs that follow strict instructions, and mindless because, without a mind, it's like a lamp without a bulb, it doesn't have an 'understanding' of life or almost anything else. It's simply a task maker that anticipates outcomes, distributes chemicals, gives instructions, stores data, prompts reactions, creates automatic responses, forms habits, and executes functions with the clear interest of optimizing the use of energy required to keep our system running. Like a clock that gives the exact time without knowing what 'time' is, the brain performs its tasks without understanding them. To be efficient, the brain maps the world we live in by predicting the best way to adapt to it and acting accordingly, reducing our uncertainty about the environment (Badcock et al., 2019) and the possibility of not surviving it. It doesn't care whether we are happy or miserable; it does not compute it. It activates almost all the processes concerned with our emotional life mainly by guessing (Barrett, 2022) based on what it has learned and stored as memories on what's more adaptive. By the way, that's when memory becomes important. Memory is more important for our brain and our survival than for ourselves—even when we may think otherwise. I'll expand on that later.

THE BRAIN: CHEMICALS, EXPERIENCES, AND HABITS

This apparatus is always active and weighs around 3 pounds. It uses about 20% of the total oxygen of the body and consumes 25% of the calories we require, which means that it uses more energy than any other organ. Two-thirds of that energy is used to send signals among neurons. While we are awake, it generates enough energy to power a light bulb with which we generate around 70,000 thoughts a day. It has tasks for when we are awake, asleep, and for when we are idle.

The brain is basically made of neurons (about 100 billion), and neurons are essentially information messengers and prediction agents communicating with each other through synaptic connections (around 7,000 each). Neurons can be seen as biological wires that conduct data among different areas of the brain through electricity. Humans have more cortical neurons than any other mammal (except maybe some dolphins and whales). Single-neuron learning depends on minimizing future surprises by constantly comparing the difference between actual and predicted activities (Luczak et al., 2020).

The brain is an electrochemical organ but I like emphasizing its electrical properties because they inform us more about its development. The human brain's electrical energy is generated by chemical processes in the neurons. Every chemical element in our body has a specific electrical charge and our neurons use these charged elements—called ions—to generate electricity (Plante, 2016). Billions of nerve impulses travel throughout the human brain and body from neuron to neuron (synapses) forming circuits that can process incoming information and carry out a response. Just a few circuits are innate; most of them are created by experience. Being traumatized becomes one of those learned circuits (a habit), but our brain has the capacity to create new circuits for safety that replace negative and ill habits.

THE BRAIN'S BEST QUALITIES

It has been said that the brain is "the most complex computational device in the known universe" (Buonomano, 2018). The high rate of energy it uses is surprisingly constant despite the wide variation in mental activity. It works more efficiently by creating automatic responses; depending on the person, from 40 to 95% of our behavior—how we think, what we say, and our overall actions—get activated automatically to adapt to our individual circumstances. This fact is essential for trauma studies because the traumatic injury creates a new program that the brain learns to use automatically and dismisses our will (until we stop it and replace it). Another very interesting characteristic of the brain—and useful for resolving traumatization—is its use of imagination. Imagining doing something lights up the brain (activates neurons) as much (and sometimes even more) than actually performing the action. In most circumstances, our brain can't really recognize the difference between real and imaginary.

While the brain is so complex and intricate, it's also very rudimentary and simple. Still, it has extraordinary characteristics; some of the ones I find of most importance for trauma studies and the healing process are shown in Figure 2.1.

Active: works all the time on generating predictions and hypotheses about the causes of its sensations (Picard & Friston, 2014). It is always changing, programmed to continuously reorganize itself, forming new neural connections as it matures and reacts to life experiences.

Complex: it consists of many different and connected parts which take more than two decades to fully mature (via myelination).

Fat: around 60% of it is fat (Chang et al., 2009). Fatty acids are among the most crucial molecules for their integrity and ability to perform but can't be synthesized by the body and must be obtained from dietary sources.

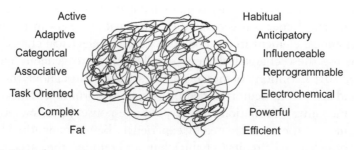

Active   Habitual
Adaptive   Anticipatory
Categorical   Influenceable
Associative   Reprogrammable
Task Oriented   Electrochemical
Complex   Powerful
Fat   Efficient

Figure 2.1 Brain characteristics

Associative: much of what we understand is based on brain activity that associates concepts, events, or mental states usually stemming from specific experiences.

Adaptive: the brain never stops learning due to its neuroplasticity. It can continue forming and reorganizing synaptic connections, and therefore adjust its activities in response to new situations or changes in the environment, particularly in response to significant environmental factors and life events. It's always learning for adaptability, survival, and optimization.

Efficient: the brain works on managing the consumption of energy in the best possible manner, predicting energy requirements before they happen.

Anticipatory: to be efficient, the brain has a predictive processing capacity to incorporate or generate not just information about the past or the present, but also future states (Bubic et al., 2010). Anticipating what's coming is relevant and beneficial for motor and cognitive control, decision-making, perception, theory of mind, and other cognitive processes.

Placebo: the mere thought that a treatment has been received has a beneficial physiological response (Pinch, 2016). Our brain is so powerful that a fake treatment can be assumed real if the prefrontal—subcortical systems that are involved in valuation, emotion, and expectation—get engaged (Wager & Atlas, 2015). Our thoughts and trust can increase the production of neurotransmitters—endorphins and dopamine—and activate brain regions linked to emotional reactions and awareness, which, when combined, have the capacity to heal our bodies.

Habitual: the brain is constantly looking for ways to save energy and creating habits is efficient in terms of not needing to 'learn' something again and again. Studies indicate that a large percentage of our behavior is not from conscious choices but determined by habits.

Categorical: the brain structures its content by creating categories automatically classifying information to predict and explain the sensory information received to create concepts, which, in terms of efficiency, saves energy the way habits do. This characteristic is dangerous for traumatized individuals since they may assign the 'dangerous' category to most experiences.

Reprogrammable: the brain has the capacity to reorganize itself, modify, change, and adapt its structure and its functions throughout life and in response to experience (Voss et al., 2017). Since the brain never stops learning, new connections can always create new circuits. Those circuits when repeated become programs of automatic action.

Many of these characteristics are key to designing healing interventions. In the same way that we can respond positively to a placebo, we can also be victims of our negative thoughts and pessimism, like in the case of the nocebo effect which works the opposite way. It's possible to convince ourselves we are worse off than we are or we could use the same adaptive mechanisms to persuade our brain that we are safe and to anticipate good outcomes.

THE TRIUNE BRAIN MODEL: A USEFUL WAY OF LOOKING AT THE BRAIN

Different professions and branches of science divide the brain differently. In trauma studies, the Triune Brain Model has gained popularity and is commonly used to explain what happens when traumatization occurs. This model proposes that, by evolution, the brain of mammals is organized into three different hierarchical layers that were adding elements: some limbic structures were added to a 'reptilian' core (called the basal ganglia) which then got over neocortical components. Figure 2.2 describes the main functions of the three different layers of evolution:

Regardless of whether the brain evolved exactly like the model proposes, it offers a useful framework to understand why we respond in such primitive ways to danger and how a more evolved part of the brain offers the way to avoid damaging alterations.

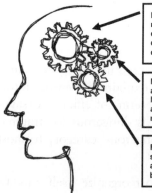

Neocortex (human brain, found uniquely in higher mammals). Key role in memory, attention, perception, cognition, awareness, thought, language, and consciousness. It hosts higher-order cognitive functions including those concerning intellect and spiritual thoughts, abstractions, morality, creativity, curiosity, and emotion regulation.

Mammalian brain (limbic system, structures influencing the endocrine system and the ANS). Support of a variety of functions including emotion, learning, long-term memory, sensory processing, time perception, attention, anticipatory affective states, autonomic control, actions/motor behavior, motivation, and olfaction.

Reptilian brain (basic survival; includes mainly the brainstem). The oldest structure known in invertebrates. Does not learn from experience; uses more automatic and habitual instinctual behaviors. Control of survival activities like breathing, heart rate, and balance.

Figure 2.2 The Triune Brain Model

Reptilian brain (or primordial)

Reptilian brain (or primordial): basic, primitive. The midbrain (periaque-ductal gray and the superior colliculi) plays an essential role in traumatization since it's part of autonomic function and behavioral responses to threatening stimuli (MacLean, 1973). It has larger participation in aggressive behavior, fighting/fleeing, the selection of leaders, compulsive or ritualistic behavior, territoriality and reproduction, conformity, and the regulation of physical housekeeping duties.

Mammalian brain (Paleomammalian complex)

Mammalian brain (Paleomammalian complex): emotional. It was assumed for many years that emotions were largely housed in the limbic system. New scientific understanding has made that belief obsolete since many scientists affirm that neurological regulation or creating memories are not under the control of one single element. Important for trauma studies is to see the lim-bic system as one of the participants in the regulation and autonomic emo-tional processes. This part of the brain hosts some of the neural networks and structures responsible for innate and conditioned fear. The prefrontal cortex (PFC), amygdala, hippocampus, and hypothalamus are structures that con-tribute significantly to regulating emotional experiences, most of which are connected to the sense of belonging as the significant component in forming and preserving family and community. Such behaviors include fear, love, hate, greed, jealousy, gluttony, selfishness, and pleasure. Over-activation of the emotional brain causes individuals to struggle with interpersonal rela-tionships, addictions, and mood regulation (Litvak & Senzee, 1986).

Neo-mammalian complex

Neo-mammalian complex (human brain or neocortex): higher-order and executive functions such as cognition, information processing, and spirit-uality are regulated here. The neocortex is connected to various subcortical structures sending and receiving information from them but the majority of its connections are from one area of the cortex to another. One of its primary functions may be the prediction of future states (Ekman et al., 2017). Ac-cording to McLean—who developed the theory—increases in size and com-plexity of the cerebral cortex separate humans from the mouse line between 90 and 100 million years and from monkeys, such as the macaque, 25 million years (Preuss, 2000). The neocortex contributes to executive functions and regulation of the nervous system in several ways: it helps stabilize emotional responses and tolerate distress; its development requires support from attachment figures. The neocortex can also be seen as comprising four regions based on the patterns of its grooves and ridges with the frontal lobe being the largest of the four. The anterior part of the frontal lobe is occupied by the PFC, a region that hosts the subtleties of the human experience. You'll hear a lot about it because it plays an extremely significant role in resolving traumatization, healing from dysregulation, or stabilizing mental health issues.

The PFC is formed by medial, lateral, and orbital surfaces. It occupies one-third of the entire human cerebral cortex. The PFC is one of the last cortical regions to undergo full maturation in humans, taking around 25 years to fully develop. Executive functions depend in large part on the activation of this region. Executive functions are in charge of decision-making, self-reflection, problem-solving, self-control, planning, the ability to sustain attention and control impulsivity, planning long-term goals, moderating social behavior, receptivity to feedback and novelty, and the ability to multitask and cognitive flexibility (Chan et al., 2008). Damage to the PFC also causes personality changes, abnormal emotional responses, and general difficulty performing in daily life. During traumatization, this part of the brain receives a very limited amount of energy, slowing down its participation. When the traumatization is prolonged, the PFC can become slow and habitually disconnected from many of the daily processes and high-order regulation. It can also slow down its maturation with terrible consequences. I'll come back to this important issue in the chapters on complex and developmental traumatization. Another important task of the PFC is to receive and translate the flow of energy and information not only from the body but from our surroundings and the people we interact with. This is the characteristic that allows us to experience life more fully.

The Triune Brain Model points out that we are as primitive as one can be, but also that we are social beings and therefore emotionally driven. Most importantly, it shows us that humans have reached a point in evolution that allows us to overcome our primitive actions and automatic decisions. The model is relevant because it uses a biological point of view to separate human behavior from the behavior of other species. This is highly important when considering that research is mainly done using animals like rats; this model offers a way to translate those findings into the human experience. Most animals' brains lack the sophistication of ours. The prefrontal functioning, for example, is closely related to the development of moral sensibility and ethical judgment (Loye, 2002) which we can't investigate in rats or any other lab subject. It is the connection between the PFC and other brain areas that allows us to make deliberate choices to be—or not to be—caring, loving, generous, considerate, thoughtful, and compassionate. These same connections allow us to understand social and cultural cues to modulate our behavior, recognize someone's suffering and needs, and offer our respect or participation (Loye, 2002). In this way, there is a big correlation between this model and the PVT, which also talks about human evolution and socialization as protection from danger that favors more evolved species. When the PFC is slow or partially disconnected, most of the healing work is to reactivate it.

Traumatizing Agents

I ran into a friend I had not seen in years and learned something interesting about traumatization by exchanging a few phrases with her. —How are you doing? Do you still live around? I asked. —No, I had to sell my place because I couldn't work anymore after I was forced out of my car at gunpoint. —Oh my! And what happened? —Just imagine the shock, I still can't sleep. —For sure! Did they hurt you? —No, I screamed so loud that the thief got scared and just ran away, but I see the gun pointing at me everywhere. —Wow! I'm so sorry. When did that happen? —It'll be 6 years in May. I've been broke and devastated since. What are the chances you find a guy in your car with a gun? Extremely traumatizing! —I imagine! I'm sorry! —I'm better now. I've been studying Thanatology and I know everything about death and how to deal with it.

It's the norm to think that what traumatizes us is the objectively dangerous nature of the occurrence we experience, or how stressful the circumstances we sometimes have to endure are. However, what's often overlooked is that what traumatizes us—and *keeps* us traumatized—is also *the relationship between the incident and our response to it*. As we learned in Chapter Two (Personalizing Trauma), the relationship with the experience (its effect) derives from how dangerous the incident seems to be (our perception) and how intensely we respond to it (our reaction). My friend's example illustrated how we can stay fixated on a traumatic event just by feeding the ANS with an idea that defeats us, like death. That's why we need to understand the additional elements that *induce*, *prolong*, or *exacerbate* traumatization on top of just danger or survival. Those factors are what I call '*traumatizing agents*.'

Traumatizing agents participate not only in activating the protective mechanisms in the first place but also in prolonging their activation. They heighten the perception of risk, keep the system in hyper-alertness, or contribute to giving up and losing hope. They affect our individual response to a situation and play a part in how symptoms unfold. These agents can be external or internal. (We already learned about two external ones, danger and survival, in Chapter One). Regardless of their origin, they all contribute to becoming traumatized at every step of the process.

> The friend I mentioned above had developed a relationship with death from the threat she experienced even though the possibility of dying from a gunshot ended as soon as the man ran away. Her chances to die went back to where they were before, or even lowered, but in her head, she was still at risk of dying, and her interest in the subject kept her connected and focused on avoiding death, which kept her system in survival mode and her life dysfunctional.

External traumatizing agents are evident since the tendency in psychiatry is to assign all the weight of the trauma phenomena to danger, adversity, abuse, and neglect. I'm adding rejection and social/systemic adversity to the incidents in this list of external agents and I occasionally add others to the list. The internal traumatizing agents are not as obvious—and for whatever reason, they (except for fear) are normally left out of the conversation. I'll explain several of them in the chapters where they are relevant, but as an introduction I want you to have in mind that we get traumatized when emotional reactions of fear, rage, shame, defeat, victimhood, guilt, etc., contribute to keeping our system in a prolonged state of alert and crisis even when the presence of the external traumatizing agents is over. Such internal traumatizing agents send signals to the brain that we still need the protective mechanisms active. In addition to the emotions, our survival circuits, rumination, negativity, catastrophizing, victim mentality, rejection sensitivity, and epigenetic characteristics are huge contributors to the development of a trauma disorder—and antagonists of resolving traumatization.

If we understand that there are factors we could have power over, it becomes easier to resolve or heal fear altogether. For example, rumination—a common habit—could be unlearned (requires practice but it can be done). Defeat, too. Defeat is a mental state that can be changed almost at will. And so on. Traumatization makes us feel disempowered, helpless, and hopeless—but

Danger/Threat Abuse Adversity Neglect Rejection Systemic Adversity	E X T E R N A L	Traumatizing Agents	I N T E R N A L	Distorted Perception Fear/Defeat Stress/Anxiety Shame/Guilt Rejection Sensitivity Anger/Hatred Rumination Victim-mentality

Figure 2.3 Main external and internal traumatizing agents

helping our system recognize the severity of the threat could give us a way out, especially in cases when it's possible to realize that objectively there is no threat any longer, even if the body keeps shaking. Figure 2.3 shows a list of the most important traumatizing agents.

PERCEIVING LACK OF SAFETY: AN INTERNAL TRAUMATIZING AGENT

Danger is the first and foremost external traumatizing agent. Besides the intrinsic level of threat of the traumatic 'object,' becoming traumatized also depends on feeling unsafe whether by recognition or by perception.

> Let's imagine an inland taipan (the most poisonous snake) going below someone's bed. If the person has no awareness of the presence of the snake, that occurrence is not traumatizing because there is no recognition of the threat. Now let's imagine a person finds that type of snake dead inside their house. If they know how lethal that snake is, they will be scared even when that snake has no capacity to harm anymore. From that day on, the person will experience a lack of safety in the house and may be hypervigilant about another one coming in.

From the example, we can deduce that lack of safety is an experience that keeps the system on alert, looking for something dangerous to happen. To avoid risk, the brain will use its sophisticated survival system to make sure that we are prepared to fight for our life. We have more than one system that protects us from illnesses, external agents, physical injuries, etc. Our immune system, for example, is designed to protect us from outside invaders using antibodies that kill germs or anything made of microbes. The same system could cause illness in its quest to protect us, as is the case of rheumatoid arthritis, a disease that develops when our immune system attacks healthy cells, causing inflammation. Similarly, the survival mechanisms in our nervous system also attack our body, causing a trauma disorder 'by mistake' in the name of adaptation. The difference between the two is that the immune system combats physical intruders, while the nervous system combats the internal, cognitive/emotional/subjective appraisal of danger. Our survival system doesn't have 'eyes' to 'see' the danger; it uses our internal experience to assume that there is a problem that needs a solution. To assess the level of risk, the brain receives signals from emotional intruders such as stress, fear, or shame. Our immune system makes us sick when it produces many more antibodies than needed; our survival system afflicts us when it produces many more stress hormones and numbing agents, causing more alterations than necessary. That's why it's essential to understand what 'threatening' really means. If we feel afraid of our own fear, we multiply the production of protections that will eventually damage our system without any protective benefits. Our mind and cognition combined could safeguard us from the consequences of the innate primitive protection. There is no more effective medicine to kill fear than our inner strength supported by determination, hope, and trust. The power of our mind can be our worst enemy or our biggest ally.

> In the example of the person that found the dead snake, living stressed from always anticipating being bitten will eventually harm their system. But being proactive in sealing possible entrances and setting traps outside could help develop the peace needed for the system to stay regulated.

FEAR AS THE MAIN GO-TO FOR SURVIVAL: AN INTERNAL TRAUMATIZING AGENT

According to Joseph LeDoux (Debiec & LeDoux, 2004), an American neuroscientist/musician whose survival circuits research is highly regarded, fear has received more scientific attention than any other emotion. According to him, "danger is ancient but fear is a recent invention" (Ledoux, 2019). He assures us that fear is not hardwired to the extent that we use it. Our assumptions about our strength (or lack of it) also contribute to their creation. For decades, fear was considered a primary emotion that manifested universally across cultures. With the advances in neuroscience, that formulation has changed. Some academics, like the distinguished professor Barrett & Simmons (2015), see fear differently, and state that instead of being universal, each one of us creates it using our experience and collecting information on what can present a threat. Debiec and LeDoux (2004) also provided a similar approach shifting from thinking of it as a 'primitive' response to defining it as a state that develops from knowing and learning. They explain that fear is a physiological state that controls behavior—preventing us from engaging in overly risky behaviors—and that it's also a learned conditioning that once learned and stored as a memory, could stay for as long as we live, becoming part of our reality and determining patterns of behavior. If we agree that fear is a conditioned response, then it follows that it can also be 'forgotten' and its reaction weakened as soon as we change our definitions of what's dangerous. According to this new paradigm, the protective mechanisms get activated by an unconscious prediction of threat that elicits fear once we are aware of the threat, dependent on the 'type of fear' we have gotten conditioned to use as a response.

While scientists debate whether fear precipitates a series of physiological responses to defend and protect our lives, or if the survival circuits do it before fear appears, for the subject of this book, it's more important to address its participation in the final results of traumatization. The fear we experience regularly (and when we are not in the wild), 'our fear,' puts us on edge automatically. That type of fear—a mental state more than a simple emotion—keeps running the processes that can destabilize us and dysregulate our system. It is learned by what we have gone through and conditioned by the acquired information from our surroundings (family, media, literature, etc.). Just think about how we are born lacking the meaning of situations or concepts considered intimidating, debilitating, unacceptable, or whatever else worth fearing, unless we learn it somehow. If we learn to fear lightning, trucks, or snakes, we will be fearful of them regardless of whether we are seeing them on a movie screen, near our house, or in our dreams. Fear can become a program that can be put into action without much thought and run for years and years even if it has no connection with what is really happening in our surroundings. That type of fear becomes the lens traumatized people see reality through, determining the patterns of their behavior, dominated by the survival primitive responses to whatever one thinks could damage or hurt us. That fear is what keeps the body in a continuous struggle for survival even in the absence of danger or threat. It becomes a traumatizing agent that keeps stressing the system to its limits. To stop it from controlling us, we need to consciously assess how threatening the thing that is scary to us really is, become proactive in finding solutions to eliminate the level of risk we are subjected to, and work on reprogramming our learned reaction.

DEFEAT AND THE POINT OF NO-RETURN: AN INTERNAL TRAUMATIZING AGENT

The dictionary definition of defeat includes "frustration by nullification or by prevention of success" when it is used as a noun. This fits the construct of 'mental defeat' which has been identified as an element in a wide range of mental disorders. What grabs my attention from the definition is 'the prevention of success.' Defeat not only prevents us from stopping traumatization but from thriving in life. Defeat is a factor that influences the development of distress and severe symptoms that debilitate individuals mentally (Taylor et al., 2011). Some studies show its presence in depression, pain, suicide, and PTSD. A high correlation has been observed between the severity of symptoms in PTSD and lack of improvement after treatment when a sense of defeat is present (Collard et al., 2021).

The possibility of losing physical or psychological integrity—when combined with a sense of hopelessness (an internal traumatizing agent on its own)—promotes a debilitating self-evaluation that becomes mental defeat and stays as a victim mentality (another internal traumatizing agent). It's this combination that turns mental defeat into one of the most important key predictors of the development of a trauma disorder (Wilker et al., 2017). Reaching the place where one loses hope of becoming the someone one idealizes can be caused by external factors like rejection, neglect, abandonment, social hate, etc., or internal factors like pain, physical illness, pervasive negative emotional states, etc., or a combination of both. Neurobiologically, mental defeat during traumatization is the crucial instance where the activation of the PSNS becomes damaging due to *the loss of inner resistance;* defeat is interpreted as a high risk of death, and therefore, the brain has to take extreme measures. Developing defeat as a mental state is what keeps the system working focusing on survival (survival mode) indefinitely because the brain translates defeat as having *given up.* Without overcoming defeat, the system will not go back to regular operation.

References

Badcock, P. B., Friston, K. J., Ramstead, M. J. D., et al. (2019). The hierarchically mechanistic mind: An evolutionary systems theory of the human brain, cognition, and behavior. *Cognitive, Affective, & Behavioral Neuroscience* 19, 1319–1351. https://doi.org/10.3758/s13415-019-00721-3

Barrett, D. L. (2022, January 9). Neuroscience says there's no such thing as free will. A psychologist explains why that might not be true. The strange neuroscience of free will explained | *BBC Science Focus Magazine*. https://www.sciencefocus.com/the-human-body/free-will/

Barrett, L. F., & Simmons, W. K. (2015). Interoceptive predictions in the brain. Nature reviews. *Neuroscience*, 16(7), 419–429. https://doi.org/10.1038/nrn3950

Behel, P. (2021). Autonomic dysregulation: An unseen epidemic. *World Journal of Yoga, Physical Therapy and Rehabilitation* 2(5): 2021. WJYPR.MS.ID.000546

Bubic, A., von Cramon, D. Y., & Schubotz, R. I. (2010). Prediction, cognition and the brain. *Frontiers in Human Neuroscience*, 4, 25. https://doi.org/10.3389/fnhum.2010.00025

Buonomano, D. (2018). *Your brain is a time machine: The neuroscience and physics of time*. New York: W. W. Norton & Company.

Chan, R. C., Shum, D., Toulopoulou, T., & Chen, E. Y. (2008). Assessment of executive functions: Review of instruments and identification of critical issues. *Archives of Clinical Neuropsychology: The Official Journal of the National Academy of Neuropsychologists*, 23(2), 201–216. https://doi.org/10.1016/j.acn.2007.08.010

Chang, C. Y., Ke, D. S., & Chen, J. Y. (2009). Essential fatty acids and human brain. *Acta Neurologica Taiwanica*, 18(4), 231–241.

Collard, V. E., Gillett, J. L., Themelis, K., & Tang, N. K. (2021). An exploratory investigation into the effects of mental defeat on pain threshold, pain rating, pain anticipation, and mood. *Current Psychology*. https://doi.org/10.1007/s12144-021-01548-3

Damasio, A., & Carvalho, G. B. (2013). The nature of feelings: Evolutionary and neurobiological origins. *Nature Reviews Neuroscience*, 14(2), 143–152. https://doi.org/10.1038/nrn3403

Debiec, J., & LeDoux, J. (2004). Fear and the brain. *Social research: An International Quarterly*, 71(4), 807–818. https://doi.org/10.1353/sor.2004.0064

Ekman, M., Kok, P., & de Lange, F. P. (2017). Time-compressed preplay of anticipated events in human primary visual cortex. *Nature Communications*, 8(1). https://doi.org/10.1038/ncomms15276

Grossmann, I., Sahdra, B. K., & Ciarrochi, J. (2016). A Heart and A Mind: Self-distancing facilitates the association between heart rate variability, and wise reasoning. *Frontiers in Behavioral Neuroscience*, 10, 68. https://doi.org/10.3389/fnbeh.2016.00068

LeDoux, J. (2019). *The deep history of ourselves: The four-billion-year story of how we got conscious brains*. New York: Viking (Penguin Random House). ISBN: 9780735223837 (hc); 9780735223844 (eb).

Litvak, S., & Senzee, A. W. (1986). *Toward a new brain: Evolution and the human mind* (pp. 145–147). Upper Saddle River, NJ: Prentice-Hall.

Loye, D. (2002). *The moral brain. Brain and mind 3* (pp. 133–150). https://doi.org/10.1023/A:1016561925565

Luczak, A., McNaughton, B. L., & Kubo, Y. (2020). Neurons learn by predicting future activity. *Nature Machine Intelligence*. https://doi.org/10.1038/s42256-021-00430-y

MacLean, P.D. (1973). The brain's generation gap: Some human implications. *Zygon*, 8:113–127. https://doi.org/10.1111/j.1467-9744.1973.tb00218.x

Picard, F., & Friston, K. (2014). Predictions, perception, and a sense of self. *Neurology*, 83(12), 1112–1118. https://doi.org/10.1212/WNL.0000000000000798

Pinch, B. (2016). More Than Just a Sugar Pill: Why the placebo effect is real. *Science in the News*. Harvard Graduate School of the Arts and Sciences.

Plante, A. (2016). How the human body uses electricity - University of Maryland Graduate School. *The Maryland University Gazette*. https://graduate.umaryland.edu/gsa/gazette/February-2016/How-the-human-body-uses-electricity/

Porges, S. W. (2009). The polyvagal theory: New insights into adaptive reactions of the autonomic nervous system. *Cleveland Clinic Journal of Medicine*, 76, S86–S90.

Preuss, T. (2000). What's human about the human brain? M. S. Gazzaniga (Ed.), *The new cognitive neurosciences* (2nd edn., pp. 1219–1234). Cambridge, MA: The MIT Press.

Schwartz, A. (2013). Polyvagal theory helps unlock symptoms of PTSD. https://drarielleschwartz.com/polyvagal-theory-unlocks-symptoms-of-ptsd-dr-arielle-schwartz/#.YbJcrvHMKrU

Steckler, T., Kalin, N. H., Reul, J. M. H., & Murison, R. (2016). *Neuroscience of pain, stress, and emotion. The neurobiology of stress* (pp. 29–49). Elsevier.

Taylor, P. J., Gooding, P., Wood, A. M., & Tarrier, N. (2011). The role of defeat and entrapment in depression, anxiety, and suicide. *Psychological Bulletin*, 137(3), 391–420.

Triune Brain. Triune Brain – an overview | ScienceDirect Topics. (n.d.). https://www.sciencedirect.com/topics/neuroscience/triune-brain

Voss, J. L., Bridge, D. J., Cohen, N. J., & Walker, J. A. (2017). A closer look at the hippocampus and memory. *Trends in Cognitive Sciences*, 21(8), 577–588. https://doi.org/10.1016/j.tics.2017.05.008

Wager, T. D., & Atlas, L. Y. (2015). The neuroscience of placebo effects: Connecting context, learning and health. *Nature*, 403–418. https://doi.org/10.1038/nrn3976

Wilker, S., Kleim, B., Geiling, A., Pfeiffer, A., Elbert, T., & Kolassa, I.-T. (2017). Mental defeat and cumulative trauma experiences predict trauma-related psychopathology: Evidence from a postconflict population in Northern Uganda. *Clinical Psychological Science*, 5(6), 974–984. https://doi.org/10.1177/2167702617719946

Three
Searching for Safety

How can we assess trauma disorders?

What does it mean to freeze?

What's retraumatization?

Is it possible to prevent traumatization?

We've been reviewing how being exposed to life-threatening situations—objectively or subjectively—sets the survival mechanisms into action. Therefore, you may want to know more about how these survival mechanisms manifest to get the whole picture. Fair enough! Before we start with each individual mechanism, let's look at Figure 3.1.

Figure 3.1 shows how the survival circuits subdivide into survival mechanisms (peritraumatic) and survival strategies (posttraumatic). Survival

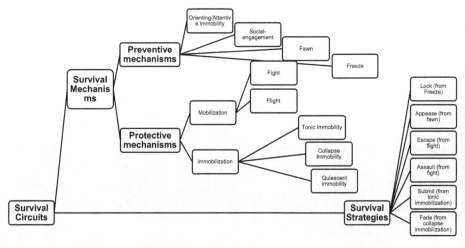

Figure 3.1 Survival circuits processes and subprocesses

DOI: 10.4324/9781003382478-5

mechanisms subdivide into two big blocks in the search for safety: (I) preventive mechanisms and (II) protective mechanisms. I'll go through them one by one in this chapter, explaining not only their biological origins but also when and how they become responses to traumatic events. We'll see how they operate and how we can identify them in the regular circumstances of our daily routines and notice when they belong to the trauma phenomena. I'll also describe the specific ways in which they can end up hurting our system. I'll explain survival strategies later in the chapter.

Preventive Mechanisms

Are you familiar with Harry Houdini? He was a Hungarian-American illusionist who became famous for his escape acts at the turn of the 20th century. Houdini liked bragging about how strong he was by withstanding hard blows to his abdomen. Fans kept punching harder and harder, and Houdini remained unharmed. Stories say that one day he was unprepared when a guy punched him by surprise. That time he got injured. Some people even say that jab was the one that caused his liver failure and death.

Houdini's story allows us to reflect on how not every 'punch'—emotional or physical—leaves a lesion even though they cause pain. The story paints a clear picture of how the level of damage depends on how prepared we are to take the blow. Traumatization would have very different results if we were prepared to receive punches—to get hurt, betrayed, left alone, and be at risk. But how to prepare for that? Since our brain is great at anticipating, just knowing that it could happen develops resilience and opens the door to acquiring whatever could be needed (resources). We have several mechanisms that give us a window of opportunity to assess, prepare, and prevent 'punches' from damaging us.

AROUSAL AND NORMAL LEVELS OF ACTIVATION

To be aroused means to be awake and ready to interact with the world engagingly when our senses perceive our surroundings. Being aroused also means that the sympathetic NS is active, similar to the processes used by nervousness, stress, or even anxiety. That's the reason some researchers consider arousal the first step in the activation of the survival mechanisms *when the stimulus perceived relates to threat.* It's hard to differentiate where arousal stops and stress begins. They all move in a continuum in terms of brain activation and maintaining arousal is a regular function of our brain. Arousal becomes part of the body's survival mechanisms when the brain anticipates that stimuli could overwhelm the system; that's when arousal becomes an automatic response toward a predicted danger. It then generates a more extreme than normal activation of the SNS (hyper-arousal). To control arousal, it is necessary to activate the PSNS, and if the sympathetic is extreme, the parasympathetic activation would need to be extreme as well, sometimes causing hypo-arousal. More on this subject later.

PERITRAUMATIC: BEFORE THE CONSEQUENCES, THERE'S THE STRUGGLE

Let me bring to your attention a concept that will become very important for assessing traumatization: peritraumatic. Peritraumatic deals with what happens before—versus after—developing a trauma disorder. It refers to whatever the system experiences during the initial phases of the struggle for survival. The term 'peritraumatic' has become a standard in the research community to separate the responses activated *while under threat* from the ones that occur in the system *after developing a trauma disorder when the survival mechanisms become the 'default.'* During the peritraumatic phase, the system uses preventive mechanisms first, followed by protective mechanisms (mobilization and immobilization). In the case of PTSD, they can be observed as sequential, but as we'll learn later on, there isn't always an identifiable event or survival sequence. Let's go over the ways the brain prevents the use of extreme measures.

PREVENTION: OVERREACTING INHIBITORS

We are naturally resilient because the brain chooses health over illness. Our natural tendency is to regulate our reactions. If we feel that our safety is being jeopardized, our resilience assists us in bouncing back to equilibrium as soon as it can. David MacPhee, a professor emeritus, says that resilience is "adaptive self-stabilization and self-organization following disturbances to a system caused by significant adversity" (MacPhee et al., 2015). As part of our resiliency, we have preventive mechanisms that can help us assess risk or look for help before we succumb to fear. What I want to emphasize is that even when we are wired for survival, we are also *wired for efficiency.* For that reason, *some of the survival mechanisms are preventive.* The traumatization sequence is energy-consuming and distracting to the rest of the system's tasks, so by activating preventive processes, the system is more effective in allocating energy and guarding the system against internal harm while preparing it for external danger.

You will notice that freeze is included among the preventive mechanisms. I think you'll be pleasantly surprised to learn that the feared 'freeze' is not what we have had in mind for a while, and instead, is a program that can help us avoid getting traumatized.

Prevention: Orienting/Attentive Immobility

We perceive a dangerous environment mainly by the information our senses collect but our awareness is normally taken by many other happenings that control our attention. So, once the brain receives some signal that creates the prediction that things are not as they should be—like an unrecognized sound or smell of burning—it redirects to focus looking for the explanation, engaging our awareness. That redirection of our focus receives the name of attentive immobility and sometimes of orienting. With attentive immobility, sensory perception increases, looking up or around or staying still and focused on listening (sensing) more carefully. This reaction is very short and may be imperceptible in humans, but it's frequently there. In terms of the changes in the brain, the superior colliculus (within the midbrain) gets activated, and there is a cardiac deceleration and a startle potentiation in preparation for what could come (Szeska, 2021). The Polyvagal Theory (PVT) suggests that we count on an extra sense named 'neuroception,' which is theorized to allow our body to scan our environment for cues of safety or danger using both branches of the vagus nerve and including a mechanism Porges calls social-engagement.

Prevention: Social-Engagement

According to the PVT, the natural way to be when mammals are safe— or when trying to make sure we are safe—is to look at someone's face or hear someone's tone of voice. We do this to confirm that they are there to provide protection, which calms our nervous system even without talking. Social-engagement is explained as precautionary, thanks to evolution among social beings (mammals). Social-engagement is driven by the activation of the ventral vagus nerve. It seems that this branch evolved directly from the hardwired mammalian need for attachment: we need to know that we are not alone, that we belong, and that we can count on someone to help us stay alive and affiliated. For infants, it means looking for the attachment figure and guessing mood and acceptance through their gestures and prosody. For older children and adults, it is looking at the possible aggressor and whoever is around, and instead of guessing the mood, establishing a connection, or predicting the level of a possible threat. New studies have found that when the eyes of two individuals meet and social gaze interaction happens, there is an interconnection between the prefrontal cortex and the amygdala that calms down the system and regulates emotional responses (Dal Monte et al., 2022).

Putting it into the context of the preventive mechanisms, social-engagement seems to be the first chosen reaction after perceiving danger when we are not alone, or after anticipating that the perceived danger is bigger than what we could handle by ourselves. If by socially engaging we find safety (someone will take care of the danger, for example), other protections may not get activated and we may avoid negative consequences. If after socially engaging we still feel unsafe and at risk, then our system will have to make use of a different mechanism. The PVT emphasizes that the ventral vagus has the power to inhibit further activation of the survival circuits.

Prevention: Fawn

This mechanism has received several different names but generally speaking, it has been ignored, most likely because it is not evident as a peritraumatic response, and because it may not be used by animals in a way that could be observed in a lab. Still, I want to include it here briefly. Its relevance as a posttraumatic survival strategy (appease) is larger than as a peritraumatic defense but still plays an important part. Porges has talked about 'Please and Appease' as ventral vagal activation. It's not hard to imagine that someone that feels threatened would try to placate the aggressor by socially engaging with them conveying a sense of submission. Social-engagement is designed to be used as a protection by projecting not only friendliness but also a sense of unthreatening to those that could seem menacing. I've seen it in front of me when working with couples; many partners go into submission, softening their voice, justifying the other, smiling, and even giggling as soon as they see the partner becoming aggressive or offensive.

Fawn could then be considered another preventive mechanism that doesn't activate the protective sequence any further. There may be some sympathetic activation, but the person will subdue aggression to gain safety. This mechanism will keep the emotions down, including bottled-up anger. If successful, the person will be safe, the protections interrupted, and just a few consequences will result, like resentment. Some people describe fawn as a mechanism where the person completely dismisses their needs and emotions, avoids conflict, and pleases others to stay safe. This description, which is more of a posttraumatic manifestation, reflects dorsal parasympathetic activity. 'People pleasers' are normally not as 'lively' or fully present; they show a dorsal vagal activation reflected as dissociation and disengagement. Therefore, fawn is not the same as submissive/pleaser.

Prevention: Freeze

This is one of my favorite survival mechanisms not only because it's interesting but because it may be the one that is most misunderstood and yet commonly encountered in people. Comprehending its purpose and operation better may help us identify it, use it, and design/apply interventions specific to it. After extended research on this particular protection (which intrigued me when I saw it as a survival strategy), I am convinced that the article written by Kozlowska et al. published by the Harvard Review of Psychiatry in June 2015 (Kozlowska et al., 2015) is the best source to understand what happens when we freeze. They define freezing as *"fight-flight-on-hold"* and make a clear distinction between this mechanism and the immobilization that becomes active later in the pursuit of survival. Most people use the phrase 'fight/flight/ freeze' when talking about survival mechanisms, which makes us think that freezing happens after a fight or flight, confusing it with the immobility that comes after mobilization fails. Most of what has been written using the triad model assumes that freezing is dissociative (and the most damaging) because it gets confused with a dorsal vagus parasympathetic activation (disconnection). But freezing, being a 'fight/flight on hold,' gets activated before fighting or fleeing, and is used, similar to orienting and social-engagement, as a preventive measure. Freezing is a healthy protection. It's anticipatory and less disruptive to our system than immobilization, especially if resolved fast. Our preventive mechanisms are not designed to stay activated for long. They are meant to be used in emergencies, helping us stay safe by doing their job, and corrected as soon as possible. Freeze, as prevention, helps hold us from attacking or escaping until we assess the best way to eliminate the risk. It prepares the nervous system to go into action but holds the hyper-arousal activation by putting the brakes on until there is space for the cognition to kick in. Because of the way our brain is programmed, we begin to respond to the emotional significance of a stimulus before we fully represent that stimulus in our cognition, and freezing is the ideal mechanism to give space for the higher-order functions to catch up.

Since freeze has been used as immobilization for so long in texts, it may be difficult to accept that it goes before fight/flight without further explanation. To be momentarily paralyzed is not the same as being immobilized. The neurobiology of each is completely different. In freeze, our muscles keep a high tone (tense), while our heart maintains its rhythm (or accelerates) as opposed to losing muscle tone and dropping heart rate as what happens during immobilization. The key difference between freeze and immobilization is that during freeze our senses are sharp, while when immobilized, we dissociate and disengage important pointers for posttraumatic processes. Staying in freeze is protective and preventive but when it is sustained for long, the person may stay in a state of indecisiveness that may become a new way to react to many circumstances which affects their behavior, identity, and even personality, but may not cause the system to go into survival mode. I'll explain this further in Chapter Six.

Protective Mechanisms

> I had a client that had an accident where they almost died. After that, they became obsessed with their health, spending hours planning and cooking their meals, exercising, and learning about better routines, best postures while sleeping, etc. They read everything available that informed them of what could cause illness or death. 'Their fear' became about their body failing them more than about having another accident, a fear that kept them shifting from mobilization to immobilization.

Protective mechanisms tax the system in an undesirable way because they distract the brain from its regular operation. They get activated if the first stages of the survival sequence—the preventive mechanisms—don't succeed at helping the person avoid danger. That's when the autonomic nervous system (ANS) moves into activating more drastic processes like fight, flight, or tonic immobility aimed at impeding the anticipated possibility of death. The processes I will describe in this section do not include what happens after a disorder has unfolded (posttraumatic), but instead describes what happens *during* the struggle for survival. I use the term 'protections' as opposed to 'defenses' to strengthen the idea that it is our system trying to protect us from adversity instead of thinking of it as a person trying to defend themselves as some theories have assumed. For many years, psychodynamic theories have used the term 'defense mechanisms' to describe ways to cope used unconsciously to avoid unacceptable thoughts, behavior, or feelings.

Using the neuroscience approach, it's easy to see how biological mechanisms are hardwired to protect us from the possibility of injury, harm, and death. Think of it this way: the design of our brain and ANS is responsible for the mechanisms' existence, while adversity and our emotional states (external and internal traumatizing agents) are responsible for their activation. I separate the protective mechanisms, according to the PVT, in mobilization and immobilization but I will divide them further to distinguish three types of immobilization as I'll explain next.

MOBILIZATION AND BECOMING STRONGER: HOW ANGER IS BEHIND AN ADAPTIVE WAY TO ELIMINATE RISK

Sympathetic activation in a defensive mode sets the body into mobilizing to either flee or fight.

Mobilization: Flight

Notice that I'm placing flight before fight as part of the mobilization mechanisms. That's because, for most, escaping is a better alternative than fighting, especially if fighting is not an option. From the time Cannon coined the term fight-or-flight (1915), some theories assumed that fight kicks off first even if a fraction of an instant later, the flight response has to initiate as well, but recent research assures that physiologically, they are the same and the sympathetic mechanics they use are the exact same ones: the heart accelerates to pump more blood to our legs, arms, and shoulders; the pupils dilate to become laser-focused on the threat with tunnel vision; the senses sharpen; organs not involved become less active or even inactive, including cognition and the reproductive and digestive systems. Still, it's worth separating them since they manifest differently even when their activation is alike. The circumstances are what influence the actions of attacking or escaping depending on the anticipated outcome; the brain's anticipation propels the action. The previous understanding came from the predator/prey model conducted on laboratory animals but people interact with challenges all the time and danger/safety is not as crystal clear as killing or being killed.

If you have ever witnessed a street fight or watched it on a screen, you can recall how people yell at each other while bringing their fists up but their bodies back; they move closer for seconds, and then they back up again like in a dance, while they continue to curse, threaten, and brood. Their bodies are attacking and escaping almost at the same time.

Our system's normal functioning is severely affected by the extreme effort of activating complex survival protections like this one even if we are only dealing with difficulties in our relationships. Flight in most animals is very simple: they run away from the danger that the vicinity of predators incites and they have miles of land to keep running away. In humans, it's not that straightforward; very rarely, running away makes us safer, especially in situations where the danger is constant. More than fleeing, we escape mentally and/or emotionally when we go through situations that we can't overcome. People resort to bars, to drugs or numbing agents, to avoid responsibility, or to believe the worst about themselves to repudiate the threat by internalizing the pain.

Mobilization: Fight

This protection is about preparing to respond to a possible attack and generating the strength to do so. In fight mode, our systems will grant us the possibility to confront the predator to beat or kill—or possibly scare by yelling—that which dares to jeopardize our life. The human brain releases stress hormones faster than we wish it would, and it becomes difficult for us to manage the surplus of energy, especially if we don't really need it. Anger and aggression are the common manifestations we see under this mechanism since anger is a natural protective reaction that empowers the person to push people away to defend their life and physical integrity.

One of the negative consequences of this surge of energy is that the brain, to empower the limbs and our laryngeal muscles, takes some of the energy from the more cognitive parts, clouding the capacity to stay rational, relational, and to make good decisions. We humans hardly use this strength to physically neutralize the 'enemy.' Instead, we use the full 'power' for raging, punching walls, menacing others with our body posture, raising our voice, swearing, and saying things that annihilate the other not physically but mostly psychologically, indirectly hurting ourselves, our relationships, and our peace of mind. An extreme example of this is 'dissociated rage' when the person goes into major aggressiveness without any cognitive filter about the possible consequences of the aggressive actions. It's not the product of 'dissociation' as the term is clinically used (because it's not parasympathetic), but the product of having the executive functions unavailable by lacking brain energy at that moment, energy that goes to our fists instead.

The failure of this protection after its activation is what pushes the system into immobilization, a process that sends our system closer to developing a trauma disorder. Failing means that the brain assumes the alterations made to empower us for fighting were insufficient if the person is still at risk, whether it comes from the actual threat or from feeling scared, overwhelmed, and helpless. If fight succeeds—becoming aware that the threat is behind—the activation of protections stops; if instead, we stay angry (and/or scared) and continue ruminating on it, the survival mechanisms might stay active, and the traumatization will get prolonged regardless of the circumstances.

For animals, failing the fight response normally means that the predator is stronger than the prey and can't be defeated. For us, it could mean feeling disempowered, incapable, or even undeserving if one never wins a fight, an argument, or a request, and if one is punished instead. For many of us, the fight response fails even before it manifests. An example here would be protesting abuse in a relationship with an aggressive person, arguing with a superior at work, or punching an authority.

IMMOBILIZATION: LOWERING OUR VITALS AS THE LAST RESOURCE TO STAY ALIVE

The next two protections are dominated by parasympathetic activation and used as a last resource. Their activation reflects how the neurons lose their strength in their communication with other neurons during the struggle, and how the numbing agents disconnect our awareness from the environment, from our body, and from many of our functions. I'm adding a third mechanism that gets ignored everywhere and has incredible value for treatment—Quiescent immobility.

Immobilization: Tonic Immobility

This mechanism and the following one (collapse) are extreme measures that animals need when they are trapped or caught by a predator after not being able to escape or neutralize the aggression. They are part of the protections ruled by the parasympathetic that intervene to keep the prey alive (at all costs) by minimizing the effect of possible physical damage caused by the predator, by trying to make the predator believe that the prey is already dead, and by keeping the vitals at a minimum to save the little energy the prey may have left. When individuals go into immobilization, their limbs—instead of being rigid—become feeble, and they lose most of their strength. This comes about after a period where the muscles retract, cramp, or spasm, and the cognition gets clouded. The PSNS activation functions as an inhibitor, lowering the vital signs and the connectivity of brain areas that consume high amounts of energy allocation—like executive and cognitive functions—lowering their power. This is the main reason we suffer from dissociative states and loss of memory if we reach this point. With a compromised brain and lack of attention, encoding memories becomes almost impossible; memory encoding depends in great part on attention and awareness.

The purpose of this protection is to help us not feel the pain caused by the struggle—whether physical or emotional—not by 'repressing' the pain but by numbing it; not by 'repressing' the memories of it, but by disengaging from recollecting most of what's happening. Most humans going into this strategy are in the struggle of not being abandoned, rejected, or unloved, and dissociating from that pain may stay as a constant at the cost of feeling like 'dead meat' which could be translated as worthless, invisible, or 'cold.' When this mechanism is used as the only one in a single event such as rape, the senses shut down and it may feel as if life leaves the body, or as if the person has left their body behind, symptoms normally identified as depersonalization and derealization.

During tonic immobility, the heightened attention gets lost and a state of disengagement with no thoughts can take over for hours. Many people call this stage 'fright' (Bracha et al., 2004) because after feeling overwhelmed, one feels helpless followed by a loss of hope with a deep sense of perturbation and dismay. One may not seem to be frightened externally, but internally, one is so scared of not having an option that the system's acute activation moves into shutdown with the same intensity. According to the PVT, the solution is to bring the system back into mobilization to reverse the flow and aspire to social-engagement. If we consult somatic-based theories, they suggest similar remedies like shaking or mimicking what animals do after being chased. Something certain is that it takes time for a brain to recover from the activation of these drastic processes.

Immobilization: Collapse Immobility

This stage has often been called 'fainting' and 'feigning death.' Fainting explains it best but the term 'collapse' may be more symbolic. Feigning death is also accurate because this type of activation could actually be lethal when there is a surge of numbing chemicals (dorsal parasympathetic activation) combined with a sudden withdrawal of levels of arousal. Fainting though is what often happens to humans: an extreme decrease in cerebral blood flow leads to a lack of oxygen—brain asphyxia—causing the failure on maintaining muscle tone and compromising the level of consciousness, therefore bringing the person to fall unconscious. There is a lot written on the description of tonic immobility and collapse immobility together as one, the way that the PVT clusters them too. When an animal pretends to be dead to avoid being eaten by a predator, both mechanisms may work together; but in the case of humans, it's hard to believe that fainting will become a response to avoid danger as in 'pretending' to be dead to push the predator away. It may be the origin of it, but at this point of our evolution, we are just suffering the consequences of the incongruence between the level of our protections and our actual need for them. Reaching this state cause a lack of recollection—whether right away or years after—of what happens during the struggle reflecting the incapacity of the brain to store information due to the lack of cerebral energy. I want us to be open to the possibility that not storing memories is not a choice (even unconscious) but a result of the way the brain works.

If this stage, collapse immobility, is described as fainting, we could conclude that it is not even a protective mechanism, but a consequence of the effort of staying alive, and the loss of hope of succeeding. As peritraumatic protection, fainting shows the exhaustion of the system as evidence that something extremely tolling happened, but if we were able to see inside the brain, we could notice how many processes shut down before the body collapses, leaving terrible posttraumatic consequences. When someone reaches this point, the chances of developing long-term PTSD (or any other trauma disorder) are extremely high. Extreme dissociation is also a way to interpret collapse even if it doesn't include the body. When the mind goes blank because enough circuits are not connecting to even having thoughts, dissociative states will be the sign that the collapse strategy consumed itself. This failure is the way people feel inside and how they remain for years. It's hard to avoid long-lasting consequences once this point is reached, but there is always the possibility to reboot to resolve traumatization and avoid the disorder.

Immobilization: Quiescent Immobility (Reboot)

Once the danger is gone and the person has been able to stay alive (at any point), there is a stage of exhaustion where the body needs to work on recovering before it can go back to baseline. This stage is included here because it is still part of the struggle to be not only alive but also stable. After the system executed extreme efforts to keep the heart beating, it's just logical to assume that it needs to convalesce before considering the survival protections as successful.

> I recently fell on the street in the middle of a crowd. The first thing people did was offer me their hand for me to stand up. I was confused, in pain, sad, embarrassed, and wondering what type of damage I was going to confront from the fall. The last thing I needed was to immediately get back on my feet. Nobody sat with me and asked what I needed. They all offered the same solution: get up, pretend you are OK, and keep walking.

We are too used to pretending and pushing to be OK as soon as possible in order to avoid the stigma of being perceived as mentally weak. But rebooting is essential and should be promoted. Some academics state that humans suffer emotionally because we interrupt our emotions instead of allowing them to unfold as they need to. Trying to be OK right after a traumatic event is also interrupting the process of rebooting. I don't know if we have this awareness instinctively, or why we don't necessarily give ourselves the time we need to recuperate what our system needs. I consider it vital for everyone—including therapists—to consider this fact and to start applying it, for example, after a processing session when the system gets activated almost to the extent of matching the worst moment of a traumatic incident. *Is there enough awareness of the importance of having the time and space to heal from the effort?*

Quiescent immobility is essential in the peritraumatic sequence to resolve traumatization and for treatment. If after going through the survival struggle there is a particular mechanism that succeeded, the person's ANS will go back to its regular way of functioning in a short period (days to a couple of months) with no major consequences. Equilibrium will eventually be re-established.

SURVIVAL MODE: THE ANS MALADAPTIVE WAY TO OPERATE AFTER BECOMING TRAUMATIZED

After going through the activation of protections and failing to achieve calmness and safety, the system stays in a lasting state of dysregulation and threat detection commonly called 'survival mode.' Living in survival mode means that the ANS is essentially operating by automatically activating the survival circuits—at any point and for whatever reason besides actual danger. When the ANS shifts to operate in survival mode, it maintains a state of hyper-vigilance that constantly looks for threats. Since negative experiences become encoded as warnings, a person's perception of reality becomes affected and their fear conditioned. In addition, their perception of threat becomes even more subjective and relentless. Living in survival mode means that the brain has suffered alterations to adapt to dangerous situations and the 'maladaptive' new way will remain. The survival mode is ruled mainly by primordial mechanisms that affect our emotional activity, reducing the participation of the cerebral cortex and executive functions as time goes by. Unfortunately, the brain will keep operating in survival mode for as long as the person fails to recover a sense of safety, and safety seems elusive due to the new perception of reality. *Regaining perspective over the past and reconnecting with the present* (if the present is safe, of course) could be a way to cancel the survival mode. By all means, there are many situations where it's not possible to feel safe because danger and threat persist.

Remember Jon? After he was attacked and beaten up, his father reconsidered his acts and showed regret to his son. Jon could have remained believing that his father was not trustworthy and stayed afraid of him just waiting for the next aggression, or he could—as he did—recover trust in the father's regret, leaving the past behind and reconnecting with the man that showed love for him in most circumstances.

RETRAUMATIZATION: THE UNFORTUNATE RESULT OF LIVING IN THE PAST

Staying scared with a system continuously feeling at risk—which I include as traumatization regardless of whether the person has already developed a trauma disorder or not—is different from being retraumatized.

Retraumatization implies that the person has already developed a trauma disorder, has lost perspective between the present and the past, and living situations similar to the traumatic ones—even if they don't present a similar level of threat—can trigger the protective mechanisms with the same intensity they had during the original exposure to traumatic incidents.

For a traumatized person, re-experiencing something similar to a traumatic situation can retraumatize the system, exacerbating the symptoms previously developed and increasing the negative change and level of fear connected to the traumatic memories. We could say that living in survival mode sets the system up to be retraumatized over and over, because the slightest threat could seem ultra-dangerous and hurtful, continuing to make the person feel unsafe and defeated with the caveat that *retraumatization is content specific*.

A CODA: WHERE THE SURVIVAL MECHANISMS LIVE IN THE BRAIN

To end the section, the following table (Table 3.1) summarizes the brain structures and the type of ANS activation that each survival mechanism sets in action.

Table 3.1 Survival mechanisms sequence and brain activity

Mechanism	Brain Structures	Activation
Arousal	Hypothalamus Pathway	Increases tone on the sympathetic branch
Orienting/ Social- Engagement	Ventral Vagus Nerve and midbrain (superior colliculi)	Parasympathetic activation, calmed and engaged
Freeze	Hypothalamus pathway; Unmyelinated Vagal pathway (opposes SNS activation); Lateral Periaqueductal Gray (LPAG); ventrolateral periaqueductal gray (opposes LPAAG)	Coactivation of sympathetic and parasympathetic components; heightened attention; enhanced vigilance to threat cues; activated and tense body muscles poised for action. The only reaction with both systems active

(Continued)

Table 3.1 (Continued)

Mechanism	Brain Structures	Activation
Fight/Flight	Hypothalamus and Lateral Periaqueductal Gray	Generalized sympathetic response; vagal cardiac parasympathetic tone is reduced.
Tonic Immobility	Extended amygdala, hypothalamus, and periaqueductal gray/or the basal ganglia. No Hypothalamus pathway with an active vagus	Restraint and fear cooccur; a shutdown response mediated by old areas of the brain that appear to activate only when newer structures (such as the amygdala) are deactivated and when freezing and flight or fight are switched off. Parasympathetic activity with withdrawal of sympathetic activity.
Collapse Immobility	Unmyelinated Vagal pathway and Ventrolateral Periaqueductal Gray; No Hypothalamus pathway	The same neural network mediates both tonic immobility and collapsed immobility (characterized by a loss of muscle tone). PRESENT bradycardia and hypotonicity of skeletal muscles. Dorsal motor nucleus parasympathetic surge; decrease in cerebral blood flow.

Source: Adapted from Kozlowska et al. (2015).

Assessing Trauma Disorders

> Imagine a tall person living in a place where the ceilings are too low, forcing the person to 'walk' on their knees. The person will do it and can become used to it, but they will never have the same ease of mobility as someone walking on their feet. That's what living in survival mode could be compared to "being forced to continue living in suboptimal conditions."

When we want to know the status of our health, even before seeing the doctor, a nurse will check our 'vitals': blood pressure, pulse, temperature, height, and weight. Then, the primary doctor may order some blood tests, probably x-rays or scans, and so on. When we have emotional pain, no scan or blood test can give us an accurate report of what's wrong with our thoughts, our impulses, our reactions, or our emotions. To explore someone's mental health, clinicians only count on their observations and the information the client provides. Even after asking clients many questions, it is possible to miss a great part of the story due to the impossibility of confirming whether the information provided is accurate, partial, or skewed. Psychometric tests, questionnaires, interviews, scales, and evaluations can help but they don't give us the whole picture or concrete data. What we have is a long list of names (diagnoses) and their list of symptoms (criteria) to identify and match the subjective and maybe incomplete report from clients.

DIAGNOSING MANUALS: THE STANDARDIZED WAY TO COMMUNICATE MENTAL HEALTH

To diagnose mental disorders, clinicians have relied for decades on the DSM produced by the American Psychiatric Association (APA), and more recently the ICD—the International Statistical Classification of Diseases and Related Health Problems—generated by the World Health Organization (WHO). Still, not everyone agrees on whether sharing a mental health diagnosis with a client is beneficial or detrimental. Some individuals claim to feel comforted by a name that explains their behavior, while others clearly feel debilitated by being assigned a name that implies a mental illness. The idea of being 'insane' carries a lot of stigmas, and even accepting that struggles are not 'real' but only 'mental' or psychological is very challenging for many. Having a diagnosis assigned could feel like the confirmation of being defective, and therefore, doomed.

Personally, I hold back from sharing the 'label' with my clients—unless individuals are curious about whether they meet the criteria for a disorder or not. I have found it very fruitful to work on alleviating specific manifestations of the uncoordinated system with the shared understanding that the design and operation of the system are, in part, the reason for the issue (instead of explaining it with a name only). Diagnoses and their criteria are better guides for interventions than for creating a relationship with the client. It's very rare to find a client that insists on getting a diagnosis once they understand the origin of their struggles and engage in becoming more whole. Not sharing a diagnosis is also a good cautionary measure since diagnosing a mental disorder is complicated and has a high margin of error.

HOW DIAGNOSES INFLUENCE TREATMENT

The diagnoses for mental health set the tone and the rules for developing treatment. History has shown that if a disorder is mainly thought of as genetic, the treatment is to medicate and learn to manage symptoms because the 'illness' is assumed to have little chance of disappearing. If a disorder is thought of as behavioral in nature, the treatment will focus on changing the individual's behavior; if some of the symptoms are considered faulty or unhelpful ways of thinking, a cognitive treatment will be suggested to correct it. Unfortunately, to this day there is no official recognition that symptoms of any disorder could spring from the dysregulation of the nervous system. Therefore, most 'evidence-based' treatments completely ignore the need to have systemic treatments. Mostly because of the mentioned issues, the majority of therapies (and therapists) have not yet moved from treating behavior and thoughts to treating the interconnected issues that stimulate unwanted actions and imprecise perceptions.

Having an official manual like the DSM or the ICD standardizes our conversations and understanding of mental phenomena. Still, what we have now for traumatization (PTSD and C-PTSD) doesn't do justice to the extensive range of manifestations that traumatized people suffer from. The same goes for many other disorders that don't include the possibility of being byproducts of traumatization or dysregulation, such as most personality disorders (PD). There are clear paradoxes when we try to use the DSM, especially relating to trauma disorders. On the one hand, the manual over-pathologizes natural responses like in the case of Acute Stress Disorder. On the other hand, it restricts the possibility of meeting the criteria for PTSD if the traumatic event is not extreme or if not all the criteria are met. The situation leaves too much space for manipulation which creates the need to distance from psychiatry in order to come up with solutions that fit the actual needs of traumatized individuals. The lack of respect that the buzz around the DSM has created has opened the door to a whole new series of problems, like self-diagnoses and the myths from pop-psychology.

POP-DIAGNOSES: THE HURTFUL TENDENCY TO CATEGORIZE OTHERS

Have you observed how writers have felt motivated to name their observations and conjectures about mental health such as who's a 'narc,' an empath, or has alters everywhere? The topic of mental health seems so hip that members of society have been contributing to spreading new social constructs or misusing diagnoses and making interpretations all over the internet. The branding contest attracts not only those interested in the science of human behavior but also those who are more inclined to accumulate likes and become influencers by coining new labels, starting new trends, or showcasing their struggles, which contributes to further pathologizing human behavior. The result is an atrocious amount of misinformation circulating on the internet, especially regarding traumatization, PD, and dissociation. This promotes self-diagnosing—or the common practice of diagnosing those we don't like, another contributing factor to developing stigma around psychological struggles.

SELF-DIAGNOSING: THE EFFECTS OF SEEING THE WORST OF OURSELVES

Mental disorders are now openly spoken about in shows/sports, voiced by many celebrities, and mentioned in the news as affecting a large number of relationships. It seems to be a trend to name people through a disorder's label (e.g. "so bipolar"). In terms of traumatization, it seems everyone believes that they 'have trauma' without having a clear idea of what that implies. Learning or believing that we suffer from a disorder may create a dysfunction that wasn't there. If a person is obsessed with finding a diagnosis, self-applying it to themselves, and reading constantly about their symptoms and characteristics, chances are high that the person could end up experiencing symptoms because the fear of being 'broken' could activate the survival mechanisms. That's the risk of self-diagnosis and the influence of pop-psychology. Of course, it could also happen after receiving a wrong professional diagnosis—which is even worse, as it will then have the weight of coming from someone with authority.

PROFESSIONAL DIAGNOSING: THE CHALLENGES OF GETTING AN ACCURATE DIAGNOSIS

It's ironic, but even when assigning a 'label' from the DSM can be as easy as comparing symptoms with a list, many individuals that suffer from emotional issues have no idea how to identify most of their symptoms. For one, many individuals see their behavior as 'normal' until someone brings it to their attention, or once the behavior is so dysfunctional that it interferes with their lives/relationships to the point of jeopardizing their stability and resulting in ultimatums. That's when they may look for a professional opinion. Even then, it's difficult for clinicians to recognize whether reported symptoms are such, or just personality traits, or maybe stories they have heard about the disorder. Clients usually look for help by reporting the difficulties in their lives, expecting solutions more than names. Still, in the case of diagnosing a trauma disorder, manifestations are so numerous and of such a different nature that it's very easy to meet criteria for several disorders and not necessarily for PTSD. Traumatized people may miss many of their symptoms and may only complain about a couple of evident ones, like diminished interest and irritability/worry, which taken out of context could receive one diagnosis for each (Major Depression Disorder and/or Generalized Anxiety Disorder). A wrong diagnosis will cause them to receive the wrong treatment, which, in turn, gives poor treatment results followed by discouragement, reinforcing the belief of being irremediably defective and abandoning treatment altogether.

'TRAUMAS,' TRIGGERS, AND CONCEPTUALIZING TRAUMATIZATION BEYOND DIAGNOSIS

I'll cover using the DSM criteria to diagnose PTSD in Chapter Five but let us explore other ways we can plan and design treatment. It's possible to conceptualize and assess traumatization using systemic perspectives but before I start I want to bring your attention to two important considerations: traumas and triggers. We are far too used to calling 'traumas' to all types of emotional wounds. We have also become very used to talking about triggers without identifying if they connect to a traumatic occurrence. When a trauma therapist's client reports their traumas, the clinician can start assessing for (a) whether the struggle has been resolved or not, (b) whether the client's system shifted into survival mode or not, and (c) whether the lingering impact comes from having experienced traumatic events or only distressing situations. Now let's see how to assess for triggers.

TRIGGER WARNING: THIS MAY NOT AFFECT YOU

The phrase 'being triggered' was introduced when the trauma phenomena became popular and people realized that their survival circuits could automatically become activated while watching/hearing/experiencing something that resembled a traumatic event. It was rapidly adopted to warn people about possible 'triggering' material on the internet, in books, videos, or whatever content was portraying situations that could disturb the consumers. In their original conception, trigger warnings were used to help people avoid getting retraumatized; it's become a widespread protection from becoming emotionally upset.

In terms of assessing the state of the nervous system and its dysregulation, it becomes important to watch out for what people report as triggering. Most of us could get upset by witnessing (in any way) violence, rape, crime, and emotionally upsetting situations without feeling that our lives or integrity are threatened. Being triggered is an actual sign of being traumatized when the situation that is activating is the same as the situation that became a survival struggle for the person. For instance, rape is a trigger for individuals that were raped, witnessed rape, or were very close to someone who was raped. Otherwise, hearing about rape is upsetting or disturbing but not a trigger. Those that are really triggered need to receive adequate support.

HOW NEUROBIOLOGY GIVES US OPTIONS

The DSM doesn't include guidelines for treatment. The APA (2022) assumes that determining an accurate diagnosis is "the first step toward being able to appropriately treat any medical condition," and that "mental disorders are no exception." That's how medical doctors treat illness, and we may agree or disagree with the statement that mental disorders are meant "to be treated as any other illness." As I mentioned before, there are no blood tests, no scans, and no x-rays that can objectively measure or identify a mental disorder. Mental disorder diagnoses are subjective and aimed at medicating, but medication has not proved effective in treating most symptoms of traumatized individuals.

Using neurobiology as a framework for treatment planning gives a different perspective to the manifestations people experience because it informs us—client and clinician—of why the person experiences so many difficulties. Having the dysregulation of the nervous system in mind gives a systemic view of the problem, adding dimensionality to the task of recognizing the needs of the individual before designing their treatment. There are many advantages of using this framework over the typical 'labeling' method of categorization. Each system has different elements asking to be considered. For example, assessing the level of hopefulness and whether defeat is the mental state from which the person operates are great predictors of the presence of the survival mode as default.

When a clinician shows a combination of knowledge and compassion, the client becomes much more responsive because they don't feel judged or cataloged with the 'mentally ill.' Sometimes, identifying the person's struggles in their body and relationships is enough to set the foundation for hope which helps resolve the traumatization and jump-start the healing process.

WHAT TO LOOK FOR: THE NUANCES OF DIAGNOSIS

If it's difficult to diagnose PTSD, which has a clear definition, diagnosing other trauma disorders is even more subjective. The criteria used by the clinician can be a misinterpretation of the construct, a personalized point of view, or a misunderstood set of experiences reported by the client. Therefore, it's good to see 'diagnosing' a trauma disorder as recognizing the components that need to be treated to recover emotional (and physical) health. It requires a laborious and paced effort that could be approached by three different assessment methods by recognizing:

- complexity of the presentation and number/type of symptoms,
- posttraumatic survival strategies currently used,
- domains that show alterations.

The next chapter covers each domain, for now let's look at complexity, survival strategies, and the range of altered domains.

Recognizing Complexity

One of the main contributing factors to developing a trauma disorder is the time in life when the traumatization occurred, and the frequency, length, and constancy of the stressors. Complexity affects the number and intensity of the symptoms. It's useful to start by identifying the core event or circumstance that represents the beginning of the survival-seeking activation; then we can move into searching for the information that tells how repeated (daily? weekly? etc.), how constant (random or unceasing?), or how prolonged the struggle was, adding when in life it happened or started/ended, and finding out the quality of what the caregiver and environment were able to provide in terms of safety, stability, and reliability.

Take "coming out of the closet" as an example. Depending on the environment the individual was raised in, it may be extremely stressful to have anticipated coming out for years, fearing getting rejected versus accepted. The complexity of the case grows if the individual's conflict started at a young age and if the environment showed animosity toward the gay community, which would make the stress constant and prolonged.

Recognizing Survival Strategies

After having the survival mechanisms running for a while, it's common to observe a dominant survival strategy in each traumatized individual. (**Note:** To differentiate peritraumatic processes from posttraumatic ones, I shift the name 'survival mechanisms' to 'survival strategies.') I say dominant because one particular strategy becomes intertwined with one's personality even when other mechanisms get activated too. Behavioral changes stem from a specific way of dealing with one's current situation under the understanding that the now-present survival mode pushes the system to find the best ways to adapt. Figure 3.2 shows the survival strategies and their main characteristics.

Noticing the strategy most commonly active informs us what type of dys-regulation the individual suffers from more acutely and if the interventions should target sympathetic or parasympathetic deactivation. It's also useful to observe if the dominant strategy (behavior) correlates with issues in the more active branch—physiology—(in Appendix A, there is a list of the main functions of each branch of the ANS). If the person presents different strat-egies without having a clear identification of which one is more pervasive, it's then necessary to assess for dissociated parts because different dominant strategies could be an indication of a fragmented personality.

To conceptualize the type of damage, it is also necessary to gauge the individ-ual's strengths. Survival strategies control traumatized individuals' emotional reactions, which implies that they learn to navigate the world under duress by developing specific skills. They could become their 'talents' even if they are not perceived as such by others; for them, their strategies could represent power and the ways they found to keep existing, especially if they got trau-matized by an environment that removed their agency and their sense of self. If there is awareness of these strategies, they can become assets not only for survival but for healing and living. For example, if someone is dominated by aggression (or hyper-arousal), they can engage in activities that make good use of their surplus of energy and strength instead of channeling it into just being 'angry' individuals.

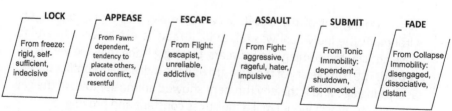

LOCK	APPEASE	ESCAPE	ASSAULT	SUBMIT	FADE
From freeze: rigid, self-sufficient, indecisive	From Fawn: dependent, tendency to placate others, avoid conflict, resentful	From Flight: escapist, unreliable, addictive	From Fight: aggressive, rageful, hater, impulsive	From Tonic Immobility: dependent, shutdown, disconnected	From Collapse Immobility: disengaged, dissociative, distant

Figure 3.2 Dominant survival strategies

I had a client that was 'angry' all the time after having suffered from serious and constant bullying in childhood; they used that extra energy to make their voice sound deeper and louder, to maintain their chest up and out, to sit at the edge of the chair to look taller; to give the impression they were bigger, stronger, and more intimidating than what they really were. That was their strategy to keep bullies from coming close which we then made it an asset.

A PREVIEW: IDENTIFYING TRAUMA DOMAINS

Assessing for a trauma disorder can include identifying the areas where the system suffered significant alterations. Instead of only looking for symptoms (following a more behavioral approach), we can look at the diverse presentation of trauma as pertaining to different domains, and all the processes that participated during and after the traumatization that got modified, causing specific dysfunction. These areas cover:

- emotional regulation
- changes in identity
- personality and sense-of-self
- agency
- dissociation
- memory
- attachment
- habits
- cognitions
- schemas
- narrative and scripts, and more.

To facilitate treatment, I find it useful to group some of these areas together. I call them Trauma Domains. The following chapters expand on each.

References

American Psychiatric Association (Ed.). (2022). *Diagnostic and statistical manual of mental disorders: DSM-5-TR* (Fifth edition, text revision). Washington, D.C.: American Psychiatric Association Publishing.

Bracha, H. S., Williams, A. E., Haynes, S. N., Kubany, E. S., Ralston, T. C., & Yamashita, J. M. (2004). *Shortness of breath, tremulousness, racing heart, and Sweating Checklist. PsycTESTS Dataset.* https://doi.org/10.1037/t19943-000

Cannon, W. B. (1929). *Bodily changes in pain, hunger, fear and rage: An account of recent researches into the function of emotional excitement.* New York, NY: D Appleton & Company. http://dx.doi.org/10.7326/0003-4819-39-2-383_1.

Dal Monte, O., Fan, S., Fagan, N. A., Chu, C. J., Zhou, M. B., Putnam, P. T., Nair, A. R., & Chang, S. (2022). Widespread implementations of interactive social gaze neurons in the primate prefrontal-amygdala networks. *Neuron, Advance Online Publication,* S0896-6273(22)00358-0. https://doi.org/10.1016/j.neuron.2022.04.013

Kozlowska, K., Walker, P., McLean, L., & Carrive, P. (2015). Fear and the defense cascade: Clinical implications and management. *Harvard Review of Psychiatry,* 23(4), 263–287. https://doi.org/10.1097/HRP.0000000000000065

MacPhee, D., Lunkenheimer, E., & Riggs, N. (2015). Resilience as regulation of developmental and family processes. *Family Relations,* 64(1), 153–175. https://doi.org/10.1111/fare.12100

Szeska, C., Richter, J., Wendt, J., Weymar, M., Hamm, A. O. (2021). Attentive immobility in the face of inevitable distal threat—Startle potentiation and fear bradycardia as an index of emotion and attention. *Psychophysiology,* 58, e13812. https://doi.org/10.1111/psyp.13812

Four
The Systemic Cost of Traumatization

How are emotions connected to traumatization?

Why is it so difficult to control our emotions?

Are false memories real?

What does it mean to have a distorted perception?

Our system suffers alterations in many of its regular processes every time it tries to provide safety. Think of the way a fever works: increased body temperature is mainly a physiological response whose purpose is to activate the immune system and combat viruses or bacteria. But once it's done its job, the fever subsides and the system goes back to normal. Something else can happen, however, when heat generation exceeds heat loss and the core temperature rises above a certain threshold or stays for longer than it should: a combination of cellular, local, organ-specific, and systemic effects occurs that puts the individual at risk of both short-term and long-term dysfunctions, including death (Walter et al., 2016). It's a useful parallel for our purposes in understanding traumatization. When fight, tonic immobilization, or any of the survival mechanisms go beyond a certain point, get activated too often, or stay activated for too long, there will be systemic effects that may leave symptoms, changes, or emotional pain regardless of whether a trauma disorder unfolds or not. This chapter explains some of those alterations, separating each of the subsystems that gets affected and labels them *trauma domains*. Each domain is explained in two ways: (1) What it looks like when it's working as it should? (2) How it gets altered?

Introducing Trauma Domains

Our system is like a fine watch made of thousands of small gears that work in coordination with each other to give the exact time. If one gear is out

DOI: 10.4324/9781003382478-6

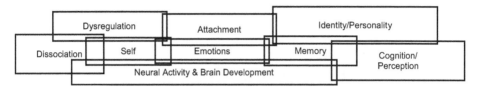

Figure 4.1 Trauma domains

of sync, it affects the performance of the entire apparatus. If we talk about our body using the same systemic approach, one where the person is seen as a whole, we can understand that traumatization causes the system to lose coordination between its parts, affecting more than one area. This finding only became clear to me after years of trying to help traumatized individuals focusing on stabilization and processing memories, and seeing how they were still unable to give 'the right time' just like the clocks. I learned that in order to conceptualize trauma treatment, the alterations in mind and body caused by traumatization needed to be included in treatment and planned for. To do that, an assessment of what areas were affected was required. I've identified nine main areas (Figure 4.1) that I place under the name trauma domains.

Since they are systemic, they are all related, but each one deserves special consideration. For trauma treatment to be successful, the alterations in brain functions, the loss of internal equilibrium, the changes in neural connectivity, and their relationship with all aspects of personality, emotional reaction, and thought processes need to be included. I'll explain the first five domains in this chapter. The last four will be described later, in the chapters where they are more connected to specific types of traumatization.

Trauma Domain #1: Emotions

A former client told me about a trip to Nepal where they visited a crematorium. From one of the burning piles, the leg of one of the corpses fell into the ground. My client reacted with disgust and horror. Their Nepali guide noticed the reaction and said: "what are you so scared of? It's only a leg. Don't you see the person is dead?" Still, my client had such an emotional reaction that was not able to sleep, eat, or enjoy the trip.

For a traumatized individual, experiencing emotions can be a nightmare. Traumatized individuals stop enjoying their full range of emotions because they become either disturbingly intense or because they disappear entirely from their radar. Since they are such an important issue when the system gets dysregulated, a surface mention of emotions won't cut it. How we manage them could help heal emotional issues, stop traumatization, and assist the autonomic nervous system (ANS) to return to baseline.

It was just recently that new research brought forth the thesis that emotional expressions are not universal and that emotions are nothing like what we have assumed for decades. Emotions are, actually, very individual. There may be a tiny piece about emotions shared by everyone, but what really makes the difference is that we express and experience them differently. I'll share a way to integrate academic definitions of emotion with what I—and all the people I have treated or supervised—feel when we talk about emotional manifestations to make it more relevant to the trauma phenomena.

THE VALUE OF EMOTIONS: A JUDGMENTAL BEGINNING

Before the word 'emotion' started being used as a psychological category during the 19th century, relevant mental states were categorized as 'appetites,' 'passions,' 'affections,' 'drives,' or 'sentiments.' People lacking mental stability (or showing too much emotion) were seen as defective and undesirable all around the world. Names used to categorize emotions had the intention of rejecting behaviors that were not accepted among the cultural values of the ruling societal groups. The word 'emotion' was used initially as 'physical disturbance.' More recently, scientists are using the term to refer to 'motivation,' while others want to get rid of the term altogether because it's now too strongly identified with the misleading idea that emotions are inborn, universal, and associated with facial muscle movements.

Let's not forget that most concepts in psychology are recent, including the study of emotions. Emotions have been studied for the last five decades without clear conclusions. Scholars have been back and forth about whether emotional reactions are a physiological response to events dependent upon the interpretation of physical reactions to stimuli (James-Lange), a physical and psychological experience happening at the same time (Cannon-Bard), that some emotions occur separately from, or prior to, our cognitive interpretation—including 'gut feeling' (Zajonc and LeDoux), as well as the premise that there are human emotions that are innate and shared by everyone (Tomkins, Ekman). The perspectives are so different that it's not hard to wonder if we have been trying to put different things in the same box as if the box 'emotions' was pre-established and everything needed to fit there. Maybe we need more boxes and new terms. I'm proposing to separate the hardwired, instinctual, short-lived reaction to certain stimuli that sets us in motion—e-*motion*—from the learned/scripted mental states that propel conditioned actions: emotionality. Let me explain why this separation could be useful.

EMOTION THEORIES: A LONG SEARCH FOR THE MEANING OF EMOTION

So far, the two theories that have been widespread and taught are the Basic Emotion Theory and the Dimensional Theory.

Basic Emotion Theory

Basic Emotion Theory (Categorical or Discrete) assumes that basic emotions evolved as ways to handle basic but essential life tasks. It states that everyone across the globe experiences, expresses, and recognizes emotions the same way spotted through almost imperceptible facial gestures. Additions to the theory suggest that their elements can be combined to form other emotions more complex in their processes. This theory started with Darwin but was developed further by Tomkins, Ekman, and by many others that have expanded on their thesis. The proposed categories to identify emotions are sadness (or sorrow), anger, disgust, fear, joy, and surprise with some scholars adding interest, wonder, distress, contempt, and shame. Each 'basic' emotion is seen as causing a specific response tendency that addresses a specific evolutionarily important need (Harmon-Jones et al., 2017). It keeps getting investigated and commonly taught even when its universality has been discredited.

Dimensional Theory

Dimensional Theory was originally proposed by Wundt in 1897 followed by Schlosberg in 1954 and used by many others for further research. It measures the degree to which the emotions are felt using two fundamental dimensions to describe them: pleasantness—unpleasantness (hedonic level) and arousal—relaxation (activation level) (APa dictionary). This theory is wise and useful even with its simplicity, as it goes to the felt-sense which involves the construct of 'affect' which is a key element in trauma studies.

- **Affect:** The term 'affect' was first used by Silvan S. Tomkins (1962) as synonymous with emotion in his affect theory but then expanded by others that defined it as the general sense of feeling of the alterations of our internal physiological states which we perceive and interpret; depending on that interpretation, we modify our behavior. Affect is only considered a component of emotional experiences. It helps us feel the changes in our body after receiving or perceiving certain stimuli. It lets us know if our level of arousal has changed together with sensations that reflect the part of the body that was set in action. Connecting with affect is how we learn to regulate our nervous system and modify our responses to threats.

Besides those two theories, there are many incredibly talented scientists participating in the quest of defining emotions. Some authors believe that we need to be aware of the stimulus before we experience an emotion, while others believe that we start experiencing the emotion before we are aware of it. Charles Darwin saw emotions as part of evolution (of course Darwin did!) explaining that they allow humans and animals to survive and reproduce (adaptive). LeDoux proposes a higher-order theory of emotional consciousness using the work of Jaak Panksepp, who coined the term 'affective neuroscience' and proposed seven primary emotional systems: Seek, Rage, Fear, Lust, Care, Grief, and Play (Davis & Montag, 2019).

After investigating a gamut of ideas, I corroborated that our emotional responses (*emotionality*) function to signal us the need to readjust expectations and to take adaptive action to survive and thrive by detecting, anticipating, and responding to challenges and opportunities according to what we have learned and stored as effective or pertinent (Anderson et al., 2019). It should be clear that all our emotions and emotional states have value even when society or religions consider them 'bad' or undesirable, or when they seem to push our behavior to unwelcome limits. But emotionality should be considered, listened to, attended to, assessed, processed, and reviewed to get the best out of our emotional experiences. Otherwise, emotions could become tyrants we learn to fear and avoid.

EMOTIONS AND AUTONOMIC ACTIVATION: MORE THAN ONE BOX FOR EMOTIONS

The limbic system is considered the dashboard for emotions and emotional manifestations in charge of our social interactions, affect, and reactions. According to the Dimensional Theory, our emotional reactions can be sensed as pleasant or unpleasant, and appraised as arousing or calming. That speaks clearly to their connection with sympathetic/parasympathetic activation and therefore, homeostatic regulation. It's also been said that emotions have a physiological component (affect) and a cognitive one (name + concepts). Let's investigate them.

Emotional Arousal

Emotional states have a significant effect on our cognitive processes, including memory and learning, perception and attention, reasoning/judgment/decision-making, and problem-solving. Attention plays an important role since it modulates focus and motivates action and behavior. When something we experience feels meaningful, our brain classifies it as relevant and stores components of it for future use, including its valence and intensity. **Valence** relates to affect and is the quality of how attractive or unpleasant an event, object, or situation is perceived. It is the value—positive or negative—that each memory gets assigned as they are encoded. **Intensity** refers to the degree of arousal (power) that our ANS experiences when the emotion is present. Emotional intensity is mainly predicted by the self-evaluation of the event that originated the response. When we predict that something is meaningful based on previous events that left a trace of emotionality and a conditioned response, our brain prepares by activating the nervous system; physiological manifestations can be noticed (affect). Traumatic events are commonly perceived as relevant and stored with a high negative valence to motivate us to be attentive to avoid similar situations.

EMOTIONALITY: EMOTION, CONSEQUENCES, AND INFLUENCES

Emotionality is what could destroy our relationships with others and with our selves. It motivates us to act, but that motivation comes from different places (innate motivational systems, scripts, or mental states). I'll separate them to see their origin and how we interact with them to better appreciate the role they play in our lives.

Motivational Systems

In addition to being part of defensive and adaptive systems, emotions can be considered also part of a reward system (Damasio, 2006). Humans have the capacity to make decisions based on choices and preferences.

Antonio Damasio proposes that "homeostasis has clear preferences, likes and dislikes" to reject or accept conditions for the betterment of our lives, and chooses optimal survival conditions over disease. This concept is illuminating. If our emotionality is basically used to interact with others, it is implicitly connected to punishment and reward, which is the way we learn almost everything. Emotionality then is formed based not only on basic adaptation for survival but also in terms of how the interactions with others make us feel. That's why emotional states are so connected with our sense of self and the values we develop. In terms of traumatization, if we learn that people who behave badly deserve punishment, we apply it even to ourselves. If we learn that certain behaviors or thoughts will be punished, we learn to shame ourselves to avoid being punished. Self-punishment and self-loathing are just too common. Being judgmental is too.

It seems more evident now that what we call emotions, especially after traumatization, are not hardwired. Emotional states develop (and are constructed) from a combination of multiple concepts, interactions, beliefs, interpretations, values, etc., that come from our ancestors, our community, our genetic and epigenetic information, and traumatic circumstances. We assign meaning to the environmental stimuli according to what we have stored in our memories, and we store memories with the meaning and values that we perceive from our environment, our relatives, friends, books, social media, and agreements made centuries ago that are passed down into our emotional information. Therefore, our emotionality is 'scripted.'

Emotion Scripts. In simple terms, a script is a mental program for action—a mental road map. Emotional scripts can be understood as *the set of beliefs and information we have gathered about a specific concept that becomes connected to an action and a feeling.* That collection informs us how to react during situations that elicit that specific action during emotional situations because they inform our brain how we are 'feeling' and what should be done. They are mostly unconscious and involuntary programs, unless, of course, we become aware of the script and participate in modifying it. Without modifying them, those scripts become the instructions our brain follows to maintain those specific mental states as constant.

Emotional [Mental] States (ES) are the product of an interaction between simple, non-conscious, automatic processes and deliberative, conscious, and controlled processes (Mayne & Bonanno, 2015). ES are the reactions that follow a stimulus that involve cognitive appraisal (or perception), subjective experience (feelings), physiological arousal (affect/body sensations), expressive motor behavior (action), and goal-directed behavior (script). They can be positive or negative. If a person stays in a negative emotional state, it'd be more and more difficult to regulate the emotional responses because the nervous system becomes disturbed but habituated to it to the extent that it becomes the person's mood.

Mood is the disposition to respond in a particular way emotionally. Mood can last for hours, days, or weeks, without the person knowing what prompted it. Moods differ from ES and from affect in lacking an object; for example, the emotion of anger can be provoked by an insult, the emotional state of anger could be the product of injustice, but an angry mood may arise even without knowing what the anger is about or what elicited it. Mood is very connected with a narrative one follows about who one is.

Depression, for example, is considered by many as an emotion when it could be an ES that becomes a mood—and then treated as a mood disorder—probably following a script influenced by experiences or values that become the narrative of being a depressed person. Many people lose their mental health because they adopt an ES as a mood, which becomes so prevalent and constant that it keeps reinforcing itself. The brain then acts accordingly. Someone in a depressed mood will have a constant activation of the parasympathetic (with all its consequences) until it becomes an automatic program that filters everything through that lens with mental and physical repercussions.

Emotionality and Society

In some cultures, countries, or families, people avoid talking about their inner life, while in others, people can't stop talking about them. Practicing specific religions, for instance, opposes the development of healthy emotional manifestations because followers may not be granted permission to acknowledge or show some inner experiences. Sometimes culture not only affects how we indicate our ES but also what elicits them. "Boys don't cry" is the typical expression that shows how cultural values can affect our behavior. Some societies find it inappropriate, sinful, or socially unacceptable to get angry, or even to laugh loudly. All those specific norms add to the scripts that will modify behavior and feeling. This becomes relevant when we talk about traumatization because some scripts are created by the influence of social values/practices that include a propensity for being shocked, alarmed, stressed, or defeated, and hence, cultural values need to be addressed in treatment.

Emotionality and Behavior

For decades, studies about emotions were based on behavior. Instead of being perceived as motivators, emotions were considered appetites or drives people needed to control at the command of others: "Calm down," "let it go," or "don't raise your voice." Emotional dysregulation was not understood in terms of biology and therefore only considered inappropriate behavior or character flaws. We have the capacity to modulate our behavior to what's socially acceptable but that doesn't mean we can always regulate what we are experiencing internally. Over time, we learn to demonstrate affective states or to suppress them according to what's expected. If our concept of emotionality is that it's bad, impure, or flawed, we will believe that we are defective and at fault when feeling emotional; if we experience or manifest it in our behavior, as we try to control the behavior, our brain may shut down the awareness of the feeling. Imposing the modulation of emotional responses has negative consequences at several levels. After developing a trauma disorder, controlling emotionality is basically unfeasible unless the person shuts down, and even then, emotional reactions will continue 'betraying' the person's will. Regulating emotional reactions is not the same as controlling emotional expression. Regulation happens when our PFC participates (gets active) and can turn off or down the dysregulated physiological activation after reflection.

Emotions and Memory

Our memories are shaped by our emotionality and our emotionality is shaped by our memories. If something is emotional, we will remember it better than if there was no emotionality present. If ES are constructs we develop from the accumulation of concepts we categorize as important (and their valence), experiencing them is connected with the activation of our nervous system. This activation is what helps identify how ES are different from person to person. One person that appraises success as happiness has a very different brain activation than someone that considers freedom as happiness. The level and type of arousal would be dissimilar in both even when they are reporting the experience of happiness. The first will be more sympathetic because success would be connected to the excitement of achieving, while the second will be more parasympathetic because freedom would be linked to less pressure to comply. Their brains will show a completely different set of neural activity.

EMOTIONAL PROGRAMMING: DYSFUNCTION IN THE NAME OF ADAPTATION

If we see emotionality as part of our adaptation and emotions as components of our innate protections, we can understand that emotionality is something that happens to us. Unfortunately, emotionality can expand beyond adaptation and end up defining who we are. When emotionality rules our behavior by following scripts that don't belong to us completely, they lose the value of their original intention. Let me use anger to explain. Depending on how we learn to express and react to our surroundings, we could see anger either as a protective way to react to danger instinctively, as a complex and sophisticated process to manipulate interactions, or as an active part of an aggressive personality. As soon as we feel someone is provoking or threatening us, we have a sudden surge of energy accompanied by burning sensations, strength in the limbs, and the desire to hit or yell that makes us argue, reject, and fight back (anger as an emotion); depending on what we have learned we need to do when angry, we will either argue calmly or violently, hide our experience or show it openly, leave to avoid the fight or stay and stoke it with words and gestures (emotional script). Imagine the fight is over but you keep ruminating about every detail said and done, comparing, justifying, and arguing in your head (anger as an ES). While staying 'angry' (maintaining the defensive circuits active), you'll be adding or changing the script depending on what you observe that anger can do to help—or jeopardize—you further. You may add the instruction to the script either to yell louder or to keep your mouth shut. Your brain will accumulate some of the information gathered from that event and store it with all previous experiences of provocation to make the script more adaptive. Unfortunately, while activated, the focus and attention are narrowed by emotionality, and cognitive processing and decision-making get compromised. The new relationship between threat and provocation associates neurons that include feelings, thoughts, memories, and physiological/expressive motor reactions (Alia-Klein et al., 2020) connecting the past with interpretations of the present, and storing new memories as emotional instructions (survival). From then on, that collection of processes will be carried as a mental state of anger. Next time your brain perceives provocation or threat, the whole circuit programmed to respond will be immediately initiated to act since it was learned as effective. The more you react like that, the stronger the circuits and the more immediate the response, making it part of your personality. At some point, you start identifying yourself with your emotionality, modifying the narrative about you. The script is unconscious, while the narrative serves as a way to explain it verbally and consciously. Traumatization amends the emotional scripts and the personal narrative for the worse. As always, it is possible to revert it by appraising whether the provocation matches one's impulses or not. It's well known that naming our emotions helps to process them. I'm suggesting to also reviewing the scripts for the emotion and understanding the emotionality they bring out aiming at being less reactive and more effective.

EMOTIONALITY AFTER TRAUMATIZATION

Traumatized people lose their capacity to interpret the meaning of their emotional arousal and thus emotions become irrelevant as signals of the present happenings; traumatization over-imposes a message of risk and transforms them into constant mental states. If sweating is a sign of arousal and excitement, for a traumatized individual, it is just a shaming trait; if heart racing is signaling fear, for a traumatized individual, it may be the sign of a heart attack. Emotional scripts are overridden by fear and translated and rewritten according to the new information gathered from the traumatic circumstances and traumatization's symptoms, psychical impulses (suppressed or acted out), hyper-alertness, and negative self-evaluation. When experiencing emotionality as exaggerated in intensity, lasting for long periods of time, occurring unpredictably, or evoked out of context (Saz et al., 2015), the memory connects them to previous experiences and the negative valence accumulates (Williams, 2002).

People suffering from PTSD tend to somatize or discharge their emotionality with actions such as aggression or accusations against themselves or others either physically or verbally. It's not unusual that traumatized individuals practice the most damaging self-talk, cursing, devaluing, judging, and criticizing themselves in ways that most may never use to refer to someone else. "You are a loser," "You got what you deserve," "I don't even know why you are alive," and statements that add to the after-traumatization script, narrative, and self-concept. Emotionality becomes a reminder of the inability to handle certain situations or achieve better results (Van der Kolk, 2014). Emotionality becomes problematic not only because it's a reminder of the traumatization even without context, but also because it's a manifestation of a person's inabilities and flaws, which in many people are attributed as part of the reason they got into the traumatic event in the first place. Traumatized individuals, most often than not, blame themselves—maybe quietly, or maybe intermittently—but they see themselves as part of the cause and, therefore, become resigned to receiving negative consequences or even maltreatment. When that internal dynamic gets externalized, they blame everyone and disconnect from their inner-self, initiating the development of personality shifts.

Traumatization changes the emotional scripts taking a central role. Narratives become all about the traumatization and emotional states are tainted by that new narrative. Resolving traumatization asks for the review of the scripts for the most important emotional states starting with fear.

Trauma Domain #2: Dysregulation

A relative of mine suffers emotionally. Their behavior is erratic and their level of dysregulation acute and peculiar. When they are in a situation they can't control and that makes them insecure, they laugh hysterically no matter where they are or with whom. It can be a theater, with an authority, or at a funeral. Their bursts of laughter are prolonged and sound very much like mockery. They seem disconnected from any sense of respect, consideration, or coherence with what's happening in the room. My relative's emotional response to stress is an example of a high level of emotional dysregulation.

Dysregulation is one of the main trauma domains that treatment should target because, without regulation, the system doesn't go back to baseline, and if the system doesn't go back as close as possible to where it was, symptoms will recur even after memory processing or cognitive interventions have been implemented.

In trauma studies, there are two different types of dysregulation mainly included: (a) autonomic dysregulation which refers to the lack of coordination between the two branches of the ANS (SNS and PSNS), and (b) emotional dysregulation which refers mainly to the extreme activation of each branch (especially of the sympathetic), overactive amygdala and other limbic structures, and underactive or disengaged areas of the PFC, which cause one to lose the capacity to modulate emotional responses. The autonomic dysregulation is not as apparent and it's basically impossible to measure. It only becomes evident in the manifestation of symptoms. Emotional dysregulation is obvious and its prominence is debilitating on its own; when we can't control the expression or intensity of our emotional states, we feel disoriented, frazzled, at risk, and even 'crazy.' Just think about the example of my relative: it must be very destabilizing to feel that they have no control over that 'nervous' laughter, and debilitating to receive the looks from those around because the laughter is out of context or appropriateness. If emotions are supposed to motivate us to act in ways that protect us and to adapt to our circumstances, when our emotionality puts us at risk, there is confusion internally and externally. My relative's laughter can irritate or infuriate some people but may be innocuous most of the time, but think about anger that turns into extreme aggression and homicidal ideation, sadness that turns into suicidal impulses, or numbness that turns into self-cutting and you may picture the gravity of what I'm talking about.

Emotional dysregulation is one of the main factors in many disorders, including 'cluster B' personality disorders, anxiety and depression, and, of course, PTSD (Dadomo et al., 2016). It doesn't only affect interpersonal relationships and the performance of essential tasks; it also causes shame and internal turmoil in daily regular activities. Just be aware that people are using 'being dysregulated' as synonymous with being emotional. Experiencing emotionality, even when intense (like furious), doesn't mean being dysregulated. Dysregulation is a symptom, an indication that the survival mode has become the default of the ANS.

THE SYSTEMIC MEANING OF DYSREGULATION

If there is a lack of coordination between the SNS and PSNS, the emotional responses get easily out of control. Think of it this way: in regular circumstances, we have the capacity to push the brake for when we get too animated (hyper-aroused) and/or the gas pedal for when we fall into a very low activation (hypo-aroused). When those processes become disabled, one may feel enraged in an instant or may feel hopeless after minimal frustration, or one may experience both extremes together. Besides the issues in the ANS, emotional dysregulation arises in part from dysfunction within the limbic system, including structures such as the amygdala, and from the failure of the cortex to manage such structures (Lesion & Lindquist, 2018). Individuals suffering a posttraumatic syndrome lose the capacity to overcome fear, they lose regulation abilities, and they maintain excessive activation to detect threats.

The lost ability of the ANS to manage the intensity and duration of negative emotional states—such as fear, sadness, anger, and anxiety—manifests as poorly modulated emotional responses which may be perceived as unacceptable (Beauchaine et al, 2007) causing dysfunction for many reasons. Someone dysregulated can't find the way to manage behavior and mood, is unable to perceive affect or interpret it correctly, finds it emotionally overwhelming and confusing, and their affective activation remains unresolved causing shame and precipitating an unpleasant and misunderstood downward spiral. People suffering from dysregulation feel either too much or nothing at all. Their emotional responses are connected to negative interpretations about what's happening, as well as to sensations in their body that can have a negative impact on behavior if they are interpreted with alarm (or a negative impact on their health if ignored). When someone reports not perceiving affect—what's happening internally—there is probably a lack of awareness primarily rooted in neural disconnection in the frontal lobes, which causes dissociation from feeling. If the ANS becomes underactive, limbs may go numb and the whole body lowers its temperature, but the individual may be unaware of those changes and only feel a lack of energy and motivation, or interpret it as dangerous, reactivating the stress response.

> A client of mine used to get so anxious in social situations that she closed her fists to the point of lacerating her palms with her nails, causing the cuts to bleed without her noticing. It was either when someone else pointed at the blood or when she felt the pain after the stressful situation that she saw the injuries. She was oblivious to the intensity of her reactions.

The loss of homeostasis may alter some of the regular vitals, making it even more difficult to understand one's emotionality. These physiological extremes may become part of what defines the person instead of being identified as markers of a problem. Ignoring those changes has psychological and physical consequences. Many people start developing somatic or medical problems without understanding that the reason is emotional dysregulation. Lactose or gluten intolerance may be two among many of these indicators that are treated independently of their origin, but also being clumsy, loud, or sweaty to name a few.

For individuals having trouble managing or recovering from extreme emotional states, even love may be experienced as extreme and may cause distress for its force and the incapacity to be modulated, especially when it doesn't match the level of engagement with or from the loved object. For instance, dysregulated individuals may feel irremediably in love with their abusers (trauma bond). Love easily turns into need, dependency, and grief, while irritation can quickly become hatred and aggression. A dysregulated person may experience both, which fragments their concept of self, causing them to doubt who they are or the validity of their feelings. Emotional re-actions are also regulated by our executive functions such as awareness and self-control, which depend directly on the state of our prefrontal cortex: how strong, mature, and active it is. But traumatization slows down the activity of the brain's frontal lobe. This means losing the capacity to interpret the sig-nificance of our emotions, their impact on our system, and their stabilization. Many people that develop PTSD recover a lot of the PFC activation com-promised during the survival struggle but people suffering from other types of trauma syndromes may not have it as easy, especially children.

EMOTIONAL DYSREGULATION AS A TRAUMATIZATION MARKER

Once traumatization unfolds as a disorder and the survival mode becomes estab-lished as default, the survival mechanisms become strategies for survival rather than for protection—and they lose the hierarchical organization they had be-fore. Due to the dysregulation of the ANS, they are activated at any moment and they are more exaggerated or intense than previously. Dysregulation origi-nates states of either a heightened activity of the sympathetic (hyper-arousal), a pervasive heightened activation of sympathetic and parasympathetic together, or a predominant activation of the parasympathetic (hypo-arousal). Those states can become the way the traumatized individual reacts to stressors or even to neutral stimuli. If the traumatized person feels at risk, they could become furious in a second, blaming others for the situation, or completely submissive, blaming themselves and apologizing; they can also move from hyper-activated to hypo-activated without any apparent reason and in any specific order. Some individuals get 'stuck' activating a particular response more often, keeping it as the dominant way of interacting with their circumstances.

The reason these reactions become dominant is that the individual learns to minimize risk by adopting a strategy that the brain anticipates as more effective than others for dealing with their surroundings—surroundings that are often, if not always, considered hostile and threatening. For some trau-matized individuals, getting angry and explosive may be the way to control abusive conditions, while for others, becoming docile and obedient may be the way to avoid the threat they feel they continuously face. Some individu-als become self-sufficient, isolated, and avoidant to be able to overcome the challenges. These learned responses are not conscious or volitionally chosen; they are unconscious adaptations of the protective mechanisms that allow the person to survive in challenging circumstances, incorporating scripts that were developed under those circumstances.

POSTTRAUMATIC SURVIVAL STRATEGIES: THE MALADAPTIVE WAY TO SURVIVE OUR CIRCUMSTANCES

The stages that the nervous system goes through during the struggle for survival are easier to observe if activated during a specific event. Once someone becomes dysregulated, and the traumatization somatized, the mechanisms don't follow a clear sequence or are not easy to predict unless they become 'habitual.' Not all people that suffer from a trauma disorder present the same characteristics. Not only are there different levels of posttraumatic dysregulation but it is also important to consider that each person's system has dissimilar circumstances to adapt to depending on their dynamics, the level of risk of their environment, and their temperament.

The strategies used by the traumatized individual during moments where there is no danger seem out-of-place to most. They create conflict in the individual's performance in society and big problems in their relationships. They are automatically activated as default or triggered easily with any stressor, especially those that are similar to the stressors faced during traumatization. Triggers could also activate different strategies depending on the person, circumstance, and type of trigger. If the person developed fear toward a punitive caregiver and anger toward the critical parent, the individual may need to use submit with the punitive parent while aggression with the other, forcing the brain to create different and disconnected circuits that will make the person act and feel fragmented.

Traumatized people easily fall into a vicious circle of dysfunction and dysregulation caused by the sense of lack of safety, plus the lack of trust, hope, faith, and confidence that follow. The dominant strategies can become so pervasive that they evolve as personality traits, and can be adapted as skills. It all depends on the relationship the person establishes with their activation.

Surviving Hyper-Activation: Getting Hyper

Hyper-arousal causes a very different set of symptoms than hypo-arousal. Hyper-arousal shows up when the person is ready to use the fight or flight response at any point. That means that it will take much less time for the person to be combative or to escape. The level of reactivity becomes intense, seems disproportionate, overwhelms the system very fast, and disempowers the person internally. People may exercise rage for power, while internally, a split could be taking place between feelings of control and lack of it. Almost

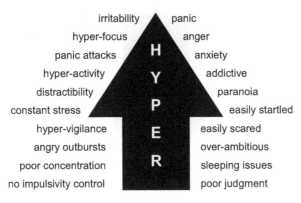

irritability   panic
hyper-focus   anger
panic attacks   anxiety
hyper-activity   addictive
distractibility   paranoia
constant stress   easily startled
hyper-vigilance   easily scared
angry outbursts   over-ambitious
poor concentration   sleeping issues
no impulsivity control   poor judgment

H
Y
P
E
R

Figure 4.2 Common hyper-activation symptoms

every time the individual becomes dominated by hyper-activation, the actions become self-destructive behaviors whether via violence, vanishing from responsibilities, impulsive sex, consumption of substances, or even disclosing too much information. For many people that are dominated by the sympathetic, it is common to observe symptoms like the ones shown in Figure 4.2.

Some people use the mobilization strategy to survive, and some people use the same strategy as a drive to work harder, avoid conflict, and be creative (passionate) about what they do. Those people show something that could be interpreted as more resilience—or a more hopeful perspective—which helps develop better skills to manage hyper-activation and to resolve the traumatization faster.

Surviving Hypo-Activation: Spiraling Down

Living controlled by immobilization strategies presents different challenges. Some people internalize the suffering, and even if they could function in society and maintain relationships, see a higher impact on their health, as seen in people who become submissive, pleasing everyone and accommodating the needs of others while neglecting theirs in their quest for sympathy, esteem, and acceptance. Living on hypo-activation could also mean living without goals, being depressed or isolated.

Some hypo-active individuals manage themselves well, hiding their suffering, but internally they may develop a sense of worthlessness and inadequacy inspired by the feeling of a small existence due in part to the lower levels of their vitals. They doubt their capacities and compensate by overextending themselves at giving (or giving up). On those living mostly in hypo-arousal, it's common to observe symptoms like the ones in Figure 4.3.

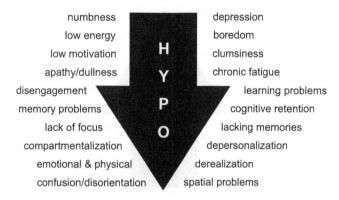

numbness
low energy
low motivation
apathy/dullness
disengagement
memory problems
lack of focus
compartmentalization
emotional & physical
confusion/disorientation

H
Y
P
O

depression
boredom
clumsiness
chronic fatigue
learning problems
cognitive retention
lacking memories
depersonalization
derealization
spatial problems

Figure 4.3 Common hypo-activation symptoms

They're in the minority, but some people learn to make the best out of hypo-activation. For those whose temperament is naturally helpful, they use dissociation to separate themselves from pain or high emotionality, and they may be inclined to engage in the service professions. Many others follow religious groups that encourage selflessness and renunciation, which for them seems easier since they don't crave much. This way of leveraging hypo-activation can give individuals a sense of purpose, agency, and hope that directs them to naturally regain balance and stability, leaving traumatization behind. At some point, with practice and direction, many people with persistent hypo-activation can make these characteristics an asset.

Shifting between Hyper- and Hypo-Arousal: Surviving by Fragmenting Our Personality

During the immobilization peritraumatic stage, among several different tasks, the production of analgesics may create disconnection among circuits which contribute to the development of division in their personality (Chapter 6 goes deeper in this matter). It's possible to observe someone embodying their combative self in certain circumstances and with specific people while becoming more compliant among other groups—without even having the awareness of such changes. They also respond differently to the same stimuli, sometimes angry and sometimes sad, and sometimes sad and angry together. The divided personality may be adaptive and functional, or it may cause the behavior to be unpredictable, not only to others but also to the person that shifts from one strategy to another without any volition. Many clinicians (or self-diagnosed individuals) have been identifying this characteristic as Dissociative Identity Disorder (DID), even though the DID diagnosis only applies when there is amnesia between the fragmented personalities, or when those fragments are completely unaware of the other's strategies. For the large majority of traumatized people, it's pretty common to use different strategies without meeting the criteria for DID. An abused child, for instance, may be submissive at home and a bully at school. Shifting may be actually *more adaptive* than activating the same strategy in every circumstance. Some traumatized individuals become very malleable and use their strategies to develop a sense of belonging instead of provoking rejection. You'll find more explanations of this subject under the 'self' and 'dissociation' as domains.

Surviving the Co-Activation of Hyper- and Hypo-Arousal: When Preventing Harm Could Be Damaging

When the freeze mechanism becomes a strategy—Lock—it maintains hyper-activation (sympathetic) either restrained or contained. For a while, I was intrigued about this, asking myself, *how could freeze become a posttraumatic strategy if it's a preventive mechanism? If it prevents us from going into a full-force survival struggle, how come I've observed many clients presenting the characteristics of people stuck in a state of indecisiveness, prepared to fight or flee but also locked up in their own restrictions, with a tension in their body that looks they are going to crack?* This strategy is present in individuals that do not necessarily meet the criteria for PTSD (or any other trauma syndrome) but are not satisfied or emotionally healthy, either. The majority of these individuals had challenging upbringings, even traumatic ones, and therefore, we could assume that their brain was ready to use the survival mechanisms but never reached the point of defeat. Still, it seems that their system suffered from several allostatic changes (explained in Chapter 6) never reaching a state of safety or trust, keeping them in 'preventive mode' indefinitely. Staying in this state (or using it as a default) takes a toll in terms of consumption of energy and because it leads to the incapacity to fully enjoy life. It may also become a personality disorder of the schizoid type when the rigidity pushes the person to avoid others.

As with the other survival strategies I mentioned, more resilient individuals that use this combination of activation are self-reliant and commonly accomplished professionally. Their relationships may not be fulfilling but they have them and know how to keep them. Since they don't feel comfortable asking for help, they develop agency even if they have no space for recognizing it. Not an ideal way to live, but an effective one if they or others learn to appreciate their resiliency. The resolution of this strategy comes mainly from awareness and decision-making.

Survival strategies could become so automatic that they may be identified as personality traits more than adaptations. Even when the person resolves traumatization or heals from a trauma disorder, the strategies they used to survive their circumstances may not disappear; they may be modulated to better serve the person though. Bringing into the person's awareness and discussing it is highly effective.

Trauma Domain #3: Memory

> I had just started puberty. I entered my shower and noticed the bathroom window was broken and a small piece at the top was missing. I didn't mind so I started showering when I saw an eye looking at me. I jumped out of the shower as if I had springs on my feet, turned off the light, and hid. I still remember the eye in the middle of the missing piece of glass as clearly as if it had happened yesterday. I also remember feeling the cold in my wet body and the traces of emotions like surprise, embarrassment, and curiosity. The last thing I remember is that the glass was replaced right away. I can almost see the full process of someone changing the glass even though I don't remember who did it (not important).

The piece of narrative you just read is all based on a couple of memorized images, the trace of an emotion or two, and a lot of thoughts I have now as an adult about how the whole picture could have looked like. It's essentially a piece of 'fiction' that my brain re-members from pieces of a real event. I wish that all of our traumatic stories would get to that point, the point where remembering feels more like fiction than a scary reality.

The way memory works is by storing the pieces of information from our experiences that are important and dismissing/deleting the rest, either in real-time or after considering what's previously stored irrelevant. Traumatic memories are managed a little differently, however, because their connection to danger gives them extra relevance. During traumatization, the brain stores pieces and emotional valence of traumatic incidents in a way that makes them seem current for a long time. They are also stored in a different place than regular memories to make them more available. Still, what our vision captures during a traumatic event is not the whole picture; what the brain perceives looks similar to those pictures where something is in sharp focus, while the rest is blurry. During traumatization, we suffer from something called 'tunnel vision.' Hence, most pieces of memory from traumatic events are not clear; they will miss pieces or they'll be absent. This is because of how hyper-focused the senses were, oriented toward whatever was threatening.

> Imagine you fell and broke your leg during a visit to a new place when your heel suddenly got stuck in a metal grate in the ground. The memories from the incident would probably be more about the holes in the floor than about what was around. The images recorded in your brain could look like the one in Figure 4.4.

Figure 4.4 Memory of a traumatic experience under tunnel vision

For decades, probably since Pierre Janet defined trauma and called traumatic memories 'primary fixed ideas,' the trauma disorder was directly identified as a problem with re-experienced memories from the traumatic incident. Later on, Freud brought up the idea of repressed memories as the issue of traumatization. Consequently, trauma treatment was focused mainly on working with traumatic memories under several assumptions such as the idea that forgetting what seemed impossible to forget—or remembering what has been forgotten—was the cure for the disorder. I'll explain how memories become symptoms but want you to keep in mind that traumatic memories stop being disturbing when they are experienced as belonging to the past and with little or no emotion connected to them. They don't disappear; they just become more integrated, less painful or neutral, and less intrusive. Even though it is well known now that traumatic memories are just one of the many disturbances of the trauma phenomena, it is still very important to know to what extent memory plays a role in dysfunction after traumatization.

THE VALUE OF MEMORIZING

Memory is another one of the constructs that keep being expanded, revisited, deconstructed, and extended as we speak. There are often discoveries that challenge the previous formulation of what memory is or how its processes work. As an adaptive mechanism, memories allow us to draw upon our past experiences to respond with flexibility in the present and plan for our future with a higher probability of success (Dudai & Eisenberg, 2004). Memory offers the possibility to connect experiences, learn, make sense of our lives, and build our stories (Camina & Güell, 2017). Memories are also essential in creating our emotions (Barrett & Russell, 2015). Memory as a set of processes is so adaptive that it is designed to forget what's not important for our survival to make space for new learnings that don't stop until we die.

Even when there are many questions without answers about memory, we have strong opinions about it; for example, we have developed the notion that having good memory is a sign of intelligence, that memory impairment and aging are the ultimate defeat, and that 'recovering' or recounting memories is healing. Those ideas are biased and partially incorrect. We have assigned to memory a preponderant level of centrality in defining our place in the world and our sense of who we are (Allen, 2018) and maybe that's why we suffer if our memory doesn't respond to us as we wish. But there are natural processes that cause deficits in the continuity of our subjective experience (Strikwerda-Brown et al., 2019), and the way we store information, and in many instances, *not remembering* is more adaptive—and healthy—than problematic. We have assumed that our brain can store everything and that if we don't remember, it means pathology. In truth, every time we 're-member,' our brain is making up a large percentage of what's being recalled. Memories are not simply a recording of the past that can be replayed at will like a book that reads the same every time we open it. Our replaying of memories is not always veridical because it's continuously suffering modifications.

Imagine you are writing an essay on your computer: the first time you write the words is the first 'memory' that the computer stores, then you read it and make modifications saving the document under the same file; the second memory is different from the first one and you may have no way to access the first 'draft.' As soon as you press 'Save' your memory is a new version of the original one with no way to recover some of the words, phrases, or syntaxes you used before. Storing information in our brain is similar to that process.

Each new memory is integrated into our existing knowledge, modifying and being modified by other memories. Our capacity to remember is limited, while our ability to forget is high. Forgetting, far from being evidence of malfunction, is an essential process that helps optimize energy use when recalling, and creating space for new information (Siegfried, 2019). Memories are stored in pieces, and each piece is stored in different parts of the brain with an assigned value each. By design, the less precise our memories are, the better the predictions about future situations our brain can make.

Let's picture you getting hit by a car while crossing the street. If we were to store every exact detail of the accident and the moment of the hit including the car's maker/color/year, the specific place it occurred, time, circumstance, etc., then your memory would only be warning you about that exact type of car in that same place at that precise time of the day. Instead, your brain simply memorizes that cars are dangerous and can injure. The information from that memory will motivate you to become more careful while crossing the street.

It is true, however, that having 'bad memory,' or rather, having deficiencies in the functioning of the processes involved in memory, can be a sign of dysfunction. There are a large number of documents from clinicians, scientists, and academics that report that memory formation, maintenance, and utilization cause symptoms connected to mental disorders and pathologies (Halligan & David, 2001). This is true when we investigate trauma syndromes. Some of the most obvious symptoms during and after traumatization relate to remembering too little, not remembering at all, or remembering too much of unpleasant occurrences, especially because memories get decontextualized from time and meaning.

HOW THE BRAIN DEALS WITH MEMORY

According to multiple new studies, in terms of neurobiology, memory and learning include a set of mechanisms by which neurons and neural systems change their input-output functions. It's important to keep in mind that there is basically no learning without memories; learning is a process by which we integrate new knowledge resulting not only from accumulating data but also from our experiences and the product of such experiences (feelings, risks, reward, etc.) which is converted into stored memories and neural circuits. There are very current important concepts to review about the neurobiology of memory that could help us understand memory processes.

- Each time we recall a memory, it changes in relation to the neural circuits that are engaged at that particular moment because the recall of the memory may require shifting networks depending on the context where the memory is needed. If we are recounting an event that is emotionally charged, we may recall certain details that won't be included if the recall is about a different situation.

> For example, if I'm talking about my wedding, I may recall the fun, the music, the ceremony, and the emotions related to those moments. But if I'm planning a wedding, I may recall the chairs, the food, the wine, the flowers, and details that are important for the future. The same memory connects to different neural circuits.

- Events that are emotionally charged are better remembered than emotionally neutral experiences. The emotionality connected to the event can be either positive or negative; the valence of the emotion gets stored in a specific area of the brain (amygdala) and linked to other structures managed by the hippocampus.
- We used to think that all memories were stored as short-term and that just a few of them made it into long-term memory. Now it's proposed that we create two memories at the same time, one short-term and one long-term, and after a while, one of them will be deleted (Roy & Tonegawa, 2017). This makes it even more relevant to delete information that won't be needed in the future since it's occupying unnecessary space.
- New experimental work has been supporting the idea that a required step in the formation of new memories is the synthesis of proteins (Pearce et al., 2017). This concept became very relevant for the healing

of traumatic memories when the construct of memory reconsolidation came about; knowing there is a process to eliminate the distress connected to pieces of the traumatic event gives us hope of removing the affliction carried by those memories.

– By the way memory processes interact with each other, the accuracy between what is experienced and what is encoded can't be guaranteed. We can't trust either the accuracy between what was encoded and what is retrieved. Even under normal conditions, memory distortions, memory failures, and false memories are part of the psychological phenomena (Radulovic et al., 2018).

– Our memories are rarely recorded as single memories. Instead, we store them in groups, overlapping those that are similar, which facilitates the association between them. If we recall one significant memory, we recall others connected by time or some other similarities (Shen, 2022).

– Memories are not only stored in our brains. The central nervous system 'remembers' painful experiences leaving a memory trace of pain, reactivity, or emotionality in our nerves and the parts of the body where the nerves were either activated or injured. The pain memory trace connects the nerves with the brain and magnifies the feeling.

– Besides traumatic memories, traumatized individuals have issues with memory encoding, storing, and retrieval. After traumatization, the brain's left side diminishes activation and loses synchrony with the right, which decreases the capacity to organize experiences into logical sequences and translate feelings and perceptions into words. The thalamus—which is in charge of relaying sensory and motor signals, and regulating consciousness and alertness—shuts down and the entire picture of what happened can't be stored in the brain as it should. Severe alterations in the hippocampus cause parts of the traumatic memory to get stored in the long-term implicit memory unconsciously and unintentionally making them be accessed not as voluntary recollection but as automatic reactions. That normally brings up negative emotionality that creates a sense that remembering is unbearable or at least overwhelming. Damage to the hippocampus causes impairments in long-term episodic memory (Anand & Dhikav, 2012) and makes it difficult to integrate future sensory information.

HOW OUR MEMORIES GET FORMED AND WHY

Even when the term 'memory' is singular, it encompasses a large classification of processes and categories. It can be divided in many different ways, but under the trauma lens, it's useful to identify memory processes depending on the function involved in their management. Trauma studies classification includes as important: short and long term, explicit and implicit, episodic, and semantic. In short-term memory, working memory is the information we keep available using attention—an important element for the resolution of traumatization. As part of long-term memory, there is explicit memory—conscious and what we normally recount—and implicit memory—what is behind actions that are automatic like walking. Explicit is divided into episodic where data from our episodes are stored, and semantic which keeps facts and general knowledge. Autobiographical memory—the memories that inform us of our lives and how we have become us—are mainly episodic but include semantic components. The autobiographical memory is the type of memory that gets greatly affected by traumatization because the traumatic information taints the concept of the person and takes a central role in the future recount of the story of who one is.

We Memorize before We Forget

Most of the texts on memory talk about three processes involved in it: encoding, storing, and retrieving. In Figure 4.5, you can see that I'm separating *consolidation* from *storing* and adding *reconsolidation* because of these processes' importance for healing. I'm also including *forgetting* as a process because it has its own characteristics and an important role too.

'Remembering' is the verb we use all the time when we talk about memories. To re-member is equivalent to saying that we *perform the act of bringing into*

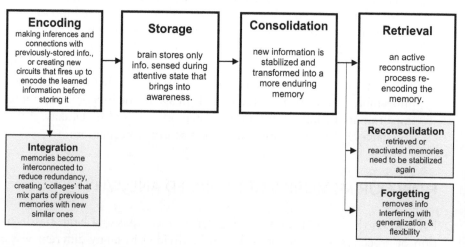

Figure 4.5 Memory processes

our awareness, again, something that was in our awareness previously. I consider this understanding essential and want to overemphasize upfront: *We can't remember something that was not in our awareness before, even if it happened.* This statement will make sense as we move on to understanding the role of memory in traumatized individuals and treatment.

It's interesting to notice that there is a conundrum in the quest to understand memory processes because without encoding and storage, retrieval is not possible, and without retrieval, it is not possible to detect whether encoding or storage occurred. It's like the chicken and the egg; we don't know which one was first. By re-membering (retrieving), we can't guarantee that the event happened because re-membering makes up part of what comes to mind, and without re-membering we can't be sure what's stored in our brain.

Imagine thinking you put the keys in a drawer: you can't know if your keys are there unless you open the drawer, but still, finding keys in the drawer doesn't mean you put them inside or that they are your keys.

All the memory processes participate in the creation and experience of traumatic memories, and traumatization affects the operation of memory brain structures and their processes. One problem is whether the memory from the event(s) was stored in its totality, another is to have memories become intrusive and distressing, and a very different thing is to have issues memorizing after we develop a trauma disorder.

MEMORY AND TRAUMATIZATION: WHEN MEMORIES DISRUPT OUR LIVES

I hope you see now that trauma disorders are not only about difficulty re-experiencing or remembering traumatic incidents. Yes, traumatization alters not only what we store but how we store it; the survival struggle affects what's prioritized and what's dismissed and leaves memory deficits (Samuelson, 2011). Flashbacks and nightmares are problems of memory and symptoms of trauma syndromes, but even though they can be debilitating, they are not the main reason people become dysfunctional after traumatization. Decontextualized memories are only part of the damage left behind in the structures that are in charge of managing memory: the hippocampus, HPA axis, the prefrontal cortex, and the catecholamine system. Let's explore traumatic memories since traumatic experiences cause their formation in three different ways:

Intrusive Traumatic Memories (Too Much)

After traumatization and for some time, pieces of memories intrude during waking states (flashbacks) or sleep (nightmares). They can be explicit, as in be clearly related to a traumatic incident, or implicit, bringing the distress without a clear connection to an occurrence.

Flashbacks are intrusive pieces of sensory information that appear spontaneous, frequently, and accompanied by some emotionality connected to an overwhelming experience whether the origin of the experience is identified or not. Pierre Janet defined them as 'pathological automatisms [that] persist as subconscious fixed ideas' (Van der Kolk et al., 1989). Traumatic memories are formed by the fragments of an overly emotional experience that pushed the system to produce high levels of stress hormones. This process causes the sensory part of the fragmented memories to be encoded as 'reminders' of risk and threat encompassing the emotionality experienced then. The reminders become more rapidly 'consolidated,' stable, and long-term. The obvious flashbacks (easy to identify) are the visual ones (images), but the ones where other *sensory* information could have been consolidated are much harder to spot and may activate responses that seem to come from nowhere. These others are in the form of odors, colors, shapes, face grimes, body postures, materials, objects, body sensations, pain, or even the specific characteristics of people (like age and ethnic background).

> Using the example of getting hit by a car while crossing the street, the brain could have stored as warnings sensory input at the moment of the strike such as the eyes of the conductor, the smell of the tires, and the pain at the impact.

Decontextualized Traumatic Memories (Too Foreign and Somatic)

Traumatic memories can be experienced out of context more in the form of emotionality and physical reactions than in the form of sensory recollection. They can be re-experienced without having any apparent connection with what's happening in the present, playing like a broken record without identifying the root of the feeling. They are experienced again and again as a distorted perception of current happenings, bringing distress. To avoid confusion between these types of traumatic memories and flashbacks, I call them backlashes.

Backlashes are connected to emotional reactions and physical sensations. When someone experiences a backlash, they experience an emotional state that feels elicited by the present but is majorly manifesting the past as part of a distorted perception, a memorized reaction, or an incomplete action. A person can perceive a situation as hurtful, dangerous, or debilitating and assign the emotionality to what they are presently facing without any awareness that what they are feeling is a reliving of a traumatic emotional memory (whether mental or physical).

We can use as an example a person that was frequently and cruelly criticized as a child for their point of view and taste. They may feel criticized every time they speak, even if others are on board or admire their point of view. They would be actually experiencing a backlash and not actual criticism, but they can't recognize the present as separate from what the body stored and reactivate, and they may even feel the impulse of running away which they may have felt but not acted on before. The memory doesn't come as sensory information or related to previous experiences, but as a real-time feeling of censure, disapproval, and need to escape, probably triggered by either a word used previously as criticism, the body posture of the other person, or even a type of laughter used while criticized previously.

Absent Traumatic Memories (Too Little)

Traumatized individuals seem affected by the fact that they can't either recall big chunks of their lives or specifics about traumatic events or call it amnesia. Many indicators point to the possibility that there are events that were never recorded, or at least parts and details of them. The brain can't register everything when it's busy trying to survive. It has been a common understanding and assumption—since Charcot and Freud—that traumatization causes amnesia but it's not been clear at this point if it includes a partial or total loss of memory since the traumatized cases they treated are not commonly seen anymore (mutism, blindness, aphasia, etc.). Amnesia, in psychology, assumes that there was a memory that then gets forgotten. *What if there was no memory? Is that still amnesia?* In medicine, amnesia refers not only to the loss of memories but also to having trouble learning new information and forming new memories. Studies indicate that the dissociative characteristics of the trauma phenomena, both peritraumatic and posttraumatic, can cause problems encoding new information and storing new memories besides the assumption that people 'lose' memories. We can use the medical model to assume that traumatization causes amnesia in two ways: (a) lack of memory and (b) loss of the ability to form new memories.

LACK OF MEMORY (AND THE POSSIBLE FORMATION OF FALSE MEMORIES)

Since most people assume all events should be in their memory, it's common to see people in therapy (and therapists) distressed and confused by not finding them. It is assumed by some schools of thought that if we don't remember, it either means that the memories are dissociated, or they are repressed. I'll cover dissociated memories in Chapter 6 but let's talk here about repressed memories. Sigmund Freud was the one that originally developed the concept of repressed memories as part of his psychoanalytic theory. According to Freud (1933), repression occurs as an unconscious push of information out of consciousness when a thought, memory, or feeling is too painful for an individual. The theory has been controversial since the beginning and it has not been possible to be proven using scientific methods. Its implications are many, in terms of treatment and in terms of what it means for those who 'recover' memories; it also has legal implications. In 1992, an international organization was created (The False Memory Syndrome Foundation) to "advocate on behalf of individuals believed to be falsely accused of child sexual abuse" after the 'victim' was put through psychotherapy techniques that were trying to recover the assumed repressed memories. The 'movement' has also been described as coming out of people who wanted to deny child sexual abuse, and sometimes their being perpetrators. The battle between accusing and denying lasted years but never found resolution. So far, it seems impossible to know when a memory comes from a real event or from a supposed event. The foundation dissolved in 2019. Psychotherapeutic techniques that utilize one or more memory-eliciting methods to recall previously forgotten memories have been scientifically discredited (Pope, 1998). Still, even when research has demonstrated that episodic memory often involves a flawed reconstructive process, there is a large number of clinicians that believe to some extent that traumatic memories are often repressed and can be retrieved; they— clinicians and clients—spend years tirelessly looking for them.

Let's think of the false memory phenomena as having a board full of pieces of a puzzle where some of the pieces evidently don't fit with the rest. Some pieces clearly belong together while some of the new 'rescued' pieces are not part of this puzzle even when they share some similarities. If the clinician finds those lost pieces—that don't match the rest of the 'picture'—but still tries to make a story out of them, the new story may develop and look like a memory, mainly due to the flexibility of our brain and the characteristics of memory encoding that we learned above, but this will be a new creation, not a recreation.

It's just too common to meet clients that lived free of depression or anxiety for most of their lives until encountering a series of 'never remembered' memories assumed by a clinician to have been repressed or forgotten, and suddenly, after 'finding the memories,' experiencing high levels of distress and traumatic symptoms that push them to extremes of the sort of suicidal ideation (Bonanno et al., 2003). I vehemently advocate for accepting the possibility that we have memory gaps from events—and even from parts of our lives—*not because we repressed the memories but because they were never there*. I also advocate not being too polarized about the false memory syndrome. Each person is different and without contaminating their memories, most individuals are able to remember *how much they didn't forget*. I've seen it multiple times: the 'forgotten' memory either (A) doesn't make sense at all as soon as the pieces start integrating, or (B) it is fully remembered thanks to all the other pieces that are available (as in the puzzle example).

From what I have explained in this section on how the brain works in terms of memory formation, it's fair to assume that not recording everything that happens in our lives is normal—even expected—and that many parts of a traumatic experience are never encoded. It's also valid to say that memories full of emotionality are not completely forgotten given how memories get consolidated. They may be compartmentalized though. It's as impossible to store everything from a traumatic situation as it is to 'forget' everything from an event that jeopardized our integrity or life (unless there are physiological problems that cause amnesia or severe dissociation which I'll mention in Chapter 6).

Trauma Domain #4: Cognition and Perception

RANODMIIZNG LTETRES IN THE MIDLDE OF WRODS HAS LITLTE OR NO EFFCET ON THE AIBLTIY OF SIKLELD RAEDRES TO UNEDRSATND THE TXET. INEDED ONE RAIPD REDAER NOITCED OLNY FUOR OR FVIE ERORRS IN AN A4 PAGE OF MUDLDED TXET (Rawlinson, 1976). IT CUOLD MKAE US THNIK THAT IT DSENO'T MTAETR IN WAHT OERDR THE LTTERES IN A WROD ARE AS LNOG AS THE FRSIT AND LSAT LTEETR BE IN THE RGHIT PCLAE, MABYE BCUSEAE THE HUAMN MNID DEOS NOT RAED ERVEY LTETER BY ISTLEF, BUT THE WROD AS A WLOHE

Were you able to read the previous paragraph? At least a part of it? Isn't it interesting how our brain anticipates the words even when the letters are scrambled? It's amazing what our brain does to save energy. It has a way of creating programs to generalize the input from our senses, predicting what we should see instead of waiting to see what's there. This is how perception works, and one of the reasons why trauma disorders are so unsettling. I enjoy showing these types of examples about perception to my clients—like the one I'm including (Figure 4.6). They all show easily and clearly that we don't see what's really there, but *what we are programmed to see*, and how our system responds to what we think we see and not only what we actually see. When we see the image in Figure 4.6, we think the black hole is expanding and our pupils dilate as if we were entering a darker place (Laeng et al., 2022).

After traumatization, our perceptual programs get 'tainted' by the experience that overwhelmed the system. Things look different from then on. The changes in perception have to do with the adaptive alteration that seeks for danger and is hyper-focus on whatever can signal threat, given the fact that the person 'almost failed' to stay alive—and now the system's job is not to take chances anymore. Everyone seems suspicious and no place seems safe. That's why most mental disorders present issues with judgment, perspective, and decision-making (Fellows, 2011).

The relationship between cognition and perception may be hard to distinguish in terms of trauma's aftermath and its healing. Traumatization

Figure 4.6 Example of optical illusion and perceptual distortion (Image credit: Laeng et al., 2022)

affects cognition due to the alterations suffered in higher-order cognitive functions such as memory, attention, emotion regulation, goal-oriented action, and problem-solving. Those alterations, mostly in the neural pathways important for the processing of sensations (Harricharan et al., 2016), have a negative impact on the emotionality connected to cognitive functioning (Hayes et al., 2012) and the meaning we assign to actions, situations, information, and reactions, from others and from ourselves. Since cognitive processes influence the most basic components of perception (Michel, 2020), *perception then suffers alterations as well.* Some evident distortions are believing that life holds no promise, that we are doomed, and that bad things keep happening. The belief that our efforts and intentions can't protect ourselves from misfortune affects our sense of agency and self-concept and perpetuates defeat as a mental state.

COGNITIVE DISTORTIONS AFTER TRAUMATIZATION

Cognition is highly related to acquiring knowledge and making sense of the information received through our senses. Autonomic regulation influences perceptions, cognitions, and emotional states by interacting with them at different levels, whether it's through changes in physiology, directing attention for meaning, memory formation, or by motivating specific mental states and actions. Interoception—the perception of sensations from inside the body—gets affected after traumatization, disturbing the capacity to detect and interpret body sensations. When someone misinterprets these manifestations, the brain fails in predicting objective outcomes originating experiences such as depersonalization, hallucinations, anxiety, and many other dysregulated states (Critchley et al., 2013). A key player in cognitive control is the PFC since it is the one that organizes brain processes for specific tasks and signals other brain structures to guide the flow along task-relevant circuits. It's also central to learning intended behaviors by acquiring and implementing goal-directed actions (Miller, 2000). Important parts of the PFC get affected by the decreasing activity caused by the survival mode. Repercussions of prolonged traumatization in terms of cognition go from having poorer spatial working memory performance, lower ability to learn new information, and reduced capacity to recognize emotions or give the right meaning to experiences, social cognition, or consequences of actions (Widom & Czaja, 2012), especially if the alteration in cognition happens during the development years and white and gray matter decrease in volume.

DISTORTED PERCEPTION AND TRAUMATIZATION

Perception is considered an active "process or result of becoming aware of objects, relationships, and events by means of the senses, which includes such activities as recognizing, observing, and discriminating" (APa). It is active because it's always guessing, predicting, and constructing representations of the world. Our expectations light up neural activity causing our brains to make predictions of the outcomes as they may unfold (Yon, 2019) guiding our decisions and movement not separated from the knowledge that our cognition has gathered, which influences what we perceive. Cognitive information influences perceptual processes, and cognitive processes depend on perceptual information.

Picture it this way: we know flowers have a fragrance (cognitive information), so when we see a flower, our sense of smell prepares to receive the information (perceptual process), and because we have smelled flowers before (perceptual information), we expect a pleasant experience (cognitive process).

The main objective of the perception processes is to amplify and strengthen the sensory information our brain receives to be able to orient and act very quickly, specifically, and efficiently (Carbon, 2014). Distinguished professor Lisa F. Barrett (and the centuries-old Buddhist tradition) says that our brain is wired for delusion and that what we perceive as real is just an illusion (Barrett, 2017). Thesis such as the fact that 99.9999999% of our body is empty space (only 0.0000001% of us is substantial matter) confirms Barret's statement since our perception makes us believe that our bodies—an illusory collection of empty spaces—are 100% 'firm and solid.' Those processes that make us believe that things are something they are not have been proposed as being part of our adaptation for survival. The perceptual processes are part of the anticipatory system that predicts outcomes and creates a world of internal representations that only exist in our heads. According to scientific findings, objective perception is impossible (Carbon, 2014). There are differences in perception across different individuals. That's why we have different tastes, why our once-beloved job or hobby becomes boring, and the reason we fall out of love. We perceive a person as perfect just to perceive the same one as despicable only sometime later. The perceptual qualities and quantities which we can process change as we age or collect new information from our experiences (Carbon, 2014). In a way, we could say that each one of us carries a different mental reality.

We all then have these processes that create a representation of reality that dictates our cognition with its consequent emotions, thoughts, decisions, memories, and so on. When we suffer from a trauma disorder, those representations get modified, as well as the processes that form and access them, without us understanding why the pictures of our reality don't match our experiences. Sometimes we are aware of this fact, but most of the time we cannot even grasp the differences. Our actions, feelings, and thoughts seem off. We lose internal and external synchrony. Others seem out of phase to us while we seem out of phase to them, which reflects that the connection between brain and body, among neurons, between organs, and amid emotional states are working out of sync. We don't understand why others don't understand us; we don't understand their behavior toward us either. Misperception becomes a frequent phenomenon experienced by traumatized individuals that may promote social withdrawal and isolation, or confrontation. Cognition and perception go hand in hand, feeding each other's dysregulated states.

WHEN DISTORTIONS AFFECT OUR WELL-BEING

The traumatized individual lives a delusion that manifests as believing they are 'insane' in one extreme or 'odd' in the other. These distortions become stronger as they get reinforced by thoughts or feedback, but it is totally possible to become aware of those influences. If sometimes the brain is prepared to base its inferences on *sensory signals*, while at other times on *expectations*, we can manage our expectations to help the brain make inferences based on them. Our mind is extremely powerful in this quest. It requires reviewing the schemas and expectations that have been using as if they were all that's true.

Schemas

A person with negative self-schemas is likely to interpret information about themselves negatively, causing further emotional issues. Schemas are "an outlook or assumption that an individual has of the self, others, or the world that endures despite objective reality" (APA). Aaron Beck (developer of CBT) has suggested that emotionally unwell individuals carry negative self-schemas that may come from negative experiences or observing negative outcomes on others, probably developed in childhood (Beck, 2002). Soon later, Jeffrey Young developed an approach—Schema Therapy (Weishaar et al., 2003)—that adds attachment theory and Objects Relations Theory to the CBT principles. Young talks about specific schemas—called Early Maladaptive Schemas—as self-defeating core themes that individuals repeat throughout their lives, creating dysfunction in most cases. This approach fits really well with the distortions that happen after traumatization, especially if it happens early in life. The maladaptive schemas formed when a child's core needs are not met seem to match the description of the ANS's dominant strategy activation, with the addition of the distortions in cognition and perception and the emotional states and responses that derive from them.

The distortions suffered in cognition as part of the traumatization aftermath manifest as a set of beliefs and ideas about how things work, who gets granted opportunities and who doesn't, the limited foreseen possibilities, the person's anticipation of how fate will limit their performance, and the functionality of the individual in society. When the traumatization happens early, the kid will carry the belief of being cursed, not capable, defective, weak, unimportant, entitled, or flawed, through life, anticipating failure, strengthening the sense of defeat, maintaining the distortions, and pushing the system to continue running in survival mode. Most schemas become so ingrained that they seem like laws written exclusively for the individual: "everything is harder for me," "nobody wants me to succeed," "I don't deserve more," etc. Facing these fallacies—and reflecting on where they come from—is a way to start modifying their circuits and the impact on the system that these schemas precipitate.

Expectations

Research has shown that our perception of the world is influenced by our expectations. Expectations serve several purposes, like keeping us motivated and engaged in our activities, planning for the future, and making sense of what we are perceiving in the present based on similar experiences from the past (Trafton, 2017). They are also used by our brain to anticipate possible outcomes. Uncertainty is extremely undesirable, and by fabricating expectations, we avoid the suffering of not knowing what will be next. By relying on prior experiences, we optimize our behavior. Our behavior is also affected by the beliefs we carry concerning the intentions and behavior of others. We create expectations and internal models about others as a way to create a representation of ourselves (Friston, 2012). The more realistic the expectations, the easier to achieve them; the less objective they are, the higher the probability of disappointment and suffering. The more emotionality carried by our expectations, the more influence they will have in our system reactions.

For most traumatized individuals it's very challenging to accurately weigh reality and set objective goals and expectations. They may either dream of becoming the best possible individual, or believe they will never be able to do 'x.' The alterations in cognition and perception affect one's capacity to know how much is too much or not enough. The fluctuations—from feeling 'extremely' needy to rejecting all types of help—are common and can become unbearable in their own right. Manifestations such as passivity or heightened anxiety (provoked by disappointment and disillusion) will further distort expectations, affecting cognitive functions, schemas, emotional responses, sense of agency, and self-concept. The downward spiral may continue getting deeper as the traumatized person fails to meet their own expectations and the expectation of others.

Individuals that get traumatized in childhood may get affected cognitively by **magical thinking**, remaining stuck on using it to manage the anxiety of uncertainty. Through magical thinking, the person may find agency, consolation, or a place 'to hide' from pain and distress, holding the belief that their thoughts, actions, and words (or any symbol) can modify the future (Vandenberg, 2019). Magical thinking is just one way to disconnect from a painful reality when expectations are not met. It causes further cognitive and perceptual decline even when it could be a resourceful defense to avoid feeling defeated. Magical thinking becomes a problem when the line between reality and fantasy is not identified, and perception gets influenced by imaginary representations. Some individuals, for example, develop the idea that their out-of-control reactions are ruled by an evil spirit inhabiting their mind, and an exorcism or something of the sort is the only viable solution. Others keep feeding the idea that their problems will end as soon as they dream of the lottery winning number. Few also develop the idea that they are invincible and can do what they please.

It may be useful to mention that some psychotherapeutic interventions promote validating the client, but validating distortions in perception feeds the disconnection with what's really going on and presents an obstacle to resolution. Challenging the distortions may not be useful, either, unless the interventions ask for PFC activation, not only on its cognitive side but also its experiential part (right hemisphere). Affect should be included while working with cognition/perception to help the distortions begin correcting.

Trauma Domain #5: Self

> I used to get confused when, randomly and unexpectedly, I found my image reflected in a mirror and wondered for an instant who that person was. "She looks familiar" ran through my thoughts in a flash. I realized one day that those moments when I didn't recognize myself were due to the distortions in my self-image that tainted how I perceived myself.

Traumatized people often suffer from the problem of not knowing who they are (or not recognizing themselves) but once one becomes aware of the concept of self, it's easier to find, form, or own it. Still, the concept of 'self' is one of the most controversial topics we can find among philosophers and scientists of all sorts (Gallagher, 2013). So, please bear with me in the quest of describing how this component of our system gets shattered by traumatization.

Being able to own a sense of self is crucial to mental health. It implies a conscious understanding and acceptance of every component that represents the person (thoughts, limitations, qualities, preferences, values, and so on). Underlying the construction of self-concept (Oyserman & Elmore, 2012) is the capacity to have thoughts where the thinker is the object, or in other words, having the capacity to reflect on what oneself is and is not, and separate it from external influences, judgment, and pressure to comply. Lacking or losing self-reflective capacities compromises the integrity of the self-concept. If the sense of who the person is develops from cognitive distortions, the damaged self-concept influences behavior and can evolve as the individual's personality. One of the obvious results for traumatized people is the constant projection of the victim role that becomes a mental attitude and a perceived identifier. Another big issue is the need to create a false-self to deal with the world that ends up ruling the system without cognitive control or awareness of the falsehood of the self that is projected. Let me describe all the components of the self and how they get affected.

The Birth of the Self

We are born without a sense of who we are. This is because we think we are an extension of our carrier—and can't recognize our bodies until we reach a certain maturation (Brownell et al., 2007). Between 13 and 18 months, we acquire reflective self-awareness, an awareness of the body being ours, which secures the development of other characteristics of the observing-self such as *self-reference* and *self-conscious emotions*. Developing an objective awareness of ourselves is the foundation to self-regulate, develop self-concept, and own an identity later (Brownell et al., 2013). Once we identify ourselves, we move to differentiate ourselves from the world, which facilitates the development of the perception of who we are as a unit, and later on, as a member of a group. The 'self' is a construct of our own making that could be defined as the connector of events in time and space into a single continuum of experience. Its basic function is the *integration of all that creates us in the context of the body we inhabit, the way we assimilate our surroundings, the circumstances we endure, and the meaning we assign to each* (Sparby et al., 2019).

We are also born without the ability to recognize our feelings and thoughts. It's the relationships with those around us and our experiences from those interactions that shape how we develop the idea of 'I.' During the initial years of our lives, we build our sense of self in relation to primary caregivers by identifying ourselves as a source of joy, or as a burden that provokes frustration, anger, or rejection in the parent. The feedback received from the caregivers on whether they value us or not will set the perception of our worth, the right to take interpersonal space, or the opportunity to engage fully with life.

Children that are not allowed to have their own point of view, make their own decisions, express their preferences, or exercise their individuation can grow up with an incomplete or compromised sense of their 'boundaries.' Babies that are ignored and not cared for may see truncated the opportunity to develop self-concept because they dissociated from that possibility early on. Not having a sense of self is highly distressing and can add to the development of a personality disorder. For many traumatized individuals with this issue, working on the missing or incomplete sense of self may be a priority, including working on traumatic memories. Working with the past will only inform the reason why the person is damaged, weakening whatever self-concept is there.

A healthy sense of self allows us to embody our desires and thoughts without the need for validation, is able to practice self-compassion and self-care, and persist from past to present (and future). Lacking self is not necessarily the result of having a traumatizing childhood. Some drugs, head injuries, oxygen deprivation, other mental illnesses, and aging can all degrade or wipe out the sense of 'I' (Epstein, 2017). We'll see in detail (Chapter 8) that an unresolved attachment as an infant is also an impediment to forming a self. If we flip the coin, we find that *we have the capacity to form a sense of self at any moment* if our brain is in good physical condition. There is always the possibility to review or build up our own set of goals, values, beliefs, ideals, and purpose.

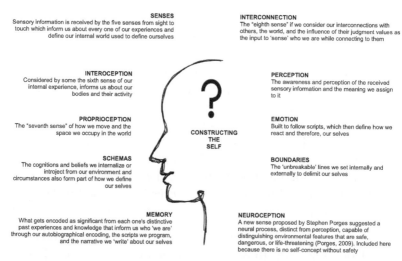

SENSES
Sensory information is received by the five senses from sight to touch which inform us about every one of our experiences and define our internal world used to define ourselves

INTERCONNECTION
The "eighth sense" if we consider our interconnections with others, the world, and the influence of their judgment values as the input to 'sense' who we are while connecting to them

INTEROCEPTION
Considered by some the sixth sense of our internal experience, informs us about our bodies and their activity

PERCEPTION
The awareness and perception of the received sensory information and the meaning we assign to it

PROPRIOCEPTION
The "seventh sense" of how we move and the space we occupy in the world

EMOTION
Built to follow scripts, which then define how we react and therefore, our selves

CONSTRUCTING THE SELF

SCHEMAS
The cognitions and beliefs we internalize or introject from our environment and circumstances also form part of how we define our selves

BOUNDARIES
The 'unbreakable' lines we set internally and externally to delimit our selves

MEMORY
What gets encoded as significant from each one's distinctive past experiences and knowledge that inform us who 'we are' through our autobiographical encoding, the scripts we program, and the narrative we 'write' about our selves

NEUROCEPTION
A new sense proposed by Stephen Porges suggested a neural process, distinct from perception, capable of distinguishing environmental features that are safe, dangerous, or life-threatening (Porges, 2009). Included here because there is no self-concept without safety

Figure 4.7 Constructing the self

CONSTRUCTING THE SELF: THE PROCESSES INVOLVED IN BECOMING

Since the self is a construct we make that exists only as an abstraction in our mind, it's not 'directly' observable. Each one of us builds it by the awareness of the information gathered from the ten different sources shown in Figure 4.7.

WHAT INTEGRATES THE SELF?

Traumatization could incapacitate the development of a sense of self if it happens at birth, interrupt it if it happens in childhood, and distort or destroy any sense of self built if it happens later. It's common to observe traumatized individuals living at the mercy of others' thoughts, opinions, judgments, or 'direction.' This lack of confidence keeps the person continuously developing a sense of being damaged, not being enough, being wrong/wronged, and not having the capacity to rule their own lives. Having a poor, damaged, or weak sense of self—or not having one at all—is a hindrance to the healing process because there may not be a 'one' involved in treatment. If this is the case, the therapeutic interventions go in loops or destabilize the system.

Ego

Freud introduced the concept of ego in his structural model (ego, id, and super id) but he used the term with more than one meaning. Fundamentally, ego was used as *agency*, always trying to win over the id and the super-ego forces, but also as *self*. From Freud on, the amount of writing produced to clarify the meaning of the term ego piles up in mountains, while pop-psychology and colloquial language have assigned their own meaning to the term. If lay people (not psychoanalytically minded) talk about ego nowadays, they most probably are talking about the part of us that is often defensive, that struggles to be perceived as better, smart, valuable, being right, self-centered, and hardly accepting making mistakes or having flaws. The way we use the term even clinically shifts from considering it an internal agent that moves between the conscious and the unconscious (as Freud had asserted), to the agent that one uses to navigate society and that keeps one's 'image' on good terms. The ego as we understand it today, it's not as 'real' or aware as Freud proposed, but instead, a psychological entity that projects strength while constantly feeling internally weak.

Now that I'm talking about Freud, I want to share the notion that there's an interesting parallel between Freud's structural model and the Triune Brain model (reviewed in Chapter 2). The Triune brain model proposes a primitive brain that is instinctual (like the id), an emotional brain that struggles for affiliation (like the ego), and the 'human' brain that strives for transcendence (similar to the Super Ego). I think therefore it is not too far off to identify the ego as *the emotional part of the self*. Because of its emotionality, the ego plays a big role in the anticipation of events connected to their place among group members in particular and society in general. The need to belong is crucial in its development. As we saw earlier, children don't have an ego (or a sense of self) until they become more aware of their surroundings and start assimilating the perception of the world from the point of view of others. They start seeing themselves reflected in the perspective, judgments, or values of those around them. The more accepted they feel, the less the ego needs to build smoke screens, and the easier it becomes to form their own concept.

False-Self (Hollow-Self)

False-self was first conceptualized by Donald Winnicott (1965) using a psychoanalytical frame referring to the types of false personalities that people create very early in life as the result of inadequate parenting (mothering according to his time) or failures in empathy and attunement, and the infant's need to comply. Followers of Winnicott have stated that those whose false-self becomes pervasive (rules the show) are not aware of the mask they wear and confuse it with their self. That means that a person governed by the false-self develops their self-concept based on their defensive 'persona' constructed to hide the 'defective one'—the one they need to negate because they don't trust that it's possible for it to be liked or loved. That hidden persona becomes psychological pain.

Under a trauma lens, distancing from well-established psychoanalytical concepts—like the false-self—it's better to choose different terms to avoid conflictive statements. I like using the term 'hollow-self' and describe it as an empty shell full of ways to survive avoiding confronting their painful reality or showing their defectiveness that may manifest some unintegrated emotional parts. I compare it with a hologram of the person; it may look identical, but it lacks awareness, self-reflection, values, empathy, and the capacity to absorb anything 'concrete' due to its immaterial nature. It's purely mental and dissociated from the 'real' objectivity of the person; it's only a projection of insecurities through a cluster of defenses that try to fit in and show a worth that they 'know' it's not there. Developing a strong self and integrating dissociated parts is a big goal of trauma treatment.

Inner-Self

Recently, the inner-self has become important in trauma studies as an agent of healing. It is considered by some to be the soul, the Buddha-nature, the 'center,' etc., or names that symbolize different perspectives on the same idea: that at the core we all are compassionate, kind, and non-judgmental since we are the manifestation of qualities such as love, generosity, joy, courage, and wisdom. In the world of therapy, Internal Family Systems (IFS)—that defines the Larger Self as the seat of consciousness (Schwartz, 2020)—considers the Self (inner) to be the one that demonstrates many positive qualities such as acceptance, confidence, calmness, wisdom, compassion, connectedness, leadership, and perspective; the model states that having access to Self is what facilitates integrating the past with the present, finding meaning in past experiences, and ending the distress from traumatic memories.

Observing-Self

The construct of the observing ego was introduced indirectly by Freud in his lecture *Dissection of the Psychical Personality* (1933), where he said that the ego can take itself as an object, can treat itself as an object like other objects, can observe itself, criticize itself, and do "heavens knows what with itself" (his words) (Freud, 1990). Since we agree that the ego is not the self, I switch the order and prefer to have *our self observing our ego* to ensure that we notice our actions and reactions and that we take ownership of them. Observing our hollow-self in vivo gives us the possibility to step back, getting the kind of distance and perspective we would have while observing a friend or family member we care for (Misch, 2000), which promotes acceptance, compassion, and self-reflective abilities. Developing an observing-self is fundamental to healing from traumatization. As long as the person stays controlled by a hollow-self that doesn't use self-reflection to understand what parts of their schemas are learned, introjected, internalized, or altered by perception, the person may not be able to manage their reactions. The observing-self is highly related to self-reflection and executive functions, which, as we know, depend on a healthy activation of the PFC. If the PFC is slow or disconnected, finding the observing-self becomes difficult, and all the healing effort is put on a self (false or hollow) that doesn't participate in the process. One of the reasons why treatment can fail.

TRAUMATIZATION SHATTERING EFFECT ON THE SELF

Traumatization leaves the person with either a weak self or a lack of it depending on its complexity and duration. If you ask someone lacking a self about their values, they will answer "my parents say I'm smart," "my friends have told me I'm x, y, or z," or something of the sort, without knowing, on their own, what to say. They lack insight into what defines or makes them uniquely them. Having a weak sense of self may be identifiable in those that lose their self in romantic relationships, shaping and fusing themselves in terms of the 'significant other,' many times suffering from codependent tendencies (their happiness is dependent on others' well-being), enmeshment with their close relatives (difficulty separating their thoughts and feelings from what their parents believe), showing an inability to create boundaries (or not knowing how to make them be respected), having scattered priorities (deficient managing their time and energy), finding challenging to set goals (not having direction), showing group mentality (creating their identity based on the ideal held by the group), suffering social anxiety, low self-esteem, not having a purpose, easily abused, taken for granted or taken advantage of, trying to meet other's definition of 'success,' and a long list of shortages that can end up as feelings of deep dissatisfaction and confusion.

For most individuals that suffered traumatization for a long period, especially early on, the hollow-self is the one that all those around them know and identify (including the clinician); some of those kids hide their 'non-developed self' while some have never 'seen' it. Therapeutically, treating a hollow-self without awareness that it's a facade may be a continuous and fruitless battle that ends up being a waste of time.

References

Alia-Klein, N., Gan, G., Gilam, G., Bezek, J., Bruno, A., Denson, T. F., Hendler, T., Lowe, L., Mariotti, V., Muscatello, M. R., Palumbo, S., Pellegrini, S., Pietrini, P., Rizzo, A., & Verona, E. (2020). The feeling of anger: From brain networks to linguistic expressions. *Neuroscience and Biobehavioral Reviews*, 108, 480–497. https://doi.org/10.1016/j.neubiorev.2019.12.002

Allen R. J. (2018). Classic and recent advances in understanding amnesia. *F1000 Research*, 7, 331. https://doi.org/10.12688/f1000research.13737.1

Anand, K. S., & Dhikav, V. (2012). Hippocampus in health and disease: An overview. *Annals of Indian Academy of Neurology*, 15(4), 239–246. https://doi.org/10.4103/0972-2327.104323

Anderson, E. C., Carleton, R. N., Diefenbach, M., & Han, P. (2019). The relationship between uncertainty and affect. *Frontiers in Psychology*, 10, 2504. https://doi.org/10.3389/fpsyg.2019.02504

Barrett, L. F. (2017). *How emotions are made: The secret life of the brain.* (p. 76). New York: Houghton Mifflin Harcourt.

Barrett, L. F., & Russell, J. A. (Eds.). (2015). *The psychological construction of emotion.* (pp. 168–180). New York: The Guilford Press.

Beauchaine, T. P., Gatzke-Kopp, L., & Mead, H. K. (2007). Polyvagal theory and developmental psychopathology: Emotion dysregulation and conduct problems from preschool to adolescence. *Biological Psychology*, 74(2), 174–184. https://doi.org/10.1016/j.biopsycho.2005.08.008

Beck, A. T. (2002). Cognitive models of depression. *Clinical Advances in Cognitive Psychotherapy: Theory and Application*, 14(1), 29–61.

Bonanno, G. A., Noll, J. G., Putnam, F. W., O'Neill, M., and Trickett, P. K. (2003). Predicting the willingness to disclose childhood sexual abuse from measures of repressive coping and dissociative tendencies. *Child Maltreatment*, 8, 302–318. https://doi: 10.1177/1077559503257066

Brownell, C. A., Iesue, S. S., Nichols, S. R., & Svetlova, M. (2013). Mine or yours? Development of sharing in toddlers in relation to ownership understanding. *Child Development*, 84(3), 906–920. https://doi.org/10.1111/cdev.12009

Brownell, C. A., Zerwas, S., & Ramani, G. B. (2007). "So big": The development of body self-awareness in toddlers. *Child Development*, 78(5), 1426–1440. https://doi.org/10.1111/j.1467-8624.2007.01075

Camina, E., & Güell, F. (2017). The neuroanatomical, neurophysiological and psychological basis of memory: Current models and their origins. *Frontiers in Pharmacology*, 8, 438. https://doi.org/10.3389/fphar.2017.00438

Carbon C. C. (2014). Understanding human perception by human-made illusions. *Frontiers in Human Neuroscience*, 8, 566. https://doi.org/10.3389/fnhum.2014.00566

Critchley, H. D., Eccles, J., & Garfinkel, S. N. (2013). Interaction between cognition, emotion, and the autonomic nervous system. *Handbook of Clinical Neurology*, 59–77. https://doi.org/10.1016/B978-0-444-53491-0.00006-7

Dadomo, H., Grecucci, A., Giardini, I., Ugolini, E., Carmelita, A., & Panzeri, M. (2016). Schema therapy for emotional dysregulation: Theoretical implication and clinical applications. *Frontiers in Psychology*, 7, 1987. https://doi.org/10.3389/fpsyg.2016.01987

Damasio, A., & Damasio, H. (2006). Minding the body. *Daedalus*, 135(3), 15–22. http://www.jstor.org/stable/20028048

Davis, K. L., & Montag, C. (2019). Selected principles of Pankseppian affective neuroscience. *Frontiers in Neuroscience*, 12, 1025. https://doi.org/10.3389/fnins.2018.01025

Dudai, Y., & Eisenberg, M. (2004). Rites of passage of the Engram. *Neuron*, 44(1), 93–100. https://doi.org/10.1016/j.neuron.2004.09.003

Epstein, R. (2017). Decapitating Consciousness. *The Awl*. https://www.theawl.com/2017/03/decapitating-consciousness/

Fellows L. K. (2011). Gottfried J.A., editor, *The Neurology of Value. Neurobiology of Sensation and Reward* (ch. 16, pp. 351–370). Boca Raton, FL: CRC Press/Taylor & Francis.

Freud, S. (1933). New introductory lectures on psycho-analysis. In J. Strachey et al. (Trans.), *The standard edition of the complete psychological works of sigmund freud* (Vol. XXII, page 58). New York, London: Hogarth Press.

Freud, S. (1990). *New introductory lectures on psychoanalysis* (pp. 86–87). WW Norton & Co.

Friston K. (2012). Prediction, perception and agency. *International Journal of Psychophysiology: Official Journal of the International Organization of Psychophysiology*, 83(2), 248–252. https://doi.org/10.1016/j.ijpsycho.2011.11.014

Gallagher S. (2013). A pattern theory of self. *Frontiers in Human Neuroscience*, 7, 443. https://doi.org/10.3389/fnhum.2013.00443

Halligan, P.W., & David, A. S. (2001). Cognitive neuropsychiatry: Towards a scientific psychopathology. *Nature Reviews Neuroscience*, 2, 209–215.

Harmon-Jones, E., Harmon-Jones, C., & Summerell, E. (2017). On the importance of both dimensional and discrete models of emotion. *Behavioral Sciences (Basel, Switzerland)*, 7(4), 66. https://doi.org/10.3390/bs7040066

Harricharan, S., Rabellino, D., Frewen, P. A., Densmore, M., Théberge, J., McKinnon, M. C., Schore, A. N., & Lanius, R. A. (2016). Fmri functional connectivity of the periaqueductal gray in PTSD and its dissociative subtype. *Brain and Behavior*, 6(12). https://doi.org/10.1002/brb3.579

Hayes, J. P., VanElzakker, M. B., & Shin, L. M. (2012). Emotion and cognition interactions in PTSD: A review of neurocognitive and neuroimaging studies. *Frontiers in Integrative Neuroscience*, 6, 89. https://doi.org/10.3389/fnint.2012.00089

Laeng, B., Nabil, S., & Kitaoka, A. (2022). The eye pupil adjusts to illusorily expanding holes. *Frontiers in Human Neuroscience*, 16, 877249. https://doi.org/10.3389/fnhum.2022.877249

Lesion, J., & Lindquist, K. (2018). Neuroimaging of emotion dysregulation. T. P. Beauchaine & S. E. Crowell (Eds.), *The Oxford Handbook of Emotion Dysregulation* (pp. 182–201). New York: Oxford University Press.

Mayne, T. J., & Bonanno, G. A. (2015). *Emotions: Current issues and future directions* (pp. 196–206). New York: CRC Press.

Michel, A. (2020). Cognition and perception: Is there really a distinction? *Association for Psychological Science*. https://www.psychologicalscience.org/observer/cognition-and-perception-is-there-really-a-distinction

Miller, E. K. (2000). The prefrontal cortex and cognitive control. *Nature Reviews Neuroscience*, 1(1), 59–65. https://doi.org/10.1038/35036228

Misch D. A. (2000). Basic strategies of dynamic supportive therapy. *The Journal of Psychotherapy Practice and Research*, 9(4), 173–189.

Oyserman, D. & Elmore, K. (2012). Leary, M. R., & Tangney, J. P. (Eds.), Chapter I, Section 4: Self, Self-Concept, and Identity. *Handbook of self and identity* (2nd ed.) (ch. 4, pp. 69–104). New York: The Guilford Press.

Pan, Shen. (2022). What is so special about episodic memory: Lessons from the system-experience distinction. *Synthese* 200(1):1–26.

Pearce, K., Cai, D., Roberts, A. C., & Glanzman, D. L. (2017). Role of protein synthesis and DNA methylation in the consolidation and maintenance of long-term memory in Aplysia. *ELife*, 6. https://doi.org/10.7554/elife.18299

Pope, K. S. (1998). Pseudoscience, cross-examination, and scientific evidence in the recovered memory controversy. *Psychology, Public Policy, and Law*, 4(4), 1160–1181. https://doi.org/10.1037/1076-8971.4.4.1160

Radulovic, J., Lee, R., & Ortony, A. (2018). State-dependent memory: Neurobiological advances and prospects for translation to dissociative amnesia. *Frontiers in Behavioral Neuroscience*, 12, 259. https://doi.org/10.3389/fnbeh.2018.00259

Rawlinson, G. E. (1976) *The significance of letter position in word recognition.* Unpublished PhD Thesis, Psychology Department, University of Nottingham, Nottingham, UK.

Roy, D. S., & Tonegawa, S. (2017). Manipulating memory in space and time. *Current Opinion in Behavioral Sciences*, 17, 1–6. https://doi.org/10.1016/j.cobeha.2017.05.020

Samuelson K. W. (2011). Post-traumatic stress disorder and declarative memory functioning: A review. *Dialogues in Clinical Neuroscience*, 13(3), 346–351. https://doi.org/10.31887/DCNS.2011.13.2/ksamuelson

Saz P. A, Bittencourt-Hewitt, A., L. Sebastian, C. L. (2015). Neurocognitive bases of emotion regulation development in adolescence. *Developmental Cognitive Neuroscience*, 15, 11–25. ISSN 1878-9293. https://doi.org/10.1016/j.dcn.2015.07.006

Schwartz, R. C., & Sweezy, M. (2020). *Internal family systems therapy* (2nd ed.). (pp. 44–48). New York: The Guilford Press.

Siegfried, T. (2019). Why forgetting may make your mind more efficient. *Knowable Magazine.* https://doi.org/10.1146/knowable-011019-1

Sparby, T., Edelhäuser, F., & Weger, U. W. (2019). The true self. Critique, nature, and method. *Frontiers in Psychology*, 10, 2250. https://doi.org/10.3389/fpsyg.2019.02250

Strikwerda-Brown, C., Grilli, M. D., Andrews-Hanna, J., & Irish, M. (2019). "All is not lost"- Rethinking the nature of memory and the self in dementia. *Ageing Research Reviews*, 54, 100932. https://doi.org/10.1016/j.arr.2019.100932

Tomkins, S. S. (1962). *Affect imagery consciousness, 1: The positive affects.* New York: Springer.

Trafton, A. (2017). Neuroscientists identify brain circuit necessary for memory formation. *MIT News.* https://news.mit.edu/2017/neuroscientists-identify-brain-circuit-necessary-memory-formation-0406

Vandenberg, B. (2019). Magical thinking. *Encyclopedia Britannica.* https://www.britannica.com/science/magical-thinking

Vander Kolk, B. A. (2014). *The body keeps the score: Brain, mind, and body in the healing of trauma.* (pp. 92–94). New York: Penguin Books.

Vander Kolk, B. A., Brown, P., & Van der Hart, O. (1989). Pierre Janet on post-traumatic stress. *Journal of Traumatic Stress*, 2(4), 365–378. https://doi.org/10.1007/bf00974596

Walter, E. J., Hanna-Jumma, S., Carraretto, M. (2016). The pathophysiological basis and consequences of fever. *Crit Care, 20*, 200. https://doi.org/10.1186/s13054-016-1375-5

Weishaar, M. E., Young, J. E., Klosko, J. S. (2003). *Schema therapy: A practitioner's guide.* United Kingdom: Guilford Publications.

Widom, C. S., & Czaja, S. J. (2012). *Childhood trauma, psychopathology, and violence: Disentangling causes, consequences, and correlates. Trauma, psychopathology, and violence: Causes, consequences, or correlates?* (pp. 291–317). New York: Oxford University Press.

Williams, M. B., & Sommer, J. F. (2002). *Simple and complex post-traumatic stress disorder: Strategies for comprehensive treatment in clinical practice* (ch. 7). New York: Haworth Maltreatment and Trauma Press.

Winnicott, D. W. (1965). *The maturational processes and the facilitating environment: Studies in the theory of emotional development* (ch. 12). International Universities Press. CT, USA.

Yon, D. (2019). Now you see it. Our brains predict the outcomes of our actions, shaping reality into what we expect. That's why we see what we believe. *Ben Magazine.* https://aeon.co/essays/how-our-brain-sculpts-experience-in-line-with-our-expectations

Part II
The Aftermath

The book's first part focused on the characteristics shared by all trauma disorders. Part II takes a deep dive into explaining each of the most significant trauma disorders and the properties that make them different. We'll see how the resulting alterations after the activation of the survival mechanisms can lead to different types of damage in the functioning of the ANS and the psyche.

Through the narration of Michaela, a young woman with a multicultural background, we will investigate how each disorder develops and how their presence (or absence) can be assessed. Michaela and the people around her will illustrate how people exposed to traumatic circumstances, despite living under the same roof and same conditions, can develop different manifestations. While Michaela is a fictional character, for our purposes, she is a combination of clients I have had and stories that come from cases I have treated or supervised. I chose to include one character and her family (as opposed to snippets of many clients) to show you how traumatic events, adversity, and other traumatizing agents such as shame, abuse, neglect, fear, anger, rejection, and social/familial factors affect people differently within the same framework.

DOI: 10.4324/9781003382478-7

Five
Identifiable Traumatization

Why don't some people receive a PTSD diagnosis even though they feel traumatized?

What exactly makes the difference between developing PTSD and not?

Why is shame so damaging?

In this chapter, you'll meet Michaela. As an introduction to her story, you'll hear her first-person narration of the sexual abuse she experienced in college and see how PTSD symptoms start showing up. While you hear about her life, look out for the role that shame plays in her experiences. As a traumatizing agent, shame—the intense desire to hide or disappear—contributes to the development of symptoms in different ways. Outlining the peritraumatic and posttraumatic effects of shame, as well as how to spot it, will not only show how it affected her but also ideally help anyone manage shame until it no longer plays a role in traumatization.

Since the criterion of PTSD is officially accepted and broadly available, this chapter uses it—and expands on it—breaking down its diagnosis criteria, identifying each of the symptoms that needs to be identified before a diagnosis can be given. It expands on the Assessing Trauma Disorders section discussed in Chapter Three to explain how PTSD unfolds using the homeostasis model assisted by a graphic representation of what dysregulation could look like.

Date-Rape: Michaela's 'Trauma'

Content Warning: This Section Discusses Sexual Assault

> My therapist just told me that I graduated, that I can stop therapy for now if I want to, or that I can choose to just go twice a month. I have mixed feelings

DOI: 10.4324/9781003382478-8

of sadness and joy. I don't want to stop having the support and comfort that my therapist gives me, but I couldn't be happier to receive the confirmation of what I have been experiencing: that my life feels whole. It feels normal! The horrible time of dread, gloominess, numbness, and shame are over. I still can remember many of the days when being at ease seemed unachievable; when sleeping was difficult and being awake an impossibility, when I was not able to look anyone in the eye, when I needed so desperately to be held but was so incapable of asking for care. Affection seemed unattainable then because I didn't feel worthy of respect or love. With the perspective of therapy, I can now remember what happened to me and I'm starting to understand how the events of my past affected my self, my system, my mind, my body, my spirit, and my family. It was going to affect my future but not anymore. My future is now mine! Let me tell you how it all started.

***

My fear of being in a relationship was still fresh after having spent my first year in college with Charles, a guy who left me hurt, weak, and feeling like nothing after months of giving him my full devotion. When I met Ritchie, I was recovering from Charles and didn't really want to date. My parents were making an effort to send me to college and disappointing them was not on my agenda. My only option was to have good grades.

Just hours after handing in a very difficult paper, a girl from my dorm texted me about a weekend trip to her friend's lake house. "It's only a small group of us," she said. I could barely hide my excitement, I was so relieved to have a party to go to for once. A lake house! How nice of them to include me!

We left Friday afternoon with Richie, a boy with wavy blonde hair who had smiled at me a couple of times but who I'd never dared to talk to. With one hand on the wheel of his Mercedes, Richie blasted the best mix and had us all dying of laughter. He locked eyes with me once or twice in the rearview mirror, and I felt a little tingly. Was he checking me out? The house looked more like a cabin and was very pretty; old but maintained, with a long deck in the back that offered a view of the lake. The abundant forest concealed us from the rest of the world. Dana or her parents were nowhere to be seen either (it was her house, Richie told us). I suddenly felt cold even though the sun was bright on my face. I got the sense that I could be one of those characters in psychological thrillers during the nice moment before the plot twist. Richie jammed the key into the lock, forcing the door open as if the house was his. As we walked around the cabin, his muddy boots left marks on the carpet.

There were three bedrooms and six of us. I felt a little drop of sweat on the back of my neck roll slowly down. Another car arrived with five more people. Three of them were guys I had never seen before, and two of them were two girls I recognized from school. There definitely weren't enough beds for eleven people. I was trying to be chill about it, but the situation made me extremely uncomfortable. Lanny seemed to be cool with it. I tried to mimic her posture.

- Where's Dana?
- Coming later.
- Can I choose my bedroom?
- Oh we're camping, we're not sleeping in the house. Dana said we can use the house for everything except sleep. You like camping, right?
- Oh yeah, I love camping. I didn't bring a tent though, does anyone have, like, an extra, or –?
- You can share mine, babe — Richie said.

I didn't like the way he smiled at me, but I was surprised and intrigued. I kind of liked and disliked his answer. For a second, it reminded me of Ishmel, a guy I dated, with an air of dominance and control that I liked to fear. I caught myself anxious at times, feeling my stomach dropping and swirling, not knowing what to do. Nothing was as my friend described it would be, or maybe as I assumed it was going to be.

The rest of the evening went so well I sort of forgot about the weird beginning vibes. I made small talk just to see if I could trust them. Everyone told jokes, ate cheeseburgers, inhaled the fresh forest air, and swam as the sun set. I was almost ready to relax when Richie and some of the guys disappeared. I felt queasy imagining some dark tricks, some bad behavior in the woods, some threat. When Richie and co. reappeared carrying pizzas, wine, and s'mores announcing that the tents and the fire were ready, I felt ashamed about being so paranoid. "My mother's legacy," I thought: privileged Catholic Colombians believe young men are not to be trusted.

We gathered around a dancing fire near four large tents already set. They were very fancy, glamping style, with everything already inside. It was suspicious because they didn't look like the tents regular people install. I tried to relax and enjoy the fun. We three girls from Richie's ride shared a tent while the rest of them used the others. As the cicadas chirped in the warm air, I overcame my nervousness, and slept like a log, counting my blessings.

***

Saturday was a full day of swimming, barbecue, and volleyball. Richie was just one of those guys who glows in a group, and he was such a good leader, too, making everything ready for everyone else. He moved with ease, anticipating our energies, our wants, our needs. I guessed he had experience organizing these weekends. I felt cared for by him. By midnight we had watched a movie inside the house, smoked some pot, and had lots of beer and tequila. I was exhausted and uncontrollably falling asleep. Richie got close to me and whispered to my ear that I could use Dana's bedroom if I wanted because she was not going to make it this weekend at all. Lanny was beside me and seemed to participate in the exchange, so, I looked at her and she seemed to assent with a wink. Richie put his arm around my shoulder and guided me upstairs to Dana's bed, gently laying me down on the pillow. He seemed extremely caring. The moment my face touched the pillow, I fell deeply asleep. I don't know how long I slept before I opened my eyes and found Richie's face in front of mine. I screamed without making any sound.

- Hey you! Finally! I was starting to feel abandoned. He kisses my cheek. Women look like angels after coming. You can trick anyone, you know? You are good at this! He slurred his words and had a big smile on his face.

Coming? Trick? I felt completely disoriented. My thoughts disappeared as soon as I tried to make sense of what he said. I felt my naked torso touching his, my senses so sharp that his words flooded my nose with a mix of alcohol, chocolate, and pot. After coming? Huh??? He covered my face with his enormous hand in a pretended caress all the way down to my breast. I felt incapable of moving. Everything was blurry. I was still like a statue. Horrified but following his hands over my reactive skin, noticing my hard nipples and my moist vagina.

The next morning I woke up in Dana's bedroom with Lanny sleeping in the other bed. I was wearing a large t-shirt that wasn't mine; nothing else, nobody else, everything silent and ordained. WTF! I didn't drink enough to black out. What happened to me? Lanny woke up enthusiastic and said we needed to take advantage of the day and ran downstairs. It was already 11:30 am. I followed her and spent the day as if everything was as it should be. I tried to participate even when I felt tense, full of doubts, disengaged, anxy.

Richie wasn't there. I kept looking around hoping to see him, but also completely panicking about seeing him. My heart pounded all day, my hands were damp with sweat, my body aching, my head full of questions. I imagined Richie telling his friends how easy I was. Where was he? The wait seemed eternal. He showed up close to 3 pm, gave me a great smile, and urged everyone to get ready to make it back on time for his girlfriend's recital. His smile felt cruel, like a stab in my heart, in my ego, in my body, in the expectations of my future. At that moment I felt as if my body had lost all strength, everything became blurry, distant, foreign. I don't even know how I got back to my dorm.

His girlfriend?!

The dream was over and waking up was the beginning of a trip with no return. I felt betrayed, used, violated. I spent the following months in free fall. I was getting sick with all sorts of issues: constant diarrhea, aching muscles, terrible headaches. I felt like my heart was literally skipping beats. The pages I read and the words I wrote were 'computed' but not processed. I felt like a machine with no soul. I was bored, absent, unmotivated, scattered, angry, sad, hopeless. I couldn't sleep and the exhaustion made me feel useless, ugly, defeated. I wasn't eating because even eating seemed to require an effort and a strength that I couldn't count on. Everything seemed surrounded by fog, a slow-motion effect that created gloomy versions of me and others, making me extremely sweaty or scarily cold.

My looping thoughts were cruel and punitive, scolding me for being so stupid, such a slut, so naive. The doubts hammered my days: did he drug me or was I just too drunk? Did Lanny plan it with Richie from the beginning? Was it really Dana's house or is it a trap for stupid women like me plotted by Richie? Did the others know? Did I do something to give Richie the idea I wanted to have sex with him? Did I want to have sex with him? It doesn't matter! I just know that I didn't consent! Did I? Lanny's wink came back to my mind over and over, and the words "you can trick anyone," and the smell of his breath, and my throbbing vagina. "You can trick anyone" kept hammering my mind; did I trick him? Or was it pure gaslighting because he was the one that tricked me? But then he asked "you know?" as if he was sharing something about me he knew but I didn't. I hate knowing I was drunk and high, and therefore I could have said or done something I'm not sure of. Memories from the trip seemed all scrambled, disorganized, unreal. Nothing made sense but I had no one to ask for advice, to bounce ideas off of, to help me find answers. I avoided Lanny even when I was consumed with questions about whether she knew. I had no courage to face her. I felt more alone than I have ever felt. I thought I was condemned to be alone forever.

Wandering around campus in a daze, I ran into a large glass window with the words "WELLNESS CENTER" engraved on it. I ventured in and filled out a form to apply for counseling. A youngish lady was my counselor and told me I could have 7 sessions. I told her how bad I was feeling but never mentioned the lake house. Too ashamed to go into it, and besides, there were huge holes in my memory that I couldn't explain. After the 7 sessions of CBT (kind of convincing me to change my thoughts), she told me to get out of bed and have fun, and gave me a referral form with a diagnosis of "Adjustment Disorder with Depressed Mood" and a brief description of how I was missing my house, my family, and "my culture." The report implied I had not made friends and had not been able to adjust to being among "Americans" and a community that was "dissimilar" to mine.

I was insulted. I couldn't stop my head from going in circles about what she said. It is true that in Queens where we lived, I hung out with all different types of nationalities and at the Midwest University I was attending, not many other people had a similar background to mine. Still, blaming missing my culture for my depression upfront was... too easy? The therapist didn't bother to ask me about my identity, my values, or what she called my "culture" or my community. She just assumed I was "other" and that I had failed to accept it and adapt to it.

Having made friends was what caused me to get into trouble, but she didn't ask much about it either. I hadn't even thought about being from a separate culture. I'm not. Was that how people perceived me at the lake house? It had not occurred to me that it had anything to do with what happened. I was born in the US and have always felt American—until the moment I was reading the report. Was what happened to me because I have a 'Hispanic' last name? Did blond Richie think he could take advantage of me because of my ethnicity? The cryptic assessment from the therapist left me full of new doubts. I wish I had not gone. I felt judged, othered, disempowered, and defeated. I spent several days upset and unsettled.

After dragging my way through the semester, I went home for the summer. Being at home made my symptoms worse. I told my parents what the counselor had said about my mood disorder in order to hide my 'sin' and to justify my lack of appetite, my days in bed watching TV, my bad mood, my apathy, my lack of interest in seeing my friends, the death of my brain. My grandma asked several times if something had happened: "Is there a guy I haven't heard of?" she kept asking. "I know there is something she is not telling us," she kept telling my mom. I stayed silent. My abuela had always been supportive of me and I used to confide in her, but this time I didn't want to make eye contact with her. I was afraid she could discover I was the slut she lectured me so many times not to be. I could almost hear using a reprimanding voice, comparing me with my mother and telling me I was going to end up like her, with a piece of shit for a husband.

My brother Ronan came home to visit. He is seven years older than me. He moved to NJ a couple of years before I went to college and I was supposed to be happy to see him. He came to pick me up to take me to his girlfriend's house. They are having a BBQ, he said. At my mother's insistence, I went. When we arrived there were a bunch of guys jumping and fooling around in the swimming pool. One guy walked toward us, saluted my brother, and put his arm around my shoulder "Look at you. Ronan's little sister! Are you still the same angel?" I started shaking uncontrollably. A tightness in my chest made it impossible to breathe, I felt dizzy and light-headed. I could swear I saw Richie at the pool. I panicked, and went to the bathroom, a cold sweat running from my neck. I'm going nuts! I think I'll faint. My arms feel numb and my hands start curling and clenching inwards. I take my purse and run out to the bus stop. I leave and stay in my room for a week.

Summer went by in a blur; I stayed in the free fall that started a few weeks back and didn't seem to end. It's time to go back to school and just the idea of it induced spontaneous dizziness and chills. I announced to my mom I wasn't going back. What a disappointment I am! She stopped talking to me. I felt even more lonely. It's already the fall and I'm still struggling to get out of the house. My grandma is trying to cheer me up and invites me to cook something for my mom's birthday. "What about Rum-Chocolate cake?" she asks and my body tenses as if it is going to break. Rum-Chocolate cake used to be my favorite. "What's wrong?" she inquires. I guess she saw my panic, my nausea, my disgust. "This can't continue!" she exclaims. "Adjustment Disorder, mis cojones! What you have is trauma and you have to tell someone what happened to you." She leaves and a couple of hours later she comes with a name and a date written on a piece of paper. "You start therapy tomorrow at 10 am."

My first encounter with the trauma therapist went fast. They mentioned that my grandma said I had strange reactions to certain events and needed help. God bless my grandma! That therapist changed everything. Even when they didn't ask or push me to talk about anything I didn't want to, it didn't take long for me to feel ready to talk about 'my trauma.'

Shame as an Internal Traumatizing Agent

Michaela just said that she is ready to talk about 'her trauma' after spending months without sharing that information with anyone. The experience with Richie was disconcerting and appalling, but let's review all the emotional states she went through from the moment she arrived at the lake house and not just after she left: the paranoia, the uncertainty, the doubts. On top of the disorienting feeling of having been sexually abused, the turbulence of emotionality and questions that kept her spiraling contributed to keeping her system fighting for survival. This continued for months after the episode. Michaela experienced a high level of shame as a direct consequence of the traumatic incident, but it was in addition to already carrying a large load of hopelessness based on her upbringing schemas, her family values, her religious beliefs, her grandmother's judgments, and maybe even her previous life experiences. (We'll find out later). It does seem like shame was dormant in her and became a huge trigger to the fear of being ostracized, punished, unworthy, rejected, and a whole list of possibilities that pushed her to hide within herself.

Michaela's experience reflects on Gershen Kaufman's thoughts about shame when he wrote, "Shame is the most disturbing experience individuals ever have about themselves; no other emotion feels more deeply disturbing because in the moment of shame the self feels wounded from within" (Kaufman, 1996). From Kaufman's reflection, I want to emphasize the words "*in the moment of shame.*" Emotions are *momentary*—so when they last and become emotional states, the complications begin. The experience of emotionality, like the one from shame, can be part of the reason some people stay in the traumatization turmoil while others don't. It's not only the memories of a traumatic situation that keep people on edge—on many occasions, *the experience of an emotional state like shame* prolongs the traumatization and stimulates a whole new set of emotional reactions. Shame acts internally as a traumatizing agent because it magnifies the feeling of hopelessness, one that impedes the system from bouncing back into equilibrium, as it happened to Michaela. Shame also causes insecurity and, therefore, fear. The fear prompts the brain to continue in defensive mode, anticipating danger. That post-event traumatization could drive individuals into a downward spiral of emotionality that may not cease until the experience is redefined and the emotional state reshaped. Not finding ways to handle certain interactions well—or, like Michaela, bearing what feels uncontrollable and unpleasant inside—reduces one's sense of agency, which could be interpreted as faultiness, promoting the need to hide even further. Emotional dysregulation and cognitive distortions cause turbulence internally and in interpersonal relationships, debilitating us to the extreme of incapacitation.

THE EMOTIONAL STATE OF LIVING ASHAMED

Shame can be described as a very destructive emotional state that goes unspoken, even in therapy; shame is many times the elephant in the room that is hardly addressed. Why? Because *addressing it could be itself shaming* and may interrupt the therapeutic relationship. Clinicians and clients rather ignore it, maybe unconsciously, or forget that it's always there, like a shadow.

The way anger promotes fighting, shame promotes hiding. It belongs to what some theorists name self-conscious emotions: those that relate to how we see ourselves and how we think others perceive us. Other self-conscious emotions are guilt, embarrassment, pride, jealousy, and similar experiences such as humiliation, dishonor, mortification, shyness, and disgrace. They require higher-order cognitive abilities such as self-recognition and public self-consciousness; each of them can participate as traumatizing agents but I'm using shame as the umbrella for all of them. There is disagreement on whether shame is or is not a uniquely human experience, but self-consciousness seems to be (Rochat, 2018). To become aware of one's self as an object of others' valuation or devaluation is to become self-conscious that one has neither met one's own nor others' expectations. Self-consciousness is a heightened sense of self-awareness and a preoccupation with one's self. This characteristic is what makes it relevant in trauma studies. Because we are social beings, we need the approval and acceptance of others to feel safe; without a sense of safety, the stress response can be activated at any point, and *shame can be the precursor to the sense of threat that elicits fear or increases its negative consequences.*

Gabor Mate says that shame is the deepest of the 'negative emotions,' and that we would do almost anything to avoid it; he also states that how much we fear shame interferes with our ability to see reality (Maté, 2003). I agree with his view, if and only if, we assume that the person learned to judge themselves harshly and to depend highly on others' evaluation. Otherwise, shame doesn't need to be so extremely detrimental. Like every other emotional state, shame is connected to a learned emotional response that follows a script. In this case, shame seems to share a script where 'being exposed' is jeopardizing and penalized, and where being seen as imperfect is negatively judged and rejected. Strict cultures (like Puritans) may suffer from this issue. In my culture (Latin), shame has a different social script and is not experienced as intensely negative, maybe because it is conceived as necessary and is even encouraged as a quality to have more of. "Please have some shame" is a phrase usually used to foment it among my compatriots. Ideally, a certain level of shame shouldn't make one want to disappear, but rather feel motivated to be mindful of one's behavior and its consequences instead of repressing behavior because it will be chastised. Being shamed feels bad because it implies being exposed, *but experiencing shame itself doesn't need to mark the person* or push them to flee by definition. Shame is very connected to our attachment needs. I have observed attachment needs beyond survival that I want to share with you as they help give context to shame and its accompanying reactions. (I'll cover attachment even more in depth in Chapter Eight.)

THE NEVER-ENDING NEED TO ATTACH

As newborns, we are so unconfident that everything feels threatening. We may think that our initial fears get resolved as soon as we grow older and stop needing our caregiver to be as close as before, but they don't. We still have big attachment needs and we can continue feeling insecure if detached (alone) all the way through seniority. My observations have helped me conclude that the need to attach goes beyond survival and is connected with more than just the need to feel safe; what I mean is that lack of safety for humans is bigger than just evading the threat of death. Safety means belonging and connecting too. Being exiled (and alone) is threatening in its own right. The triune brain model facilitates picturing the three different levels of hardwired attachment we require to feel full safety.

Basic Attachment Needs

For our primitive brain, the need to survive is the number one priority. Attachment at this level means having someone to provide for the basics such as food, shelter, temperature control, protection from external agents, alleviation of physical pain, and so on. Caregivers need to be reliable for the baby's system to trust that they won't die of hunger, dehydration, cold/heat, or pain. The caregiver should be available, close, consistent, and responsive to satisfy the essential needs for the baby to develop a secure attachment to the caregiver at this level. As adults, we need someone we can count on in order to feel that we won't have to confront obstacles by ourselves.

Belonging Attachment Needs

As social animals, we need to belong. We can't live in isolation, and not belonging is as scary as perishing. This is obvious at birth, but may not be as evident later. What differentiates humans (and primates) from all other species—besides our disproportionate cortex—is the complexity of our social lives (Dunbar & Shultz, 2007). At this level, the need to attach is satisfied by feeling that we are part of a group, hence, not alone. Due to evolution, socialization is specifically driven by the need to minimize predation risks. Belonging and the desire to belong are deeply rooted human motivations that mold our thoughts, feelings, and behaviors (Baumeister & Leary, 1995). Being part of a group, accepted, and included helps us feel safe and protected, and leads to a more secure life, especially if we are also comforted, supported, and nurtured. The communication between individuals is regulated by the emotional brain (or limbic system), which sets emotional connections, giving space to the formation of emotional states that will reflect healthy capacities throughout our lives. Romantic relationships are so essential for our existence for the same reason, and why cheating is so devastating: it puts the bond at risk, and with it, the perception of stability for the nuclear family (even when in most cases, it doesn't). Being a social species has many advantages but it also has costs as it foments competition among members of the group and animosity against 'outsiders.'

Connection Attachment Needs

As far as we know, our neocortex has capacities that no other animal possesses. *The attachment needs of the more evolved part of our brain relate to connection at a higher level.* Feeling connected in a deep way to another human being (or to something bigger) makes us feel that we exist. Contributing to a big cause substantiates our existence. Connection gives us purpose, motivation, acceptance, hope, reciprocity, and, at some point, the feeling that we can transcend.

If attaching is designed to provide safety, I'm proposing that the need doesn't disappear until we achieve fulfillment. Let's see how shame is connected to our attachment needs.

THE SELF-CONSCIOUS STATES THAT LEAVE A MARK

Besides shame, other similar processes that pound directly at a sense of self also influence traumatization. Table 5.1 shows the most common understanding of the trauma-relevant self-conscious processes.

Table 5.1 Self-conscious processes

Process	Characteristics	Consequences
Embarrassment	When other people find out one has done something that disturbs some norms (especially own) but without further consequences.	Strong affective reaction; instantaneous rush of adrenaline. It comes fast and normally leaves as fast.
Humiliation	Being caught inappropriately crossing group boundaries and having the transgression exposed; always inflicted by another person, normally unjust, and benefits from spectators.	Creates resentment, injures dignity and self-respect; leaves the mark of an emotional wound; its memories may be difficult to forget.
Dishonor	Actions/behaviors that cause losing approval from others with whom values are shared.	Damages the reputation of the person in front of those who care about the same set of values and causes huge amounts of shame.
Disgrace	Equivalent to dishonor but in the eyes and judgment of the Creator or 'Giver of Grace.'	Exposes someone as if they had 'brought shame upon' themselves.
Guilt	Feeling responsible for some action or inaction that carries the evaluation of having been harmful, negative, unacceptable, dishonest, or damaging.	Has an implicit motivation to make amends, apologize, or correct the behavior.
Shame	"a painful set of affective and cognitive states typified by self-judgment stemming from a perceived transgression of social/cultural norms or expectations" (Saraiya & Lopez-Castro, 2016).	Associated with a negative evaluation of the self, withdrawal motivations, and feelings of distress, exposure, mistrust, smallness, powerlessness, and worthlessness.

Guilt and shame are similar and many people can't separate them. The main distinction between them is that while guilt relates to having made a mistake, shame makes the person feel as if they are a mistake. It's also noticeable that while guilt can facilitate empathy, shame disrupts the ability to empathize. Guilt and shame typically tend to co-occur in many situations maintaining a significantly strong correlation (if one increases, the other increases too). Guilt is also debilitating, but it's easier to get rid of it than shame because it motivates us to act, while shame motivates us to disappear.

Shame—as the opposite of pride—arises when we believe that we are damaged in some way, including self-valuation, others' valuation, and the interaction between them. We could even say that shame is the internalization of others' negative judgments; the values and opinions we hear and perceive from childhood are what write the shame script.

> Think of cultures where being overweight means wealth and promotes pride, while in others it is seen as a flaw in character. Nobody feels shame naturally because of their weight until they learn the value assigned to it.

Also interesting to notice is that shaming is used to attenuate positive affects such as excitement and enjoyment when those manifestations seem inappropriate to the norms of the group. Shaming is one of the most common methods used to regulate women's and children's behaviors. It's common for children to learn to feel ashamed for engaging in completely normal and healthy behaviors because it's 'convenient' for the caretaker or teacher to 'modulate' their behavior to make discipline easier. It's also common to shame women for not being feminine enough, or for wanting more than what women 'should' want.

As a simple spontaneous emotion, shame motivates us to refrain from acting in unapproved ways, but as a chronic emotional state, it pushes us to hide, to be forgotten. Since shame is a social emotion, it leads to destructive forms of banishment from self and others, creating a separation from loved ones, social groups, or communities. Depending on the script one carries, the brain's anticipation of negative outcomes can activate or intensify protective mechanisms. Ultimately, the absence of hope that others might have empathy for one's flaws could be interpreted by the brain as defeat, taking over the survival of the system. Feeling worthless or defective implies losing support and affiliation, which, in essence, could feel equivalent to social death. The possibility of being 'canceled,' for example, could be as scary as dying because

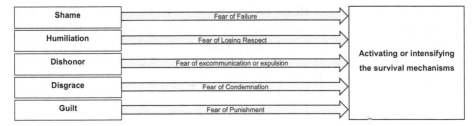

Figure 5.1 Self-conscious processes as traumatizing agents

as humans, we need acceptance for stability. *The fear of not belonging is traumatizing.* Figure 5.1 summarizes self-conscious emotions and how they relate to fear and become traumatizing agents.

THE PHYSIOLOGICAL CONSEQUENCES OF THE NEED TO HIDE

As we clearly know by now, the autonomic nervous system (ANS) can get hyper-active when we are in crisis. Our brain could easily interpret shame as a crisis and activate the ANS's survival protections when bonds fail and relationships break (Tangney et al., 2007). The shame response could be felt as extremely painful. In its more intense form, it's experienced as being stunned or shocked with sensations in the skin of the face and neck, pain in the stomach or nausea, tightness of the throat, and a strong sensation of imploding or exploding in the chest, manifestations that may seem impossible to hide. Its response could be so strong and disturbing in terms of physiology that it could initiate the flight mechanism that follows the wish to disappear, or it could go directly to parasympathetic activation, immobilizing the individual as in helping them 'disappear.' On many occasions, the shame response's intensity is directly proportional to the intensity of the perceived rejection (actual or expected). The accumulation after long exposure to shaming means that every time the person experiences it, the sense of inadequacy increases as well as the negative valence of the experience. Therefore, the probability of having self-esteem deficits, depression, anxiety, addictions, and some other mental issues is high.

In the case where shame activates the flight response, the surge of energy commonly ends up being used toward oneself; the system is so rejecting of the self that the impotence and defeat circuits fire up, over-regulating emotional responses, shutting them down, and moving into parasympathetic almost chronically. Shame develops social signals with facial and body postures that can be recognized across cultures as 'smaller' (taking up less space), sunken chest, low gaze, or 'not there' body language. Shame can be an agent that promotes the activation of protections but it is also considered a symptom of trauma disorders. As a symptom, it takes the form of avoidance when the person isolates themselves to hide their internal chaos. Shame is also contagious and transferable if someone takes or projects their shame on others.

Michaela carried shame from her mother for being a sexual being and acting in ways that were penalized by their cultural/religious beliefs. Shame took over her thoughts, fearing rejection and punishment, but mainly her future's possibilities, which kept her survival protections activated. She became terrified of being discovered, and seen as naive and immoral, as something she didn't mean to be. It's sad to uncover that this scenario is all too common among individuals that are subjected to sexual misconduct.

The Cost of Hiding

Shame plays a role after exposure to danger, but also during and before. People that often feel the activation of shame are at a higher risk of developing PTSD and its complex versions. Studies have consistently found a strong association between shame and PTSD, particularly following rape, sexual abuse, childhood abuse, and intimate partner violence (Saraiya & Lopez-Castro, 2016). In general, individuals who suffer from a trauma disorder live life under an altered biological and psychological reality that is hard for them to understand and explain. It gives them a sense of lack of control, of separation from reality that generates itself a sense of failure and powerlessness. Their emotional experiences create a sense of being weak and ineffective among several value judgments that are considered shameful, and this experience of shame adds to the impact of the traumatic event itself during and after the threat adding to the emotionality.

However, the traumatic experience may be seen as a disappointment. When one fails to protect themselves, the symptoms can act as a confirmation of deficiency, which amplifies the shameful mental state. This creates a self-perpetuating cycle from which it can be difficult to escape. As a result, traumatized individuals keep shying away from all expressions of connection and affection from others, feeling undeserving of them (Kvarnstrom, 2016) and fearing being seen in their unfitness, deep down fearing further rejection. When either (1) there is no acceptance of oneself, (2) there is no self, or (3) the awareness of self-existence doesn't develop, the person feels a deep sense of shame. This contributes to the development of a strong hollow-self that hides the deficient self-concept. Shame is strongly connected to personality disorders where the strong feeling of shame denotes a weak or absent sense of self. They don't hide themselves, but they hide whatever shames them.

In a circular process, traumatization reduces the resilience needed to metabolize shame, and shame inhibits the formation of resilience to resolve traumatization. In terms of dysregulation, shame contributes to maintaining the state of lack of homeostasis for two reasons: (a) wanting to disappear demands a surge in parasympathetic, while (b) fearing being rejected keeps the sympathetic producing stress hormones, which is a process that mimics the struggle for survival.

Shame also has another aspect when it becomes internalized. When a person feels ashamed for the single fact of being part of a family, group, community, or culture, they may hide their feelings, sometimes even from themselves. They may internally feel ashamed of being part of a group that is considered by others as flawed, and they may do everything to hide the fact that they feel that way. In many cases, self-criticism comes from the words and behavior—even unconscious—of those in power. Powerful societies institutionalize the devaluation of others with the use of words that convey disdain, disrespect, contempt, or scorn toward specific groups. Most of the 'isms' are forms of devaluing others, building ashamed communities, and taking away the dignity and resilience of their members by exercising humiliation and rejection. As Rich Hanson wrote: "The contempt of others becomes hatred of the self" (Hanson, 2015).

> The shame that Michaela experienced for being perceived as 'other' by the university counselor had an impact on her self-concept and also impacted the way she dealt with her emotional responses after she left school. It may have been the reason she left, as the possibility of being 'other' made her feel unsafe, rejected, and maybe internally unworthy.

If Shame Becomes Pervasive

When we are frequently shamed during the years when our brain is developing, we become emotionally conditioned to feel ashamed in similar situations even if we bear no responsibility. Shame can become a pervasive state of being without having done anything shameful (Hu, 2021). According to Erickson's Developmental Stages, shame develops at around 1.5–3 years of age, a time when kids develop a sense of personal control over physical skills and a sense of independence. Supported kids that are encouraged to succeed achieve the virtue of will, increased independence, confidence, and security in their ability to survive. But criticized, rejected, and neglected kids develop feelings of inadequacy, become overly dependent upon others, lack self-esteem, doubt their abilities, and carry a constant sense of shame. This conditioning may stay present for life unless there are interventions that shift it.

Passive Shaming: When Shaming is Disguised

We can all identify active shaming when people use phrases like "I can't believe you did that," and "Shame on you!" especially in front of others. But shaming can also happen passively, without words. *Passive shaming is practically synonymous with emotional neglect.* It occurs when a parent fails to meet the developmental needs of their child, as when they ignore the child's desire to share their day, their preferences, and their experiences. It happens among adults too. Ignoring someone emotionally is a way of 'accusing' them of being unimportant and invisible. Indirectly, the sent message is of being a burden, unaccepted, unwanted, undeserving, or irrelevant. Passive shaming can be as damaging as active shaming and is typically harder to identify and work with, as the person that carries it retains no narrative or episodic memory of "what did not happen" (Benau, 2020).

Reducing the Impact of Shame

The way to address shame without shaming it is not necessarily by naming it. Most other emotional states respond positively by naming them but telling someone that they seem ashamed invites them to hide further until they develop a strong observing-self that can take it. One way to introduce it is by recognizing all the situations, beliefs, words, and actions that could be shaming to the client from the macro to the micro, for example, starting with the big picture that religion or societal values one has been taught about certain behaviors. Normalizing and reviewing what the person assimilated and carry by default, and then keeping them by choice, resolve the shame. Considering culture and expectations is also useful. Identifying what type of behaviors society pushes or demands on them facilitates finding why they want to hide. Noticing the effect they have on the system could be an invitation to be more caring about oneself.

Developing PTSD

> The date-rape from Michaela's recount would be considered by many as the traumatic event in her story. Under a broader lens, the three-day weekend could be seen as the 'single-event' considering that she felt, in her words, "one of those characters in psychological thrillers" from day 1, to the day after when Richie mentioned his girlfriend. Michaela was anticipating something bad from the beginning. She used preventive mechanisms—orienting and social-engagement—to calm herself down. She may have gone into 'faint' when she found herself in bed with Richie but we can't be sure because she was not completely conscious; therefore, her memory may not be fully reliable. It seems that she stayed in 'freeze' the morning after the sexual encounter, looking forward to, but also fearing seeing Richie again, unsure what to feel and whether he was authentically interested in her or if he drugged and abused her. Once she heard about the girlfriend, she went directly into hopelessness, tonic immobility, and defeat.

Everything seems to indicate that Michaela developed PTSD after the event since the survival protections were evidently activated and she showed symptoms for months. Still, not every person will suffer from a posttraumatic disorder even in cases where all of the protections became active during shock, disaster, affliction, or unbearable situations. For that reason, cases like Michaela's need further conceptualization. Chapter Three described how the survival protections get activated sequentially until the system either bounces back to baseline or shifts to operating in survival mode. There are additional ways to explain what makes the system shift into a new way of functioning. First I'm including a visual representation of how the sympathetic and the parasympathetic lose coordination, and then I'll add an explanation of how the ANS gets dysregulated using the HPA/SAM (the hypothalamic-pituitary-adrenal/sympathetic-adreno-medullar) axes.

PTSD DEVELOPMENT AFTER THE DYSREGULATION OF THE ANS

There is a fascinating understanding in science about how everything in the Universe behaves in waves. Even when something may appear to be motionless, it's actually vibrating, oscillating at various frequencies. Therefore, it's useful to picture the activity of our nervous system as an oscillation. The elements that participate in the oscillations are arousal and rest states.

Being awake is a state of arousal in which there is an interaction between consciousness and whatever in our environment stimulates our senses. At the other end of that spectrum is the sleep state, characterized by limited mobility and reduced responsiveness to environmental stimuli. Moving in between those two is the resting-state, which includes the state of being awake but without a task (idle). We can picture the behavior of our nervous system oscillating between states of activity and states of disengagement in a graph that would look like the one shown in Figure 5.2.

Those oscillations happen out of our awareness. The arousal state is governed by the SNS and the rest state by the parasympathetic in a coordinated effort to continuously balance each other out to secure homeostasis. When there are stressors, the arousal may surge and the oscillations may spike. Depending on how much the system is stressed or tensed, a larger wave of resting-state may follow, needed to compensate for the effort of the arousal to maintain a regulated system as shown in Figure 5.3.

When the stressor is too intense, and there is an appraisal of danger, the activation could be such that the person may feel overwhelmed. Not only does the level of arousal increase, but the brain may interpret the jump as an instruction to activate the survival protections. Once the protections become activated and fail at achieving their goal of protecting the system, the parasympathetic will give up its normal way of working in coordination with the sympathetic. Instead of balancing each other, the SNS and the PSNS would both try to exercise their dominion. The highs could feel like exasperation, enraged, unsettled, and manic, while the lows would feel like depletion, fatigue, despondency, or lack of engagement. It's considered that the person may have developed a trauma disorder when their ANS is constantly

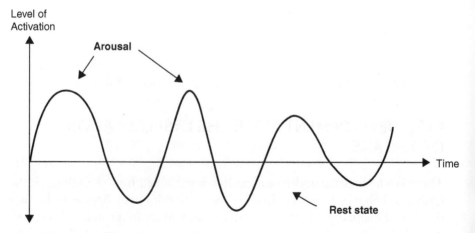

Figure 5.2 ANS oscillations

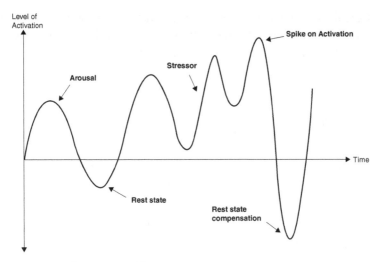

Figure 5.3 ANS oscillations caused by stress

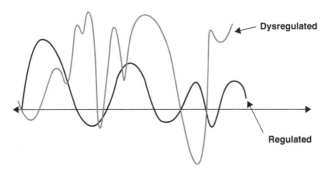

Figure 5.4 ANS dysregulation versus regulation curve

dysregulated (as default). Figure 5.4 shows a representation of how the oscillations lose harmony once the system gets constantly dysregulated.

HOW PTSD DEVELOPS WHEN HOMEOSTASIS IS LOST

A large amount of the published work about the stress response and survival mechanisms includes descriptions of either the HPA/SAM axes or the hyperactivation of the ANS. However, these systems can't be separated because they work in a highly coordinated way and are physically connected; the nerves from the ANS innervate the HPA/SAM axes. Activation of the ANS and HPA/SAM axes in response to stressors follows a hardwired, preprogrammed coordinated sequence (Rotenberg & McGrath, 2016). Our ANS activation stimulates physiological changes through the work and instructions of its two branches. If they deviate their attention from equilibrium to survival, the system loses coordination and we suffer lasting modifications—diagnosed as PTSD.

Mobilization Attempt

Our system moves from the stress response into emergency mode when we feel not only stressed but extremely fearful. This makes the SNS respond by becoming hyper-active, preparing our system to face the situation we fear. There are several physiological changes needed to be able to confront the risk or escape from it. Figure 5.5 describes the main changes.

These changes are mostly regulated by the HPA axis, which constitutes the interaction between the hypothalamus, the pituitary gland, and the adrenal glands. They control the system's reactions to stress and regulate many basic body processes. If we continue feeling afraid, *overwhelmed* and with a sense of *helplessness*, the brain will continue anticipating a negative outcome and the activation of the HPA will be prolonged, producing more stress hormones, which normally results in interference with its negative feedback loop (designed to counteract changes), and therefore, with the homeostatic processes.

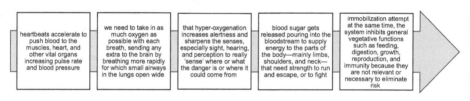

Figure 5.5 Timeline of sympathetic physiological changes during crisis

Figure 5.6 Timeline of parasympathetic physiological changes during crisis

Immobilization Attempt

If we are not able to achieve safety by mobilizing, the brain will make use of other protections which make changes that maintain us alive but almost lifeless with severe consequences on our regular functioning. Figure 5.6 shows the sequence of what happens during immobilization.

Loss of Equilibrium

The PSNS facilitates the immobilization responses by withdrawing its in-hibitory effects (Porges, 1995, 2007), which means that when the ANS is in emergency mode for too long, the parasympathetic ceases trying to stop the sympathetic activation and there is a loss of coordination; they will ex-ercise their functions separated from each other. That lack of coordination means that the most important characteristic of their design—maintaining homeostasis—will no longer be the default.

The other factor that affects homeostasis is the interruption of cortisol's nega-tive feedback loop. If the SNS stays active as in crisis, the brain will continue pumping cortisol into the body. An excess of cortisol affects the function of many organs, and could even destroy neurons in the hippocampus, amygdala, and other parts of the brain. It becomes toxic to our system. If the cortisol pro-duction runs for too long, it gets depleted and low levels of cortisol would keep the individual in a state of fatigue, weakness, and low mood for an indefinite period, causing a deficiency. Many studies have found unhealthy very high or very low levels of cortisol in traumatized individuals (and their descendants).

Why do we stay in a state of fear even if the threat is gone? Because fear can re-produce internally like a virus that becomes resistant and mutates. The script of fear that we carry may have taken years to be formed; traumatization adds a whole new story of what's dangerous and fear becomes a much more reac-tive and pervasive emotional state. The new script will assume catastrophic consequences and will grow like fire in a dry wildland.

Because the brain is assigning as much energy as possible to the processes of surviving, cognition slows down. In such a situation, *acting* becomes more important than *thinking*. Therefore, the adult capacity for objective thinking and decision-making gets hijacked and cognition becomes cloudy, slow, or in-operative. The addition of other traumatizing agents, like shame, adds to our emotionality, increasing the perception of risk and ruin. The additional trau-matizing agents contribute to prolonging the state of alarm. The ANS will have no choice but to take over many of the regular functions and volitions. The inability to restore a functional and stable internal environment causes many diseases; when homeostasis fails, organ systems function less efficiently to the point of malfunction. Trauma disorders have *psychological* repercussions but they are mainly *physiological*. The maladaptive state of the ANS will manifest as a set of symptoms that eventually will meet the criteria of PTSD. Figure 5.7 shows the sequence of the peritraumatic process that ends up as PTSD when the point of being overwhelmed is surpassed and hopelessness becomes pervasive.

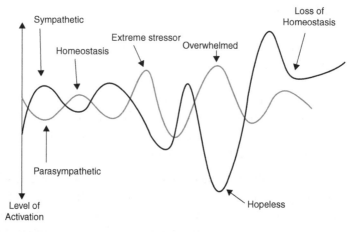

Figure 5.7 PTSD development using the homeostasis model

What happened to Michaela is a helpful example of the consequences of 'stoking the fire.' She couldn't stop thinking about the event at the lake, internally reliving all the signs of danger she ignored, and all the details of the weekend. These thoughts were what kept her in a state of losing hope for the future and disconnecting from the present. She couldn't concentrate or focus because her brain was busy recalling fearful, shameful, and defeated narratives, and then because the numbing agents were exercising their disengagement influence. Once she gave up and left college, she was really prolonging the use of immobilization. Her less-evolved structures took over and she became dysregulated and defeated, amplifying the negative effects of the protective mechanisms, getting worse as time went by.

WHEN DEFEAT BECOMES AN ENDURING MENTAL STATE

PTSD is a severe disorder. Its symptoms move from mild to critical, can be just a few or many, and can last weeks or years. If we see it, as we did in this section, as a sense of hopelessness with the loss of homeostasis, we can deduce that the psychological consequences become intertwined with the physical ones. When we lose internal equilibrium, we will have to endure dysregulation, and the lack of coordination among organs and systems will shake our way of living and the perception of ourselves, of others, and of life itself. Figure 5.8 shows visually how PTSD unfolds or can be avoided.

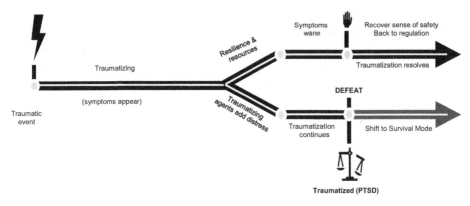

Figure 5.8 Developing PTSD (or not)

PTSD as the Framework for Diagnosing All Trauma Disorders

When Michaela looked for professional help, she was first diagnosed with Adjustment Disorder. This diagnosis was based only on assumptions (as she didn't disclose the event at the lake). If she had disclosed the rape, many clinicians would have assigned the label of PTSD; even when the first time she looked for help, she may have not yet met PTSD criteria. It's common to think that the diagnosis correlates mainly with the event and to assume PTSD from having only the incident as the cue. Maybe because 'trauma' is used to refer to the event and to the disorder, having suffered 'a trauma' may be assumed to cause trauma. But the event is only one of the criteria among seven. It is also important to consider that it may take many sessions before the client discloses the circumstances and all the symptoms they are experiencing. Still, in many cases, clients focus on reporting the most disturbing symptom and ignore others. We will see later how Michaela was not aware of many symptoms she already suffered from.

Emotional experiences are not objective, and therefore, finding words to describe them is not as straightforward as we might wish. For instance, some people lack the vocabulary to describe their feelings, while some people stop feeling altogether after developing PTSD. Besides, *how could one know if shoulder pain or getting angry at noisy people is related to something that happened many years back?* Talking about PTSD symptoms is challenging because each person manifests the alterations in their functioning in different ways. The most commonly mentioned and identified symptoms are flashbacks, which could be so intrusive that it's easy to point them out; they normally include reminders of an unmistakably traumatic incident. People see the face of the abuser. They may have recurrent dreams of car crashes, blood, and ambulances. They may see knives as weapons despite having been oblivious to them before being hurt by one. But flashbacks normally fade away as time passes, while backlashes may become more prominent even when undetected as related to the incident. Avoidance is another symptom that may seem easy to identify when the traumatized person is aware of the whereabouts of the traumatic event, but there are fewer obvious ways to avoid that are harder to be identified as a symptom: avoiding sensory input out of their radar like certain sounds or smells, or opulent people, or tall women, or things that may not have logic for why they are repudiated.

> Michaela had the intrusive image of Richie's face, but she also had a lot of other symptoms that she didn't even know were related, like her lack of concentration, her second-guessing, her random palpitations, the way she was avoiding her friends, school, her reaction to being perceived as 'an angel.'

Unfortunately, people suffering from PTSD—even in its simplest or mildest form—develop many symptoms that may not be mentioned in the DSM or are left to interpretation. The symptoms reported by and noticed in traumatized individuals are so numerous that medical doctors and clinicians may see them as separate and attribute them to different disorders thinking that it will be easier to manage them if tackled separately. Even the traumatized individuals themselves describe symptoms as if they were different maladies, from depression and anxiety to think they suffer from Bipolar Disorder, DID, or ADHD. Many others will simply feel that they are losing their mind, feel uneasy all the time, or believe they are 'broken.'

EXPLORING THE DSM'S PTSD CRITERIA

It has been said that PTSD is a disorder created by society and its politics (Summerfield, 1999); still, it's the reference point to all trauma studies even when it follows a model that is not systemic. I'll use the most recent revision of the manual's criteria to describe how to diagnose someone for PTSD (please see Appendix B for an exact text from the DSM) but I'll also go beyond by including what neurobiology has taught us; a way to encompass all the components that intervene in the phenomena. First, I expand on the first criterion: exposure. Then, I add some neurobiology principles to the symptoms' clusters, look for traumatizing agents and complexity, and analyze peritraumatic mechanisms used during the struggle as well as any posttraumatic strategies adopted.

A. Exposure

The first criterion talks about exposure "to actual or threatened death, serious injury, or sexual violence" in four different ways (see Appendix B). The ICD has an even more extreme criterion for the event stating that the person needs to have been exposed to an event or situation "of exceptionally threatening or catastrophic nature, which would be likely to cause pervasive distress in almost anyone." If we follow that 'filter,' very few people would be diagnosed with PTSD.

The fifth version of the DSM added (probably motivated by the 9/11 events, to include firemen, first responders, and witnesses) very specific ways to have been exposed to the traumatic event(s) that reflect something that is called 'vicarious trauma'—the damaging effects of repeatedly witnessing or hearing stories regarding the aftermath of a traumatic incident. This was a positive addition that opened possibilities for the subjective experience of danger. Still, everything emotional is subjective, and therefore, very individual. The DSM-5-TR doesn't explicitly include the individual's challenges and the fact that how traumatic an event is, rests on each individual's resilience, their available internal and external resources, and their personal perception of what they categorize as "threatened death, serious injury, or sexual violence." PTSD can develop after many more events than just the ones listed in the manual. Let me elaborate on the three listed circumstances:

Threatened death: someone can fear for their lives when a gun points at them or a knife is pushed into their throat, but also when the chances of 'succeeding,' thriving, or 'making it' in their future disappear. I know people who utterly believe that they won't survive if their loved one dies, if they divorce, or if they become homeless. I also know people that feel they would be killed or sent to concentration camps if democracy ends. Children could fear death for much less. Sometimes people become suicidal after one of these tragic events, and the involuntary and impulsive presence of suicidal ideation is life-threatening too.

Serious injury: a 'serious injury' is subjective too but also relative. Imagine someone has an accident and their ribs break. For some people, it could be considered a serious injury, but for an athlete, it could either be (a) a professional hazard—processed quickly, or (b) extremely damaging if it causes an impediment to their career.

Let's also remember that PTSD becomes a thing when the symptoms stay for at least a month consistently and constantly; otherwise, the experience may just leave some negative memories and some nervousness, but not a mental disorder. It is not the job of the clinician (or anyone) to categorize how 'serious' the person's incident was without considering their response, their relationship with the event, and the consequences to their psyche.

> I know someone that felt severely injured as a teen after an acne infection because of the way their skin looked after; the loss of self-esteem and thoughts like "nobody will ever want to kiss me" meant "I'll always be alone." For most, this is a terrifying thought and clear hopelessness for the future.

Sexual violence: the word 'violence' bothers me (and many people) from this DSM criterion. What if the grandfather penetrates the grandchild gently? What if someone like Michaela gets used sexually, without consent, but 'amicably'? Does the person then have no right to be treated for PTSD? The 'violence' qualifier obviously needs to be reconsidered when assessing for PTSD.

Expanding PTSD Symptom Clusters

Even though my suggestion is to investigate what each cluster means for each person, as well as the variations on how the symptoms manifest, the PTSD criteria from the actual version of the DSM (5-TR) is a foundation. Let's see the criteria one by one with an eye toward how they could be re-thought.

B. Intrusion (Re-Experiencing)

Under this criterion, there are those intrusive recollections that can appear unannounced at any point, during the day and night in several ways, mainly unwanted upsetting memories, nightmares, and flashbacks that cause emotional distress. Flashbacks are the symptom that traumatized people most report but they may be referring to the vivid and involuntary intrusions easily identifiable. The DSM-5 description of flashbacks implies that they are dissociative reactions where the individual feels or acts as if the traumatic event was recurring. These memories could be images; yet they could also be body sensations, odors, colors, sounds, flavors, or any fragment of the sensory information stored during the traumatic event and encoded as automatic reminders of the incident that assist in the task of anticipating risk. What is dissociated is the awareness of their connection with the traumatic incident because the pieces of the memory get decontextualized as we saw in Chapter Five. When the intrusions are different from images, it becomes more difficult to recognize them as re-experiences.

Imagine you get bitten by a snake. The flashbacks per se—like the silhouette of a snake—may not seem to be as debilitating, but the image brings up the emotionality that was experienced during the event, and also the pain in your leg and the fear/horror/shock of seeing a snake biting your leg. The emotional valence stored comes back very alive and adds to the emotional reaction created by the memory itself, possibly carrying additional emotional responses like fear of amputation because of something you read about the consequences of getting bitten. The fear of amputation and disability could become paralyzing, even becoming chronic physical pain in the area where you were bitten. These fears could go beyond, causing extreme anxiety and even paranoia if they are left unattended, or if you relive the memory too often and keep reading about amputations (rumination and obsessiveness are also internal traumatizing agents). The fear can grow to the extreme of causing psychotic breaks (not as common) where you could see imaginary snakes coming at you.

In this category, if we separate feeling and acting from the listed criterion B (Appendix B), we could name the intrusion that promotes action a backlash (commonly overlooked). Having an emotional reaction to something or someone that behaves or reminds us of a similar situation, not as sensory information but as an emotional experience that motivates some extreme action, is more debilitating than just feeling the past emotions elicited by the flashback. The relationship with the traumatic incident of these invasions passes unnoticed during a backlash because it doesn't seem connected to the past: the person experiences it as real and as present as it can be instead of merely noticing it as a reminiscence. When the person experiences something similar to an experience that left a negative imprint without clear sensory information (only emotional), the emotionality will present itself decontextualized. Since it's harder to recognize backlashes as reminders, they become *re-experiences* of what is hurtful—retraumatizing the individual without any type of notification, and causing further dissociation. Backlashes are retraumatizing until they are recognized as re-experienced traumatic memories and processed as such.

> Michaela could have a strong reaction if someone behaves in a caring way because that's the emotional experience she may have stored as a sign of danger—since Richie seemingly took care of everyone at the lake (and her, technically, when she was tired). She may not be able to separate the present from the lake experience, and she might feel emotionally upset and at risk even if the caring gesture is not even directed toward her. A backlash could make her assume (unconsciously) that caring men are abusers or bigots looking for prey, and activate her system inadvertently to run, punch, scream, or any unexpected distressful action, retraumatizing her system.

C. Avoidance

This cluster is described as "avoidance of or efforts to avoid distressing memories, thoughts, or feelings about or closely associated with the traumatic event(s)" and "avoidance of or efforts to avoid external reminders (people, places, conversations, activities, objects, situations) that arouse distressing memories, thoughts, or feelings about or closely associated with the traumatic event(s)." That criterion includes the word 'effort' in both descriptions which makes avoidance sound like a voluntary activity. There are descriptions—in the psychodynamic theories—of avoidance considering it to be a 'coping' mechanism instead of a symptom. Even when it can be a conscious decision, avoidance is based on automatic reactions of the ANS most of the time. Although it can be recognized as behavioral or cognitive— as in avoiding acting the way that 'caused' the threat—especially if there is a belief (or distortion) that the person may have brought to themselves about what happened, avoidance is mainly unconscious. It can be physical or emotional as when someone avoids taking taxis, singing, caring people, wearing red, or whatever actions seem dangerous for no apparent reason. That's when avoidance is problematic. If a person decides—willingly and consciously—to skip something dangerous, I'll refer to it as resilience, since it implies having awareness, which makes it not qualify as a symptom.

Avoidance can be seen, from a neurobiological point of view, as the continuous use of the flight response, which uses escaping to get rid of the pervasive hopelessness that translates as a failure. Hyper-vigilance (a dysregulation symptom) together with the lack of trust impels avoidance not only of reminders but of life situations in general. The part of avoidance that reflects this automatic behavior can be seen in the unconscious evasion of certain stimuli without understanding the reason, as well as in the unconscious impulse to escape from responsibility. Phobias could also be included under avoidance. It's easy to observe that some traumatized individuals are phobic toward something. They may not know why, and the phobia may seem completely unrelated to any occurrence; nonetheless, they may develop an irrational fear of, or aversion to, something or someone, or to specific actions, causing them to be perceived as righteous, intolerant, pious, rigid, sensitive, or unsympathetic and even weak or exaggerated.

> Michaela meets criterion C since she tried consciously and unconsciously to avoid people or situations that reminded her of the lake, and then she avoided college altogether probably because being perceived as 'other' put her at risk.

D. Negative Alterations in Cognition and Mood

There are seven options under this criterion, all easily described in terms of brain alterations or under the perspective of the domains I described in Chapter Four. The "inability to recall important aspects of the traumatic event" is a problem of memory encoding and consolidation, whereas "having overly negative thoughts and assumptions about themselves or the world" are problems of perception, sense of self, and emotions like shame and guilt. The "exaggerated blame of self or others for causing the injury" is connected to alterations in perception as well, which also falls under the disconnection among brain areas related to negative affect, difficulty experiencing positive affect, and isolation after feeling shame and guilt.

These symptoms were also present in Michaela since she developed and rehearsed overly negative thoughts about herself, blamed herself for many details of what happened, and was very depressed with a loss of interest in activities. She was also self-isolating and feeling alone.

E. Marked Alterations in Arousal and Reactivity

This cluster addresses symptoms that are manifestations of the hyper-activation of the sympathetic nervous system: "irritability or aggression, risky or destructive behavior, hyper-vigilance, heightened startle reaction, difficulty concentrating, and difficulty sleeping." The traumatized brain loses the capacity to regulate emotional reactions, control impulsivity, assess situations with objectivity, calm down, or relax due to the hyper-active threat detection and anticipatory learned reactions plus the dulling of the executive functions. On many occasions, the reactions are seen as so out of proportion that the person gets confused, not understanding why they are judged as irrational since the level of reactivity and intensity of the emotional states seems completely justifiable to them. That confusion moves them to blame others or to feel misunderstood and victimized as a way of explaining their experience. In general, these uncontrollable reactions also cause shame, doubt, guilt, and fear of rejection, which amplify the sense of hopelessness that kept the person in survival mode in the first place, making symptoms worsen and prolonging the dysregulation.

This criterion was less obvious in Michaela except maybe for the difficulty sleeping and concentrating. This criterion relates to hyper-arousal and the activation of mobilization protections. Michaela's temperament combined with her family's style was not inviting for this type of manifestation. It may have been present but she either didn't report it because she wasn't aware of it, or she suppressed or internalized these symptoms.

Additionally, there are criteria F, G, and H that also need to be met before diagnosing (Appendix B). The fact that all the criteria are needed to diagnose PTSD presents its downsides. There are modalities that help desensitize the emotionality of traumatic memories, and when the person stops having intrusive memories, according to the DSM, the individual stops meeting the criteria for PTSD. That doesn't necessarily mean that the other symptoms disappear too. Still, the results from those studies add to statistics that show that, for example, working with the traumatic memories resolves PTSD, which is a fallacy and a trick of diagnosing.

References

Baumeister, R. F., & Leary, M. R. (1995). The need to belong: Desire for interpersonal attachments as a fundamental human motivation. *Psychological Bulletin*, 117(3), 497–529. https://doi.org/10.1037/0033-2909.117.3.497

Benau, K. (2020). Shame, pride and dissociation: Estranged bedfellows, close cousins and some implications for psychotherapy with relational trauma. Part I: Phenomenology and conceptualization. *Mediterranean Journal of Clinical Psychology*, 8, https://doi.org/10.6092/2282-1619/mjcp-2154

Dunbar, R., & Shultz, S. (2007). Evolution in the social brain. *Science*, 317, 1344–1347. https://doi.org/10.1126/science.1145463

Hanson, R. (2015). *From Shame to Self-Worth: Development of Shame Spectrum Feelings in Childhood*. https://www.patheos.com/blogs/justonething/2015/06/from-shame-to-self-worth-development-of-shame-spectrum-feelings-in-childhood/

Hu, J. (2021). Shame, vulnerability, and change. *Journal of the American Philosophical Association*, 1–18. https://doi.org/10.1017/apa.2021.21

Kaufman, G. (1996). *The psychology of shame: Theory and treatment of shame-Based syndromes* (2nd ed.) (pp. 5, 16). New York: Springer Publishing Co.

Kvarnstrom, E. (2016). *Treating PTSD as a Shame Disorder, and the Role of Compassion*. https://www.bridgestorecovery.com/blog/treating-ptsd-as-a-shame-disorder-and-the-role-of-compassion/

Maté, G. (2003). *When the Body Says No: The Cost of Hidden Stress* (1st ed.) (pp. 12). Toronto: A.A. Knopf Canada.

Porges, S. W. (1995). Cardiac vagal tone: A physiological index of stress. *Neuroscience and Biobehavioral Reviews*, 19(2), 225–233. https://doi.org/10.1016/0149-7634(94)00066-A

Porges, S. W. (2007). The Polyvagal Perspective. *Biological Psychology*, 74(2), 116–143. https://doi.org/10.1016/j.biopsycho.2006.06.009

Rochat, P. (2018). The ontogeny of human self-consciousness. *Current Directions in Psychological Science*, 27, 345–350. https://doi.org/10.1177/0963721418760236

Rotenberg, S., & McGrath, J. J. (2016). Inter-relation between autonomic and HPA axis activity in children and adolescents. *Biological Psychology*, 117, 16–25. https://doi.org/10.1016/j.biopsycho.2016.01.015

Saraiya, T., & Lopez-Castro, T. (2016). Ashamed and afraid: A scoping review of the role of shame in post-traumatic stress disorder (PTSD). *Journal of Clinical Medicine*, 5(11), 94. https://doi.org/10.3390/jcm5110094

Summerfield D. (1999). A critique of seven assumptions behind psychological trauma programmes in war-affected areas. *Social Science & Medicine*, 48(10), 1449–1462. https://doi.org/10.1016/s0277-9536(98)00450-x

Tangney, J. P., Stuewig, J., & Mashek, D. J. (2007). Moral emotions and moral behavior. *Annual Review of Psychology*, 58, 345–372. https://doi.org/10.1146/annurev.psych.56.091103.070145

Six
Prolonged Traumatization

How exactly does our health get compromised through constant exposure to danger?

Can traumatization prolonged damage be neutralized?

Is it possible to regain some of the lost functions from prolonged traumatization?

We've now seen what something awful looks like both through Michaela's eyes and the process of diagnosing PTSD. In this chapter, Michaela's early romances will illustrate what happens when the 'something awful' transcends a singular event and repeats or becomes constant. The prolonged circumstances can either be evident, or they can fly under the radar (even when the system starts adapting by making modifications to its operation based on them). While our system assists us in those situations, nothing is unbreakable. This chapter will emphasize two concepts: endurance and harm. *Endurance* because abuse and recurrent or prolonged traumatic circumstances require endurance. *Harm* because we will see how when that endurance fails, the person suffers long-lasting damage.

Guys: Michaela's Romances

Content Warning: This Section Discusses Sexual Misconduct

Once I was able to get the lake trip out of my chest, I realized that there were things about my past relationships that I had put in a drawer and locked away. Charles came up one day during therapy and a lot of stuff started pouring out of me.

Charles

I met Charles during the first week of college. It was the first time I'd lived by myself or away from home. It was very exciting to feel free. The campus was huge with a mix of very old and new buildings, full of open

DOI: 10.4324/9781003382478-9

space and places to go for long walks, and lots of people around my age chilling on the quad. Charles was one of those guys who spent hours lying on the grass. I was walking from one class to another, confused about how to get to the right building. I guess I looked lost because Charles asked me if I needed directions. He walked me to my building, put his number on my phone, and told me to call him. I texted him "Hi" a couple of days after, but he didn't respond. A few days later I got 'lucky.' I saw him at the cafeteria and we talked.

- Did you find your class? He asked
- I did but I got lost again on my way to my dorm. This campus is so confusing.
- Yes, that happens to me all the time. I lived in several different foster homes and I never knew where my room was. I'm always lost.

It broke my heart when he said that, imagining what it'd be like having no family and no home. I don't know if that was the moment I lost myself. From then on my relationship with him became a romantic nightmare. Soon after that day, he took me to his dorm. Our make-out quickly became sex, quietly, without any type of ceremony. It was very weird to be with him, and sort of nerve-racking. In a way, I wanted to protect him, but I also felt like I couldn't because I never knew how he was going to react.

As the months went by, Charles became absent, as if he was a different guy. His "Mr. Hyde" started to make me feel guilty for everything. His constant accusations, aggressiveness, and menacing posture paralyzed me; his rejection and criticism made me feel completely useless. I'd whimper for hours, not knowing what to do. When I asked, Charles gave me all sorts of nonsensical explanations for his mood: he had headaches "from the crushing weight of the world" and told me he was doing poorly at school and on his writing because we rarely had sex. He said the ache of my beauty and the way I'd look at other guys — certain I was cheating — had blocked the flow of his creativity. He made a snide remark about having no money because I ate too much. One day he just stopped responding to my texts for a few weeks and then justified it saying it was because my extra pounds "destroyed my Platonic ideal of a body." Being with him made me feel wildly insecure but I couldn't stop myself from loving him. I was sure his moods were symptoms of his past. Once I got irritated after an insult, and instead of apologizing, he put his fist near my face, sneering "who do you think you are?!" He slammed the door behind him and left me shaking.

I think I had become used to his temper and unpredictability but one day I just couldn't bear his negativity and accusations and snapped. I threw my glass into the wall. I didn't recognize myself. I had never done something like that. You're crazy! He yelled and left. Didn't hear from him again. I begged him to talk to me, to take me back, to give me another chance. He blocked my number.

That's why when the invitation to go to the lake house came, I said yes right away. Probably why I got so enthusiastic about Richie too. I really wanted to get over Charles because even when I kept myself busy, I was hurting. I felt like a failure wishing I knew how to be a better girlfriend, feeling like I wasn't good enough for him. I racked my brain for answers, reconsidering everything about our relationship. It's true that we didn't have much sex. I had a lot to study. Still, I wanted to have sex with him, but he always wanted me to go down on him instead. It made me feel dizzy, and my lips and hands were numb for hours after. My grandmother had put such horrible ideas in my head about sex that it was always a conflict for me. I was not sure if I was a good lover or a sex slave. But I said nothing, like so many times in my life. Thinking about Charles made me think about other guys. There were not many but they were significant.

My 'dog'
I was 14 when I had my first boyfriend. He was my cousin. Well, not really. He was the son of one of my mother's close friends, but we aren't blood-related. We've known each other since we were babies, well, since I was a baby and he was already a boy. He was 5 years older than me and used to play with my brother when his mom visited. The year my older brother Ronan left home for college, he came to watch TV with me. I was around 10. I don't remember exactly how but at some point he pretended to be a cute dog nuzzling my ribs with his nose. It tickled and I was laughing and he started licking my face. He kept poking and I kept laughing, and he started licking my neck, my arms, everywhere, pretending to be a dog the whole time. One day the 'dog' put his tongue in my mouth. I was confused but he made me laugh and everything he was doing felt good. That happened several times and the 'dog' always ended up showing his affection by licking other parts of my body. The visits were not frequent because of my mom's work schedule, but I looked forward to seeing him. It was a mix of excitement and fear before, during, and after his visits. My heart pounded in my chest so hard that I thought it would explode. I was afraid we'd get caught, but I was also afraid we wouldn't get caught.

When I was around 13, he told me I was his girlfriend. I felt really happy but kept it to myself in case my family didn't approve. Because I was his girlfriend now, I let him lick me more and more, until one day he said "it's your turn." He brought his pants down and taught me how to lick his balls. He then proceeded to finger me while licking my neck. Now I know I had an orgasm. I still get embarrassed remembering and saying it, but it still turns me on. It felt so good that I was sure my mother could hear me down the block at the nail salon. But he took off like a torpedo before my mom came back.

My mom found me sitting on the floor all sweaty and breathless. She slapped me in the face and asked me what had happened. I told her he was my boyfriend and that he had given me a kiss. I don't think I was that convincing, because she left, and didn't say a word to me for weeks. It was excruciating. I spent days and nights wondering if she would punish me somehow, maybe by not allowing me to see him again.

A couple of weeks later I was turning 14 and my father whispered into my ear that my mom was throwing me a birthday party. At dinner my mom 'announced' she had talked to 'my 'aunt,' that her son was in love with me, and that he had asked my mom for permission to be my boyfriend and he was coming to my birthday. I felt so embarrassed, surprised, and excited too. Was she organizing an 'engagement party?'; Wow! Like in the movies!! Yes, movies from the times of the pilgrims, maybe. Was making it 'official' helping them feel it was right to leave a 13-year-old girl alone with an 18-year-old guy until she was moaning? In any case, I didn't know what 2 + 2 was then and I felt happy with my mom's approval and 'support.' I had a boyfriend, and he made me feel sooo good. I was euphoric, especially after telling all my friends about him. I realize now that he had agreed to be my boyfriend, likely to avoid being accused of molesting me.

When my 'boyfriend' came to the party, I felt like a queen. My boyfriend, at my party! All the attention was on me. So much attention that I didn't have a second alone with him. I was dreaming of a 'formal' first kiss and some romantic declaration, I guess, but it didn't happen. I'm not sure why, but he ignored me like I was someone he'd never met. He seemed anxious like he just wanted to get out of there.

My first boyfriend didn't last long. He went 'traveling' shortly after the party and I never heard from him again. I longed for 'my boyfriend' for a long time. It wasn't only the dog play, but the attention and excitement that I felt waiting for his next visit, especially without the fear I'd felt previously now that we were official. I fantasized about his tongue until I met Ishmel.

Ishmel

A new girl came to live in my neighborhood just two houses from mine, Andreea. She was born in Romania and had lived in three different countries before moving to NY. She was already 19 and applying for college, which meant that I could still be her friend for a whole year. I loved her instantly—not romantically, but as a friend, someone who opened up my world. She talked about her sexual skills so casually. She teased me about my virginity. She had at least three guys begging her to go out with them every week, and some weeks she went out with all three even when she had an official boyfriend, Ishmel. Ishmel used to pick her up on weekends, and many times he didn't bring her back. Her parents were both alcoholics and didn't care much about how she spent her time. Ishmel was older than us and not from our neighborhood. He was tall and thin, with warm eyes framed by square eyeglasses that made him look like a doctor. When he looked at you, his eyes examined every inch with fearsome intelligence. I could see why they were together. What was weird is that Andreea liked talking about her occasional dates but didn't like talking about Ishmel. I never asked. Ishmel started showing up more and the three of us hung out before they left for the day. I was working part-time at a nearby supermarket and I was surprised to see her waiting for me outside when my shift ended. While walking home she stopped, held my arm, and said "Let me ask you something. Do you like Ishmel?" "Like him? What do you mean? Sure! He's nice" "I mean liking him as in wanting him. He says you do and he says he wants you too. I can make it happen" she responded. I was shocked and speechless. "But he's your boyfriend" is all that came out of my head. She smiled and said no more. She didn't mention it again, but in the coming weeks, she became very interested in how I looked. "Your clothes don't suit your body," she told me. "I want you to wear my mini skirt." I began wearing some of her sexy outfits and she also made me wear makeup when Ishmel was coming. Something was going on that I was not able to pinpoint, but I was feeling attractive for the first time even when sometimes I was ashamed for looking so slutty. Still, I was feeling great, laughing loudly for no reason, and all tingly as if I had had 10 cups of coffee whenever I saw Ishmel's car approaching.

On a random Saturday evening, Andreea picked me up saying she had a surprise. She dressed me up and walked me to a park nearby and told me to wait there. She left and two minutes later I saw Ishmel's car. He stopped in front of me, lowered his window, and told me we were going for a ride. I just obeyed and jumped in. We drove while talking about some of the girls he had dated and asked me what type of guys I liked. We didn't mention Andreea at all. Soon enough we were kissing and making out. After that day he began texting and picking me up after work. I couldn't believe what was happening. My feet didn't touch the ground. I felt outside my body as if my body had stopped being mine. He really liked me. Sometimes the thought that he was still my best girlfriend's boyfriend crossed my mind, but it was easier to join him in pretending she didn't exist. It felt as if I was two Michaelas instead of one. When I was with Andreaa, I hardly remembered Ishmel, and when I was with him, she was not real.

A couple of weeks went by and he was kissing me for what seemed like an eternity when he whispered "I really like you!" He then lowered his fly and brought my head down into him. He was giving me directions on what to do. When we finished he drove me home and kissed my cheek. "You are worth every penny" he mumbled. I couldn't sleep for days. I was confused but also extremely happy. He liked me, I liked him, and Andreea was about to go to college. She had been admitted to a couple of places in California and had decided to move to LA. All the way to the other coast. That's probably what he was waiting for. I'm sure that once she moves, we will be together, I thought. He spent the following two months teaching me how to be a good lover in the cutest little hotel. He was giving me money to avoid my mother finding out about me missing shifts at work.

Andreea was finally moving to Cali, and I was feeling liberated from my guilt. I was very hopeful and certain about how solid my relationship with Ishmel was. He picked me up one Sunday evening bringing a nice pink box with him. "Open it!" My heart was jumping. I was sure he was going to ask me to be exclusive and I was so ready to say yes. But inside the box, there was a cute t-shirt with a card. "You are wonderful! Hope you can come to visit in California. Kisses, Ishmel." Long pause. "Visit in California? What do you mean?" "Yes, LA" "You are moving to California?" "Yes!

Are you surprised? didn't Andreea tell you? I have business in LA and SF. I asked her to apply there because I need to move back. It has been our plan for a year." I couldn't say a word. "She would be happy to have you visit. You'd love it. Please come. We could teach you a lot more things."

I cried for days. I didn't even say goodbye to Andreea. How could I? I felt so ashamed and defeated. I didn't know if she knew and if she could have forgiven me for trying to steal her boyfriend. I couldn't hate Ishmel either, even if I wanted to. Andreea was so much more beautiful and interesting than me. She did send a text saying 'they' were going to miss me. "Love you always. Hope to see you soon" she signed. I even entertained the idea of visiting them but it was pure fantasy. I had no time or money to travel. I worked double shifts during that summer to save for college and applied to go to a good school far from home. I spent the following year focused on my school work, avoiding guys in general, and Eastern European people in particular. I also avoided eye contact with my family members. I just wanted to disappear from their sight.

Therapy helped me realize what was underneath Andreea's interest in me looking sexy. She sold me! I had been used by both as a piece of merchandise, like a toy. I guess I 'knew' it but neglected to become aware of it. To realize what their actions and intentions really meant was many times more damaging than the actual abuse—or the breakup.

Stress as an Internal Traumatizing Agent

From what we now know about Michaela, we can see that the reaction she had at the lake (and right after) was most likely the result of a combination of that weekend with having been abused on several previous occasions. She may have not been completely aware of the different ways in which she was sexually abused before Richie, but her system was well-primed to anticipate abuse even when her cognition preferred to categorize it in romantic terms. It seems that she managed her stress and fear from the three different instances of abuse by compartmentalizing, which is a form of dissociation. We can also see some indications of dysregulation in the way she acted confused and fearful about her cousin's conduct and the possibility of being caught, then secretive, the way she compartmentalized during her relationship with Ishmel, and, finally, submissive with Charles. Much before the lake, Michaela's shame and preoccupation were evident; she even mentioned that she felt defeated after her experience with Ishmel. What did all of this mean for her system? Let's find out.

Extreme stress—whether sustained or spiking continuously—is what many scholars have identified as the main reason we develop complex presentations of traumatization. It is actually common to find descriptions including the phrase 'traumatic stress' to refer to the studies of the trauma phenomena. Let's deconstruct stress to understand it better (and how to manage it), and look deeper at how the way we deal with it internally makes it traumatizing.

HOW STRESS BECAME QUOTIDIAN

It wasn't until the 1950s that the word stress was used to describe how we feel when nervous or under pressure. It didn't even exist in psychology as a concept until Hans Selye coined it in 1936 taking the term from physics (Szabo et al., 2017). Selye—a Hungarian-Canadian endocrinologist—joked about choosing the term due to his inadequate English and about how he should have preferred calling it 'strain syndrome' but it was too late. 'Stress' was quickly adopted as a household term. From then onward, studies found that psychological stress was *as powerful as physical stress* at inducing the body's emergency responses. Before stress was popular, being nervous or worried was the way individuals described their unsettled states, but worry was seen as a deficit in behavior, while being stressed (and its connection to performance) has been used as a sign of engagement. For many years, stress was spoken of as an issue of busy and productive individuals, such as corporate executives or college students. It seems that social media has heightened the pressure to perform and achieve and made stress pervasive even among children, not to mention the stress that the threat of climate change has inflicted on younger generations. We now know that stress comes with serious consequences on everyone's mental health. I'm not saying anything new, but I do think it's worth pointing out how despite this widespread knowledge, we do very little to stop it (and the damage it causes). Just notice (at this moment) the state of your neck and shoulders. *Are they relaxed? Or are they tense?* If you check several times a day, more often than not you will notice that it takes effort to release the tension from your muscles. Most of the time our body is tensing, which means that we maintain a level of stress almost as a default. Unfortunately, stress is not only a fad or a fancy term; stress is a reality for our nervous system, one that's highly connected with the development of trauma disorders. The stress response belongs to the same system that gets activated while in danger (mainly mobilization). Stress, defined as protection, is the process that promotes survival by rapidly responding to threatening environmental conditions (Britannica, 2022) and adapting. That adaptation is what, at some point, could become a trauma disorder of the complex type when, instead of having a strong reaction once, the person lives in a continuous state of stress, causing small adjustments to the system's operations.

In a neurobiological sense—and relevant for traumatization—stress has also been defined as "a state of threatened homeostasis" (Chrousos, 1997) because its toxicity affects our internal equilibrium. There is a classification of stress called 'toxic' because of the excessive amount of chemicals that stress can infuse into our system—mainly cortisol—'poisons' our blood. Stress keeps the system in a state of alertness that becomes a hindrance to optimal functioning. But it doesn't need to be that way. Even noticing the tension in one's body many times a day and intervening by releasing it out may be enough to stop it from escalating and intoxicating our blood and organs.

THE SEMANTICS OF STRESS

To understand its relevance in trauma studies, it is useful to differentiate between stress, stressors, and stress response. Let's use 'stress' to refer to the experience we get when we are under pressure or tension that elicits a reaction. The tension or pressure is *the stressor*, while the reaction is *the stress response*. Let me expand on this important difference.

Stressed

Stress—the process that strains our functioning—moves in a continuum, from simple tension to the starter of traumatization. Stress, to put it clearly and simply, is how we force or tense our body and system when we are alert or under duress. Tensing the muscles is the natural way our body uses to defend against injury and pain. Remember Houdini? He used to tense his abdomen to be able to stand the jabs that fans were inflicting; the day he didn't, the jab went all the way into his liver. But if we get tense, our brain believes that we are trying to protect ourselves, and that interpretation may cause our body to tense further. It's a vicious circle that doesn't resolve until we instruct our brain to unwind and relax.

Stressors

Stressors are the factors, emotions, stimuli, or actions that cause us to feel agitated, tense, or threatened. Figure 6.1 shows the different ways to classify stressors.

There is a long list of stressors that include mental stress, physical pain, addictions, working under dangerous conditions, abusive bosses, discrimination,

INTERNAL	EXTERNAL	PHYSIOLOGICAL	PSYCHOLOGICAL	ABSOLUTE	RELATIVE
thoughts or behaviors that come from expectations, schemas, values, experiences, etc.	situations that we perceive as difficult to control or unmanageable (deadlines)	put a strain on the body (pain, illness, etc.)	interpreted as negative or threatening (loneliness)	affect everyone (terrorism, pandemics)	interpreted as such only by a few people (ghosts)

Figure 6.1 Types of stressors

loss, marriage, illness, etc., or whatever challenges our sense of agency. They can go from mild to severe and go from acute to chronic, including intermittent and seasonal. We could say that *traumatic events are stressors* and that *some stressors could be traumatizing agents, but not all stressors are traumatic* by default.

Stress Response

The stress response could be described in simple terms as the anatomical and behavioral changes during exposure to stressors that put the nervous system in a state of alert, setting it up for action. It includes a set of processes that prepare the body to tackle the challenges perceived and anticipated when facing internal or external stressors explained under mobilization in Chapter Five. Its purpose is to protect the system from avoidable damage. For example, when a person goes through invasive surgery, the stress response activates body processes to attenuate tissue damage, excess bleeding, numbing excessive pain, etc. Unfortunately, the stress response is also activated even if the possibility of damage is not as severe as anticipated by the learned fears of the individual. In cases where the stressor is actually intense, repetitive, or prolonged, the physiological changes made by the stress response may be more detrimental than helpful. We will see later that the stress response activates allostatic processes that make changes in our regular functioning and that at some point damage our system. Aside from trauma disorders, the stress response has been identified in many studies as the initiator of biological alterations associated with the start (or the exacerbation of) a wide spectrum of physical and psychological illnesses, including anxiety in its worse manifestations.

ANXIETY: WHEN STRESS BECOMES HABITUAL

Anxiety is defined differently depending on the author or the branch of science it's studied under, but it is almost always connected to uncertainty.

As a spontaneous emotion, it is the experience caused by ambiguous circumstances, manifesting as fleeting uneasiness and distress by anticipating that something might happen (Grupe & Nitschke, 2013). Additionally, anxiety can be an emotional state learned and modeled by experience that anticipates the worst (catastrophizing). It is also considered a secondary emotion, or an emotion that is a reaction to a primary emotion—fear—which connects it to stress and causes the stress response to get activated.

> Michaela described her uneasiness as anxiety, connected to a sense of not having any certainty about what was going on when she first got to the lake. When she felt her stomach dropping, that was her body sending her signals that it was anticipating something bad. At some point, she 'relaxed' or perhaps she stopped hearing the messages from her body. This could have been because she was used to dissociating when she felt at risk.

Anxiety can also be seen as the internalization of stress that becomes a habit, or, further, a program that runs automatically without the need for a stressor: a learned, subjective, and created experience that operates automatically and without much volitional control. It means not only being hyper-aroused, but having a constant reaction toward every circumstance that brings thoughts of doubt or concern, stops us from sleeping or relaxing, and keeps the system shooting stress hormones as if it was under threat. Remember that every habit our brain creates is replacing (or nullifying) our capacity to engage with our actions, and that every habit can be modified once we become aware of it.

Trauma Domain #6: Dissociation

> Michaela's romances have one thing in common: her dissociation. We read how she missed recognizing the ways she was being abused in different circumstances, but also that she used fantasizing as a way to cope with emotional hurt, that she had out-of-body experiences, and that she was able to compartmentalize to avoid responsibility. It's soon to tell, but her level of dissociation may be rooted in even earlier traumatization. In this section, you will learn that dissociation manifests in different ways.

The whole dissociation construct is extremely important for trauma studies. Dissociation—the separation of realms of experience that would usually be connected (Putnam, 1989)—may be the key that opens the door to the survival mode. Before reaching a state of dissociation in the survival struggle, the person may suffer many 'scratches,' 'bruises,' and 'small injuries,' but once the person goes into disconnecting functions, the wound becomes a real problem due to the laceration in the psyche and the injury to the system's operation. Theorists have found that the more extreme the response to the traumatic event, the more pervasive the dissociation, and the greater the dissociation, the more acute the symptoms of the trauma disorder. Deconstructing dissociation could be a book on its own; the topic of dissociation has become a key player in the world of psycho-pathologies inescapably connected to traumatization. Its connection to disorders like DID (Dissociative Identity Disorder—formerly known as Multiple Personalities Disorder) has given it a prominent place. More and more literature is becoming available about the interesting phenomenon that has become so broad it could be seen as an umbrella term. The dissociation umbrella covers an extensive set of different manifestations, processes (Brown, 2006), and experiences of what it means 'to disconnect.'

DISSOCIATION: A MAIN PLAYER IN THE TRAUMA PHENOMENA

Dissociation got its initial attention as a pathology in the times when 'trauma' became part of the mental health conversation. Pierre Janet is attributed as the first to report it as a symptom in connection with hysteria, which he described as "an illness of the personal synthesis" and as "a form of mental depression characterized by the retraction of the field of consciousness and a tendency to the dissociation and emancipation of the systems of ideas and functions that constitute personality" (Janet, 1907). He also wrote about how traumatic memories influenced behavior and personality, and intruded at any point in life triggered by reminders of the traumatic event (Van der Hart & Horst, 1989). He was already talking about the importance of resources when he stated that the dissociation of memories was a consequence of "the depletion of mental resources" (Oathes & Ray, 2008). Because of Janet and his observations, followed by Freud and Breuer, dissociation got a prominent place as a pathology derivative of traumatization.

More recently, the importance of dissociation has exponentially escalated due to the undeniable connection with the consequences of suffering a trauma disorder during the developmental years, and the fact that kids' systems go into dissociation fast as it seems to be the most viable way to protect themselves from the pain of being abused, neglected, and confronting adverse circumstances. It has also become more clear that individuals dissociate while trying to escape from threats, and that dissociation becomes a pervasive symptom for many of the individuals that stay traumatized. Pathological dissociation arises as a peritraumatic characteristic and also as a posttraumatic symptom.

Peritraumatic Dissociation: A Protection

Dissociation that happens during traumatization (in the immobilization phase) is called peritraumatic dissociation and is an implicit byproduct of the survival mechanisms. It may stay as a symptom, or it may resolve soon after the person's autonomic regulation goes back to baseline. That's not difficult to picture, but the interesting question is whether 'peritraumatic' applies to traumatic incidents that occur not only once but recurrently for years. Since a constant level of stress can prolong traumatization, the survival protections could be turned on and off as the sense of dread is experienced over and over—until the neural circuits get disconnected more permanently. Dissociating then may become a habitual manifestation in the individual's 'personality,' commonly in a child that survives an inescapable unsafe situation for whom disconnecting from the present is an adaptive strategy (such as incest).

> We could wonder whether Michaela had suffered from dissociation before her cousin abused her, or if she learned to dissociate during the years when he abused her, even when she didn't acknowledge consciously that she was extremely stressed. She said she was experiencing fear of both being caught and not being caught, which may refer to the fear of possible punishment which could have been a stressor. We still don't know the dynamics with her mother.

It has been suggested that peritraumatic dissociation is a key variable in understanding clinical disorders with roots in interpersonal traumatic experiences during childhood that link the overwhelming experience with what seems unbearable (Schimmenti & Caretti, 2016). Peritraumatic dissociation is also key in understanding the modifications and adaptations of the personality of the individuals that maintained a level of fear and hopelessness in life that caused them to disconnect. The aftermath of peritraumatic dissociation leaves gaps in awareness, identity alterations, memory formation dysfunction, cognitive and executive deficits, avoidant behavior, decontextualized intrusions, and different types of numbness. Even if a person doesn't develop a complex trauma disorder, some of these dissociative manifestations may remain.

Posttraumatic Dissociation: An Adaptation

Peritraumatic dissociation increases the possibility to dissociate later (Fullerton et al., 2000), but it goes further than that; the activation of the dissociative mechanisms during immobilization (tonic and collapse) indicates that the person's autonomic nervous system (ANS) had to use its most extreme processes to go through something subjectively considered terminal, and difficult alterations to repair (or to revert) had to be made. Not only may the person dissociate constantly after a traumatic event, but they will most certainly suffer from more than one dissociative consequence such as affect compartmentalization, disrupted memory encoding, time distortion, slowing down of some cognitive functions, and some type of memory lag. Under survival mode, dissociating becomes a constant prompt to processes that consume abnormal amounts of energy which decreases the activation of certain brain functions to harmful levels that eventually become unavailable.

DISSOCIATION IS NOT ALWAYS A PROBLEM

Ways to dissolve stigma and find more mental health solutions include refraining from using terms that perpetuate old beliefs (and create new stigmas). When someone uses the word dissociation, it's valuable to mindfully listen to the details of the experiences that person is describing before jumping to conclusions that pathologize natural occurrences. I'm using 'natural' to refer to what's programmed in our system to fulfill a function by design. It's natural to sneeze when we smell pepper, it's natural to tear when we are sad (or the eyes irritated), and, so it's natural to dissociate in certain instances (daydreaming is dissociative, for example). The misinformation from social media and the tendency to push for some medical issues to become part of the 'popular' culture carry the risk of never reaching a hopeful understanding of what happens to us psychologically. When it comes to dissociation, it may seem harmless to pathologize its manifestations, but the number of individuals diagnosed with a dissociative disorder has increased exponentially. When someone carries the belief that to experience dissociation means to be severely damaged, that idea is more harmful to the psyche than the dissociation itself. For instance, if panic and anxiety result from a dissociative experience, it may be because the experience gets interpreted by the individual as catastrophic and then panic and anxiety become the agents that promote disconnection, a vicious downward cycle. We could stop the fall into despair before it starts if we de-pathologize some of the dissociative experiences. However, normalizing dis-sociation could lead to dismissing dissociative states that debilitate the person going through them. Michaela is a good example of someone with a tendency to dissociate that was not spotted by anyone including herself until it became dysfunctional. That's the reason I'm dedicating several pages to explaining the continuum dissociation moves through, from 'natural' to pathological.

'DISSOCIATION': AN UMBRELLA TERM FOR DISCONNECTION

I say that the term dissociation is an umbrella term because many occur-rences have been deemed dissociative and the term keeps being semantically open, which could lead to conceptual confusion. Figure 6.2 shows the differ-ent types of occurrences that are called dissociation.

In addition to the options in Figure 6.2, the term is still applied to name a 'defense mechanism' of avoiding emotional pain in the service of the ego, following psychoanalytical views. What neurobiology says is that avoidance of emotional states is not the same as dissociating from them. Avoidance can become a habit, and yes, it can make us less aware of emotions, but that type of disengagement is less lasting than systemic dissociation. As it's used in psy-chology, it moves in a spectrum going from very short-lived mental breaks to more permanent withdrawal; from an instant of disconnecting (the dialogue

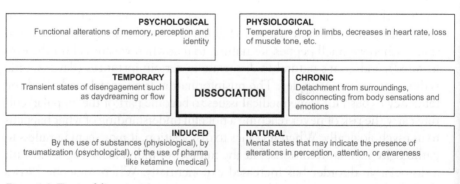

Figure 6.2 Types of dissociation

in a movie) to chronic disconnection (emotions, memories, functions); from forgetting where we left the keys, to complete amnesia (forgetting years of one's life or what one 'part' did); from a desired altered mental state (getting drunk) to 'psychosis-like' symptoms of chronic and debilitating disorders (delusions). In short, dissociation moves from very natural, short-lived, and common occurrences to long-lasting pathology.

As you can see, dissociation refers to all sorts of experiences different in nature. The reality is that it's present to some degree in everyone and can be experienced at any time by us all. It has been calculated that 80–90% of individuals experience dissociative symptoms at least some of the time (Bruce et al., 2007). Though this book is about traumatization, I don't want to limit the conversation about dissociation to its pathological manifestations because as we talk about it today, it causes fear, and we know that fear prompts survival mechanisms. Dissociation can be a result of traumatization, but dissociation could become a traumatizing agent when it is defined and anticipated as an undesirable or abhorrent experience. One of the objectives of this book is to help reduce fear. If we are less afraid of experiencing altered mental states and are able to identify what and how we dissociate, we will be able to make those episodes temporary, as opposed to partaking in generating further alterations in consciousness.

Let's start then with a useful way to understand dissociation, separating the different ways in which the occurrence could affect our lives. Table 6.1 lists the elements that dissociation makes inaccessible to consciousness by interrupting the continuity of.

Table 6.1 Aspects affected by dissociation

Time	Feeling Real	Identity	Motivation	Memory	Emotions
Lack of conscious presence and orientation toward present-tate and distortions perceiving time	Disconnection to the physical body, the space it occupies, its volume and size, and/or its sensations	Disconnection from the self or the idea of who we are as a unit, separated parts or identities with specific characteristics	Lack of goal-directed behavior including no purpose or energy, mental fatigue, and involuntary motor activity	Amnesia that goes from 'highway hypnosis' to inaccessible memory details, actions, or long periods of life	Loss of the capacity to recognize certain affects, their meaning, expression, range, value, or motivations

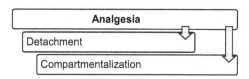

Figure 6.3 Dual model of dissociation

THE ANALGESIC QUALITY OF DISSOCIATION: COMPARTMENTALIZATION AND DETACHMENT

There is not much written about the benefits of dissociation. Still, several of the models and definitions also apply to non-detrimental dissociative experiences. For instance, Holmes et al. (2005) suggested a dual model of dissociation that identifies at least two distinct categories in all their expressions—*detachment and compartmentalization*—each one easily distinguishable from each other in their definition and mechanisms (Brown, 2006) (as shown in Figure 6.3).

Both detachment and compartmentalization include very positive, adaptive, and protective characteristics before they cause problems. When dissociation becomes dysfunctional, both categories are connected to the anesthetic byproduct of the survival protections that I'll explain next as part of the neurobiology of the phenomena.

Analgesia

It's well documented that dissociation is ruled by parasympathetic activation, especially when it's not working in a coordinated manner with the sympathetic. The parasympathetic extreme activation could cause circuits to disengage and lose awareness and missing parts of what's going on around with or without serious consequences, or could promote the overproduction of numbing agents which decrease vital functions, slows down communication among neurons, and misses to encode information of the situation among some of the consequences.

Think of when you get a cut and the wound feels numb for a while, indicating that the natural 'analgesics' are working to help you avoid the pain. Similarly, when we experience stressful situations, the PSNS increases the production of endogenous opioids to undo some of the activity of the sympathetic. Analgesics work on the psyche similar to how they work for the body: they detach us from pain, which in the case of the psyche means shutting down our awareness of painful experiences to help us tolerate the assumed 'imminent' distress. But they also have side effects; if the promoted production is low, it'd be equivalent to taking an aspirin, but if the pain is assumed strong, our self-produced analgesics would have the effect of painkillers like oxycodone. This protective response causes changes in cerebral blood flow that contribute to slowing down cognitive functions (brain-fog), generating perceptual disturbances (blurriness), impairments in memory encoding and retrieval (forgetfulness and amnesia), and failure of engagement (dullness). In more extreme circumstances, the excess of endogenous analgesics (among the main factors) disrupts the connectivity in the brain, causing more severe, lasting, and pathological effects on disruption and disconnection internally (amnesia, learning, regulation, motivation, etc.) and externally (engagement, motor activity, awareness, attention, etc.).

Detachment

As a peritraumatic phenomenon, detachment is undertaken in the name of adaptation. During threat, the PFC inhibits emotional processing and reduces sympathetic activity; parasympathetic activity increases, and the activity in the cortico-limbic brain system (including the production of analgesics) make the system skip the process of storing memories (painful and not painful), recalling experiences (overwhelming and regular), and of distancing awareness from affliction. Detachment could also be expected when mild situations disturb us, or when one needs to separate the focus from the surroundings to regulate and calm down. The sense of detachment may relate to numbing an emotional experience, disconnecting from the sense of self, and detaching from the body or the world around, even if the sense of reality testing is preserved and intact. For example, one may detach from one's body in the wintertime if one doesn't have appropriate clothes to get by in inclement weather. One knows it's cold, but one stops feeling it. Still, the fear of feeling detached may cause detachment to become chronic if it's out of one's awareness. A better example of functional dissociation is the state of flow, where people get to the peak of their creativity by detaching from their surroundings; if you combine that process with fear, then the person can experience feeling distant from their body and freak out, causing further distancing.

Compartmentalization

Besides using opioids to numb our experience of pain, endogenous analgesics have another use: to assist us by controlling some processes that are normally under our control. That's basically how compartmentalization functions. The reason? To slow down some neuron activity in certain regions of the brain to isolate areas that, when connected, may imply conflict. Keeping us less immersed in a consuming experience—by compartmentalizing it—separates chunks of information from each other, helping to manage emotionality more effectively. For example, by compartmentalizing the emotional states and information related to work from the emotionality and information about family life, we could be much more effective in both environments. Here we see that disconnecting some circuits from others can be positive and not necessarily lead to dysfunction unless it becomes habitual and interferes with family dynamics or accountability. Many spouses complain about having their partner 'forgetting' about them and replacing them with their jobs. The reduction in neural activity in certain areas can cause the loss of the ability to consciously control processes or actions that couple the sense of self with perception, planning, and decision-making. This is less desirable even if it is still adaptive.

The exaggerated intervention of the PSNS can cause several areas of the brain to change speed and power when it comes to communication, altering some previously formed circuits and creating new less efficient ones. In turn, these altered circuits interrupt communication and use different processes. Amnesia, anesthesia, pseudo-hallucinations, and motor disturbance fall into this category. The new circuits may start firing up independently, which may explain, for instance, the presence of different 'self-states' that could go from the standard internal different points of view to having extremely different personalities. This type of division (known as structural dissociation) is also protective and adaptive, but it may be debilitating if it is out of one's awareness or control, as it happens after traumatization. When dissociated identities develop a whole set of individual characteristics unintegrated from the self, mental processes become debilitated and can easily become pathological.

Interestingly, compartmentalization and absorption have been proposed as psychotherapy strategies to diminish the impact of disturbing emotional states (Bowins, 2012), which means that if we de-pathologize the construct, we may accept the possibility that dissociative states could be *volitional and under our control*, and even helpful during healing.

DISCONTINUITY: USUAL VERSUS ANOMALOUS

In the DSM-5, dissociation is defined as "a disruption of and/or discontinuity in the normal integration of consciousness, memory, identity, emotion,

Table 6.2 Dissociation: usual and anomalous manifestations

Discontinuity of:	Usual Dissociation	Anomalous Dissociation
Consciousness	Losing connection (lack of awareness) with surroundings on common activities (sleeping or being absorbed in one's thoughts). E.g., Daydreaming (harmless or not).	Extreme experiences of separation from reality like derealization, or experiencing certain psychotic symptoms like hallucinations. Also maladaptive daydreaming (engaging in vivid and imaginative thoughts for hours on end, neglecting real-life relationships and responsibilities, resulting in clinical distress and functional impairment (Soffer-Dudek, N., & Theodor-Katz, 2022).
Memory	A disruption of memory when the brain loses interest in learning new information that has previously been stored. In cases like driving home, no new memories are stored.	Incapacity to recall years of one's life (having been disconnected from feeling pain in challenging moments). Memory issues storing, accessing, and confusing the time/place/meaning of events. Not recalling actions, thoughts, or interactions with others in a selective way (under specific altered states and identities).
Identity	Behaving differently around different people (discontinuity in identity without consequences), e.g., being 'the responsible one' within a family setting and 'the funny one' among friends.	Lacking recollection of specific behavior under dissociated states. The development of 'alters' or dissociated personalities; fragmentation of the psyche, creating internal polarization and emotional conflicts between what is wanted and needed. When individual dissociated selves are stronger than the whole and take control over the personality, and the behavior can become a PD.

(Continued)

Table 6.2 (Continued)

Discontinuity of:	Usual Dissociation	Anomalous Dissociation
Emotion	Disconnect during painful or uncomfortable emotions. E.g., giggling upon hearing something upsetting or while anxious.	Emotional disconnection or lack of awareness of emotions (alexithymia). The chronic loss of the capacity to perceive different emotional states.
Perception	To stop perceiving the surroundings while distracted; easy to reconvene and refocus. E.g., reading a book without not knowing what was read.	Perceptually disconnecting from the surroundings (derealization). Not cognitive disconnection; the person still knows what's real, but the experience is a disconcerting, unrecognized mental state. E.g., sounds may be perceived as muffled, distance as too far or too close, etc., miscalculating the height of a step making one stumble, or feeling a body sensation that makes one scream in terror.
Motor control	Hunching is an unconscious response to shaming situations.	Suffering from paralysis of one or more limbs, ataxia, tremors, and dystonia.
Behavior	Mannerism dissociated from one's awareness. E.g., twirling one's hair while thinking or idle nail-biting.	Tics develop their own circuit that gets activated without one's volition.

perception, body representation, motor control, and behavior." But who hasn't felt a version of this in their day-to-day lives? Not everything about dissociation means pathology. Some behaviors are simply part of the human experience, not symptoms—even when they're a little uncanny. I'm going to take the liberty of deconstructing the DSM dissociation definition and give some examples of every type of discontinuity from what's usual to what's pathological (Table 6.2).

Pathological Dissociation

Since there are many individuals for whom dissociation impairs some of the processes essential for thriving and fully enjoying life, it may sound odd that I 'defend' dissociation. Seeing dissociation as a protection might sound romantic, but I am fully aware that it loses that touch in instances where it represents the breaking point from health to dysfunction. Dissociating could even be seen as the point where the brain loses hope of continuing to operate as it was and shifts into a disconnected (partial) brain communication, or as the task that intervenes in retraumatization (with dissociative states such as backlashes) without one being aware. Even after recovering from traumatization, it's hard to reestablish connectivity on circuits that got disconnected given that dissociation may have altered emotion processing and memory, interoception and attention regulation, self-referential processes, cognitive control, and arousal modulation (Krause-Utz et al., 2017). When the brain 'learns' to operate slowly, it's hard to bring it back to speed. *Remember how our brain is designed to keep our bodies alive without caring about the psychological cost we have to pay?* Well! Just as plants sting and some insects camouflage to avoid predators, humans dissociate. Disconnecting from pain—or submitting when there is no better option—is a real protection even when it ends up leaving us in that state of submission and disengagement for long; it becomes a true impediment when some brain functions disconnect our will to participate in the battle of being, when our chemistry reduces our level of engagement and control, or when the disconnected circuits affect our perception chronically; we stop seeing the 'big picture.' Dissociation becomes pathological when it becomes unconscious and impossible to control. (It actually never gets *impossible* to control, but it may feel as such. The brain can always relearn, create, or reconnect neural circuits even when the effort required seems huge.)

Dissociation can become a mental disorder on its own as in Depersonalization Disorder, or be present as a symptom of several mental disorders like

ASD and PTSD as well as BPD, schizophrenia, affective disorders, OCD, and somatoform disorders among others (Pec et al., 2014). *When is dissociation dangerous?* Extreme dissociation makes people almost inert, and thoughtless. When there is amnesia involved because the disconnected circuits are those of memory, the person may have beliefs and schemas separated from each other, which could make them behave in extreme ways without being able to recall the behavior. Dissociation can also cause fainting. When the brain slows down so extremely, the brain may not receive enough oxygen which can cause loss of consciousness and even non-epileptic seizures.

Abuse as an External Traumatizing Agent

Michaela's candid narration about her romantic relationships makes it clear that she was abused by several people and was unable to acknowledge it. Molested and awakened sexually by her cousin, groomed and traded by her 'best friend,' sexually abused by Ishmel, and emotionally abused and gaslit by Charles. She blamed herself. She may even have trouble accepting the use of the word 'abuse' in her experiences. This came about due to certain dissociative tendencies she was showing, as well as a lack of guidance and a habit of seeing herself as not good enough—the unfortunate consequences of having been used early in life.

Do you remember that when a trauma disorder develops after an identifiable situation (like date-rape), fear and our survival needs are the main traumatizing agents? You might also remember that shame, stress, and anxiety can play a role in launching survival protections or in sustaining their activation longer, and that gaining control of them requires our active involvement and engagement. Unfortunately, there are many other issues we may not have any power over, like abuse, an extremely relevant traumatizing agent in the development of a more complex presentation of a trauma disorder.

The word 'abuse' may immediately bring thoughts about maltreated children, battered women (domestic violence (DV)), and rape. Those are indeed very significant types of abuse, and probably the best-studied ones. Many (or all) types of abuse can put us at risk, especially when they happen at an early age. There are even more faces of abuse than the obvious and they happen at all ages and across many different circumstances. Even when it occurs in situations that would not be considered dangerous, like in codependent relationships, abuse can leave lasting wounds, contributing to allostatic changes that can end up as Complex PTSD (C-PTSD). I'm going to focus on those in this chapter.

While abuse in adulthood may not have the same profound effect on the brain as being abused as a child, it is still very important to consider. It is sad to learn, for example, that seniors are as frequently abused as children (mostly by their family members), that partners abuse each other to the extreme of 'soul-death,' that teens get virtually abused to the point of suicidality, and that people of different ethnic backgrounds than those in dominant positions get abused and maltreated as a norm. You would be surprised to know how many people get abused by their bosses, landlords, teachers, clients, therapists, or friends. When there is an imbalance of any type between two entities, whether real or assumed, there is potential for abuse. Individuals that have disadvantages and lack resources of any sort are not only subjected to abuse but may become numb to it without understanding that something inflicted upon a person without consent can have very damaging consequences on their mental and physical health.

> I worked for a non-profit organization as a volunteer for several years. The type of abuse I witnessed and suffered in that place was worse than the overt cases of abuse I have seen in any other environment. The mental undermining was inflicted under the cover of the organization's mission, which used the goodwill of its members to exploit them. I'll describe in Chapter Nine how this type of abuse becomes systemic.

THE EXTENT OF ABUSE

In psychology, abuse is considered the cruel, demeaning, violent, or invasive behavior of one person toward another. Maltreatment is the general umbrella under which all the different types of abuse lay, with the addition of neglect. Many people treat abuse and neglect as one, considering neglect a form of abuse. I prefer to separate them; neglect, as an act of omission, causes a different type of damage than abuse (an act of commission), especially if we consider how our many survival mechanisms get activated. I'll cover neglect in the next chapter.

What is abusive may not be solely dependent on the act, but also on the perception of the act and its consequences on the abused. Some individuals are prone to be abused for their submissive stance, naiveté, inexperience, a disadvantage of some sort, or their dissociation. Others that learn to protect themselves may be more aware when abused, putting their foot down to stop it, laughing and brushing it off, and even forgiving the act. Let's remember that some mistreated individuals become aggressive, violent, rebellious, or abusive themselves; it's documented that a huge number of abused individuals abuse others. Individuals that were traumatized by abuse may re-experience abuse—often as backlashes—even when the later acts inflicted are not abusive per se. They develop intolerance and feel abused easily regardless of the act or its intentionality.

There are cultural factors to abuse, too. There are more permissive cultures or communities where boundaries are non-existent, or where sarcasm, mockery, and criticism are not penalized as much. Some communities still exercise physical punishment as an accepted formative parental right. With children, some guidelines apply to every country (even when in practice they are not followed) like the guidelines that the WHO provides together with studies, statistics, and interventions to prevent and correct common abusive practices on children. But for adults, besides DV, torture, or prolonged social abusive situations like racism, there is almost no social or legal protection or acknowledgment of the multiple ways people get abused in the open every day.

TYPES OF ABUSE

There are many types of abuse. Some books focus solely on a single one such as sexual abuse. What's important in this chapter is the connection between abuse and trauma disorders, and how we can avoid traumatization even if we

PHYSICAL	SEXUAL	EMOTIONAL
Any harsh treatment that includes damaging the person's body such as injuries that cause bruises, welts, burns, abrasions, lacerations, wounds, cuts, bone/skull fractures, and other injuries after being slapped, punched, choked, kicked, shoved, hit, pushed, or inappropriately administered with drugs or physically restrained	Any non-consensual sexual activity that is committed by force, fear, or mental/physical incapacitation including coercion and the use of substances like alcohol or drugs. It varies in its level of severity and the type of behaviors which include rape, statutory rape, sexual touching, sexual exploitation, sexual harassment, stalking, sexual talk and enticement, and sexual molestation	Words and non-physical actions that hurt, belittle, weaken, manipulate, or frighten a person. Interactions that distort, confuse, influence, or dominate a person's thoughts and behavior, affecting perception, the sense of who one is, and shaking emotional stability through intimidation, manipulation, objectification, gaslighting, yelling, swearing, obsessive jealousy, etc. causing mental distress

Figure 6.4 Types of abuse

encounter ourselves in abusive situations. I'll cover child abuse more in the next chapter, whereas here I'll focus on the abuse that happens in adulthood. Figure 6.4 shows a description of the main types of abuse.

WHEN ABUSE JEOPARDIZES OUR INTEGRITY

Almost all abuse has the potential to jeopardize one's life, but only sometimes actually does. Therefore, abuse is traumatic but not always traumatizing. **Physical abuse** is traumatizing because it is clear to everyone that it can jeopardize the life of the abused. It is not uncommon for what starts as physical abuse to end in death. **Sexual abuse** (sexual misconduct) is traumatizing and shockingly pervasive. It causes great emotional damage and it doesn't respect age, social or financial status, education level, intelligence, race, or any other qualifier for the person that commits it or the one that suffers it. The mental and emotional consequences of sexual misconduct can last years, even with one event, because it creates all types of confusion, disorientation, and shame, together with loss of dignity and self-worth. **Psychological abuse** may be perceived as the least damaging but in fact, it could do much harm, in part because it could go under the radar for years without getting repaired, especially not by the abuser, who is the one expected by the abused to correct the wrong.

Emotional abuse can become the norm in a dynamic, inflicting a level of damage that may go unnoticed until it depletes the internal and external resources of the abused, breaking the person's will or inner stability. It may not be evident how it jeopardizes the life of the abused, but it could be so damaging and debilitating that it could cause the abused to attempt to end their own life. Abuse is traumatizing when the abused individual falls into despair, probably not seeing the way out of it, or when it weakens the person at the level of fearing not for their life but for their sanity. It's not easy to assess how traumatizing the abuse is because every person may have a particular relationship with their abuser or the abuse itself. Some abused individuals believe that enduring 'bad mood' or 'difficult moments' from others (partner, parent, child, elderly, etc.) is a sign of love, while others shut down by default thinking it makes them better people. That's why, within the realm of sexual abuse, for example, it's important not to rush into calling out the dynamic as abusive in order to protect the 'victim,' condemning the act without much investigation. The risk of shaming the person instead of validating their experience is high. (Read my article 'The Power of Labels: Why We Need to Rethink "ABUSE"' for more information.)

> The situation between Michaela and her 'cousin' illustrates a type of non-traumatizing sexual abuse. It seems that Michaela didn't feel victimized despite the 'abuse' lasting three years. She only learned that it had been abuse years later when she heard of statutory rape and understood the guy's bad intentions of what the game meant. There's no doubt that what the cousin did was a crime, and legally, he should have paid for it. But for her, it was an act of closeness and playfulness, and she maintained that fantasy in her mind for years without considering it threatening. Her narration sounds like she found it comforting and probably useful to escape from situations that were more stressful. If she had been treated as a victim when that abuse was discovered, she would have been disconcerted and ashamed.

THE RELATIONSHIPS THAT KILL OUR STRENGTH

Abuse is interpersonal by nature and one of its consequences is C-PTSD. Some people call it relational trauma, but most complex traumatization is relational (interpersonal), and using that term may be easily misinterpreted because there are other syndromes that are also relational. People in abusive relationships develop dynamics that include tactics for establishing power and maintaining control. Sometimes power is lopsided by the nature of the relationship (jobs, parents, etc.), but sometimes both parties struggle to gain control over the other (partners, friends, coworkers, etc.). For instance, physically abused individuals may need to develop emotionally abusive tactics to control the aggression (example: "I'll kill myself"). The tactics on both sides could include intimidation, isolation, punishment, denial, blaming, coercion, threat, humiliation, belittling, or other ways to manipulate, confuse, and objectify. In many of these situations, abuse is either cyclical or subtle, and therefore not easy to identify, not easy to confirm and report, and maybe easier to excuse. Did you follow the Johnny Depp (actor) and Amber Heard (ex-wife) (John C. Depp, II v. Amber Laura Heard, 2022) trial? The amount of abuse on both sides was over the limit and knowing who the abused and who the abuser was became almost impossible.

You may have also heard the term 'love bombing' used as a technique to manipulate someone into an abusive relationship by using bursts of affection and 'unselfishness' to gain or regain control over the aggravated. The love bombed feels special and one could not call it abusive since it'd invalidate their own worth. Love bombing is also one-way abusers use to transact for forgiveness and 'buy' another opportunity after the situation becomes extreme and intolerable. Name-calling, humiliating, negating, criticizing, controlling, shaming, accusing, blaming, punishing, isolating, discrediting, and denying can create and exacerbate anyone's insecurities to the extreme of 'losing' oneself and becoming an appendix of the abuser. This defines a codependent relationship where the abused feels in debt and can't find happiness unless the other shows signs of satisfaction or acceptance. The abused individual may lose all self-concept and respect, flooding their thoughts and concerns with the actions, demands, behavior, accusations, and needs of the abused. The abused may not find ways to grasp the level of risk they are subjected to because the risk rises from discontentment with the self. There is a real threat here in the form of pathological dissociation, self-harm, illness, and suicidal ideation.

Michaela's romantic partners abused her without anyone noticing. Her cousin and Ishmel abused her sexually while Charles mainly abused her emotionally. Charles's gaslighting was more detrimental than the sexual abuse, at least for as long as she was oblivious to how she had been sexually used—and the implications of it. The sexual abuse became detrimental when it happened again, at the lake, once she was more aware of what sexual abuse was. However, the mental debilitation she showed after Richie was probably caused by the extent to which Charles's emotional abuse had depleted her inner resources.

Mental Undermining

All types of abuse, but especially emotional abuse, have one purpose: to debilitate someone's will and undermine their capabilities in order to obtain personal gain (control, submission, obedience, pleasure, independence, financial benefits, etc.). This type of abuse doesn't put the person's life at risk, but does shatter their sense of self, sense of belonging, stability, confidence, and can vanquish their will to live. This is achieved mainly by constant mind games, devaluation, scheming, cunning, deceiving, and tricks of the sort that can be summarized under manipulation and gaslighting. I'll expand on them to clarify some of the misinformation about what they entail since they are intentionally abusive and not only casual practices.

– **Manipulation** (psychological) is a subtle way of abuse that may not be recognized by those around—or even by the manipulated. Manipulation conveys an artful, unfair, and insidious way to gain control over another person's thoughts, emotions, and actions. Many people manipulate others just to get what they want, but here I'm using emotional manipulation as a type of traumatizing *abuse*. Manipulation can be exercised through a wide range of methods with or without a plan that goes from using understated ways—like begging with a soft tone of voice—to sophisticated 'Machiavellian' strategies. A person that is constantly manipulated can suffer from distorted perceptions, disturbing emotions, disorientation and confusion, and a drained sense of self, agency, and self-esteem that are conducive to feeling hopeless and like a failure (McGinn, 2008). Lacking resilience combined with reaching hopelessness causes the person to live defeated and afraid of potentially being abandoned, replaced, rejected, or expelled. It can cause complex traumatization on its own, contribute to living in survival mode for as long as the relationship lasts, or inflict pain slowly, draining the capacity of the system to adapt. This type of manipulation is included in many descriptions of personality disorders such as narcissistic PD and how people suffer from relationships with those affected by the disorder. For the person with a PD, manipulation may be a skill developed to survive but for the manipulated it means constant pain, conflict, and disempowerment.

– **Gaslighting** is one of the most effective ways to manipulate and debilitate someone emotionally by making them doubt their own reality, aimed at making individuals seem or feel 'crazy' and insecure (Sweet, 2019). Its purpose is to gradually undermine the person's confidence in their ability to distinguish what's true from false and what's right from wrong and to put the responsibility of the relationship problems on the gaslit. The mounting doubts result in weakening the abused and driving them to adopt a dependent or submissive attitude. Gaslighting has become a popular term used almost as synonymous with lying, but gaslighting is not a simple practice; it requires technique and consistency. The gaslighter needs to know the other person really well to leverage on the known weaknesses to increase their insecurities and make them believe they are not well, that they are the ones to blame, and that they are the ones with distortions. Gaslighting is no doubt abusive since it's a repeated and intentional practice. It's much more common among romantic partners (or even professional colleagues) than between parents and young children. Kids consider what their parents say as the laws of the Universe, so they don't require sophisticated manipulation strategies such as this one. Gaslighting is also common in societal contexts. Racism, for instance, has been perpetuated by the premise that the oppressed misfortunes are their fault.

Objectifying

Objectifying a human being is a subdued way to exercise abuse with traumatizing consequences. Objectification is a central notion of feminist theory (Nussbaum, 1999) but extends beyond sexualization. It's straightforward to identify when the person is used as an object sexually but there are many other ways to objectify a person to the extreme of dehumanizing them or stealing their power without exercising any evident abuse. *All humans have the primordial need to be seen, heard, and understood.* When someone is treated as an object—even when unintentional—their primordial needs are implicitly unmet, and therefore, it becomes almost impossible to develop a healthy sense of self or establish healthy relationships and boundaries. Consequently, they may either tend to make relationships transactional and use themselves as currency or accept whatever is offered to them because of their depreciated sense of self-value (LaCroix & Pratto, 2015).

People that tend to objectify others are those that lack empathy, see everything as self-referential, and are normally ego-syntonic, which means that objectifying others is acceptable to the needs and goals of their false/dissociated-self, the 'whatever it takes to survive' one. This is not only about semantics. People that objectify others are not emotionally well. Most objectifiers suffer from a personality disorder—like narcissistic PD—and lack connection with executive functions related to morality and sentiments like compassion or love. Most live in survival mode since they can remember. They are not born intrinsically vile but suffer from severe mental issues and disconnection between several of their brain centers. It's also the case that individuals learned to objectify others from someone they respected that did it (a parent, for example); those individuals can rectify their behavior as soon as they understand what they are doing. Still, those in relationships with them suffer the consequences of being treated as a thing, a gadget, or a piece of property; experiences that are extremely de-formative and painful. The same happens with social practices that objectify a whole group of people such as 'blonds,' migrant workers, or even athletes.

I'm using the Nussbaum/Langton framework (Langton, 2009; Nussbaum, 1999) in Table 6.3 to show objectification for all individuals. These situations may not be traumatizing on their own but can become traumatizing agents, especially combined with other types of abuse or with reduced resilience and lack of resources.

Table 6.3 Types of objectification

Type	Definition	Example
Instrumentality	Being treated and used as a tool or instrument to obtain benefits or satisfy others' goals.	Any worker who is treated as a 'pon of a chess board,' moved around as the boss pleases without giving them validation, recognition, fair remuneration, or respect for their work, dignity, and value. They are removed or replaced as soon as they break, fail, ask for more, or verbalize their needs.
Denial of autonomy	Individual's treatment implies they have no capacity to act on their own or at their will.	A wife that is seen as an accessory or just as a helper around the house, or a son/daughter deprived of the right to decide what profession to pursue.
Fungibility	A person is not recognized in their individuality and is treated as interchangeable with (other) objects.	A mother that loses a blond baby girl and changes the name of her daughter with the name of the deceased one and dyes the girl blond.
Violability	When someone is violated in their integrity and value as if they were objects that could be disposed of, broken, used, or traded.	Hurting a son/daughter as revenge against the spouse.
Ownership	If someone is made to believe they belong to the other, and therefore the 'owner' has the right to buy or sell, damage, hurt, and even kill them.	People who ask their partners or children to have sex with another person to obtain favors or money, or when a partner chooses friends as cuckolds for their wives/husband just for fun.

(Continued)

Table 6.3 (Continued)

Type	Definition	Example
Denial of subjectivity	When someone's experiences or feelings are dismissed, not worthy of attention or concern.	A person sends a friend to pick up his drugs in an unknown neighborhood because they don't want to take on the risk themselves.
Reduction to body	When someone is treated as if only part of them were relevant or seen.	A parent that brags about the son's big strong arms and only includes him when there is a need for physical actions that demands strength.
Reduction to appearance	If someone is treated a certain way because of their look or physical appearance.	A family member that 'shows off' one of the kids because they are 'beautiful' and dismisses, ignores, or rejects the other siblings. In this case, both siblings suffer the consequences of objectification.
Silencing	When someone is treated as if they cannot speak.	A kid that doesn't learn to speak because the caregiver speaks for them.

Trauma Bonding

I want to include trauma bonding here not because it's a type of abuse but because it is the result of certain types of abuse—such as objectification—that perpetuates abuse, promoting traumatization. A trauma bond is the kind of attachment a person develops with their abuser disempowering the individual that lives in a state of defeat, covering it over with the mirage of being in love.

> Michaela was convinced she was in love with Charles, most probably because she saw him as someone that could give her some care and validation. But this didn't only happen with Charles. Throughout her life, she lost objectivity and developed a bond with people that did not see her worth and only saw her utilitarian value to them, like Andreaa, Ishmel, or her cousin. Those experiences obviously undermined her self-concept and worth.

Developing C-PTSD

> To make it easier to understand complex traumatization, let's imagine a cut made by a blade to first explain PTSD. The cut made by a blade is an easily identified cause of an injury. It's also straightforward to see how the wound from a cut heals using the body's natural protection system: it bleeds, itches, burns, hurts, gets numb, gets swollen, and so on until it develops a scab, and eventually closes and scars. Now, to understand C-PTSD, instead of a cut imagine an abrasion that results from scraping the skin. When you replace the blade with a hand file, rubbing the skin constantly replaces the cut). Our natural protections get ready: blood vessels will turn the tissue red and there will be swelling too, etc. But as the filing continues, you may see how a blister appears, or maybe some tiny drops of blood depending on the severity of the rubbing. As soon as many of the skin layers are removed, the skin will start bleeding. The wound will ooze a pinkish fluid, which may be a healing agent. Imagine the filing stops for a while and the skin begins healing, but then the rubbing starts again, stops and starts again, and again. There will be a point where the body won't be able to protect the area. An infection may occur because the protections are not enough; now the

wound is exposed to other attacks. Our system is designed as such that, if we stop rubbing, there will be crusting, and at some point, the wound heals. However, if the filling doesn't stop or if there are bacteria (external) or diabetes (internal), the other agents will create an ulcer and the process of closing the wound will be disabled.

In the previous chapter, we were able to follow the development of PTSD after an identifiable traumatic event using the homeostasis model. It was relatively easy to track because the process of traumatization in those cases is a sequence of activations that take place in a short period. But for a trauma disorder to unfold in its *complex* type, the person may endure traumatization for years (the constant rubbing before the infection). What happens to the nervous system during constant exposure to danger, as well as persistent states of insecurity, doubt, confusion, or other situations that cause fear and shame or constant traumatic stress? Does that follow a different activation of our survival mechanisms? When the source of traumatic stress can't be pinpointed, there are complications. *Were Michaela's activities with Ishmel stressful or was betraying Andreaa more stressful? Was Charles's abuse the 'rubbing' or was it actually the fear of being abandoned again?* If it's not possible to conceptualize traumatization by identifying the event (because the stress is caused by several different traumatizing agents and is suffered through a prolonged period), it is even more difficult to picture the moment when the system loses its equilibrium. How then could we recognize when the system becomes chronically dysregulated? This question may have been in the mind of researchers that saw that a new way to conceptualize equilibrium and internal regulation to explain this conundrum was sorely needed. Thankfully, a new construct was born around 1988 called *allostasis*. This section is dedicated to explaining allostasis and the moment it 'fails,' causing the system to stay in survival mode and originating the development of a disorder identified as C-PTSD.

THE COST OF CONSTANT STRUGGLE

Judith Herman, a pioneer in the current studies of the trauma phenomena, dedicated part of her research to the treatment of incest and traumatic stress. In 1988, she suggested a new diagnosis: Complex PTSD. Herman and others (like Christine Courtois and Julian Ford) saw that it was necessary to describe the symptoms of long-term traumatization stating that PTSD was not enough.

They were able to bring attention to the matter and, since then, a lot has been discovered about the consequences of prolonged exposure to life-threatening situations such as DV, sex trafficking, torture, or persecution. In this section, I want to also shed light on the prolonged exposure to traumatic circumstances that are not as clearly identifiable as the mentioned situations.

It is not difficult to picture the stress suffered by someone living with a verbally or physically abusive individual, or by someone harassed or constantly abused sexually. Those individuals, especially as adults, may be able to notice their level of anxiety when the abuser approaches, but those that go through the type of experience I implicitly described under 'mental undermining' in the abuse section, subjected to constant manipulation and gaslighting, or having lived a life feeling like an object and having been used as such might not show clear signs of the constant stress of their struggle because the fear is not toward the abuser but toward their own schemas about their inabilities. Observed externally, they are not seen as 'fighting for their lives.' Those that have developed a trauma bond and believe they love the abuser get easily dismissed. The lack of empathy or understanding for their pain could make it feel as not important or real, regularly received with a "relationships are difficult" type of statement and an expectation to keep enduring it. Their struggle may be directly connected to wanting to find reasons to 'keep fighting' without having the support of their own body to do so. Once someone reaches that point, a point of implicit futility, even if they have not shown clear signs of prolonged stress, they may develop C-PTSD because their system may not be able to take it any longer, shifting gears directly to immobilization mechanisms and survival processes. This type of traumatization can develop after constantly being abused by a partner, relative, or at work dealing with a superior or a whole team.

Adult individuals that have reached a resignation level of not being considered, or have given up the idea of having needs as others do, lose motivation to engage with life; they feel like failures and their brain then anticipates defeat. The type of circumstances (fear, insecurity, doubt, submission) causes allostatic mechanisms to be working non-stop, especially those that numb pain. Let's see what that means under the trauma lens.

ALLOSTASIS: AN ADAPTATION MODEL TO PROLONGED STRESS

Walter Cannon—the same scientist that coined 'fight or flight'—defined homeostasis as the major principle underlying physiological regulation and called it the 'Wisdom of the Body' (Cannon, 1932). That phrase describes how a coordinated way to keep physiological parameters stable is the response of a group of physiological and behavioral processes (Ramsay & Woods, 2014). For many years, the homeostatic model (and construct) was extremely well received and used to generate further hypotheses, stimulating research and motivating experimental findings. At some point, further research identified situations that appear inconsistent with the basics of the homeostatic model and a large number of new propositions appeared. From those propositions, the model that has gained more recognition has been the one presented by Sterling and Eyer (1988) named *allostasis*. Sterling and Eyer coined the term 'allostasis' and described it as the adaptive process that organisms use to *adjust to new or changing environments* (Ramsay & Woods, 2014), i.e., *remaining stable by being variable*. The allostasis model has been able to challenge the homeostasis one—after almost a century—without contradicting it. Allostasis is an extension of the previous theory but offers a broader postulation and expands its applications. Allostasis is relevant to trauma studies because it explains active processes by which our bodies 'adapt' to potential threats or stressors by making small changes to maintain internal equilibrium and promote survival (Peters & McEwen, 2012). Allostasis allows our brain to automatically predict and prepare to meet the body's demands before they arise (Barrett, 2020). Allostasis extends the concept of homeostasis to reflect the adaptation process that responds to physical, psychosocial, and environmental challenges to our system (Logan & Barksdale, 2008) with minimal expense of energy. As it is postulated, the allostatic model facilitates adaptation, while the parameters associated with homeostasis do not. In short, we could say that homeostasis maintains stability through (assumed) constancy, while allostasis maintains *stability through change* (adjustment).

Constant exposure to psychosocial stressors—like the possibility of being repeatedly injured by physical, verbal, or emotional abuse—contributes to adverse health outcomes due to the tension and demands they put on the system. Stress is identified as one of the main processes that initiate and maintain allostatic mechanisms running (Ramsay & Woods, 2014). For example, in an especially stressful environment such as living or dealing with an aggressive person, an individual may maintain a high level of blood pressure compared to those living in a less-stressful environment. Through allostasis, that person's system 'learns' to live with the elevated level of blood pressure, making other small changes in order to maintain the system in equilibrium.

An important aspect of allostasis is the notion of *anticipation*. Anticipating the actions that will be needed (learned as effective from previous experiences) is the most efficient ANS regulator (Peters & McEwen, 2012) and offers the possibility of adaptation given the capacity to mobilize and re-solve the challenges quickly (McEwen & Gianaros, 2011). The changes that occur during stress responses (many times assisted by apprehension, worry, and anxiety), like hormonal changes or structural alterations in the limbic brain, are more easily reversed if they are conceptualized under allostatic processes. Allostasis is a clear exemplification of the natural tendency of our body to heal and be well. Allostasis is preventive and protective against stay-ing within suboptimal operation—developing emotional disorders—since it helps avoid losing balance as fast as homeostasis had proposed.

So far, it sounds like allostasis could save us from the perils of our envi-ronment, but if it were so, C-PTSD wouldn't exist, right? Well, everything breaks if it reaches its limit. The construct of allostasis also gives way to the 'allostatic load,' the wear and tear of allostatic processes.

ALLOSTATIC LOAD: REACHING OUR LIMITS

Allostatic load is explained as the cost of having been exposed to elevated or fluctuating production of chemicals caused by repeated objective or sub-jective challenging experiences (Guidi et al., 2021). Even when allostasis processes are helpful to our system making adjustments that avoid greater damage, there are repercussions from the depletion caused by repeated cy-cles of allostasis. At a certain point, turning these processes on-off-on-off becomes inefficient. After constant, prolonged, or non-habituated use of allostasis, the system can't continue making changes; it overloads. That crucial moment is called allostatic load. Reaching that point over-activates the production of stress hormones—pro- and anti-inflammatory cytokines first—and metabolic, cardiovascular, immune, and reproductive markers lose balance. Allostatic load then results in failed allostasis, causing pathology, dysfunction, and chronic illness. Allostatic load causes lasting damage to the brain, nervous system, and organ systems. For example, an individual that had learned to live with high blood pressure reaches a point where they can suffer a stroke, a heart attack, or kidney failure.

DEVELOPING C-PTSD ONE ADJUSTMENT AT A TIME

Upon reaching allostatic load, the brain knows by then that the small 'ad-justments' were insufficient. The ANS then shifts to emergency mode to save it. That's when it can be said that the person has developed C-PTSD.

The ANS takes over, keeping the system running in survival mode. Operating after the allostatic load is reached causes chemical imbalances as well as perturbations in the daily rhythm, and, in some cases, atrophy of brain structures (McEwen, 2000). Under allostatic load, the hippocampus reduces its size, which influences aspects of what will be stored as episodic and declarative memory. The amygdala increases its size and its neuronal proliferation, keeping the system hyper-alert, looking for any cue of a possible threat. There is also a loss of neural activity in the cortex when high levels of chemicals (catecholamines such as epinephrine) have the potential to weaken the PFC connections and interfere with adequate cortical performance.

We could then conclude that C-PTSD is a disorder of the ANS that is caused by the cumulative burden of allostatic changes following a prolonged period of constant use of the stress response that reaches a point of overload.

Assessing and Diagnosing C-PTSD

We can see from Michaela's recap of her romances that even though they were all abusive, she didn't show evident symptoms compared with the ones she showed after the lake (except dissociative characteristics). We can assume that the moment of allostatic load occurred during the lake's weekend, when she read the report from the counselor, or somewhere around those days. Her dominant strategy seemed to be submission and self-devaluation which manifested as low self-esteem, a tendency to escape mentally, and her need to be loved. Unfortunately, she doesn't include her physical health in her narration except for her burn-out; it's normally useful to check on the person's health because that's where the allostatic load shows more clearly. Look for irregular hormonal levels and problems on the neuroendocrine (diabetes, menopause, hyperthyroidism/hypothyroidism, etc.), cardiovascular (arrhythmia, etc.), immune (slow scaring, digestive issues, frequent infections, etc.) and metabolic (obesity, high blood pressure, etc.) systems.

Does C-PTSD mean more damage than PTSD? Prolonged traumatization causes many more alterations and the changes are not obvious until they become unbearable. In PTSD we saw that all the symptoms show up at once and they start fading away shortly after the threat is gone. It's possible to bounce back to baseline when the alterations happened during a short period. In the case of allostatic load and long-term traumatization, going 100% back to baseline might be impossible if the modifications happened slowly, too long ago, or were too many. The individual with high blood pressure due to allostatic changes may have that characteristic forever even if allostatic load never happens. Small changes may not be obvious or even considered symptoms and only when they add up, they can reach unhealthy levels. But that's why it is so important to resolve traumatization instead of allowing it to continue running, deteriorating our health and well-being.

USING PTSD TO DIAGNOSE ITS COMPLEX VERSION

The latest version of the DSM doesn't include criteria for C-PTSD for us to use as the basis for a diagnosis. Therefore, we need to rely upon other tools. The WHO includes C-PTSD in their newest edition (ICD-11) and states that PTSD (C-PTSD) is "a disorder that may develop following exposure to an event or series of events of an extremely threatening or horrific nature, most commonly prolonged or repetitive events from which escape is difficult or impossible (e.g. torture, slavery, genocide campaigns, prolonged domestic violence, repeated childhood sexual or physical abuse)" (WHO, 2019). To grant the diagnosis, it asks for all the diagnostic requirements for PTSD and lists additional criteria: C-PTSD is characterized by severe and persistent: (1) problems in affect regulation; (2) beliefs about oneself as diminished, defeated, or worthless, accompanied by feelings of shame, guilt, or failure related to the traumatic event; and (3) difficulties in sustaining relationships and in feeling close to others (Appendix C lists the whole criteria from the ICD-11).

As you can see, it proposes criteria that are difficult to meet, especially in terms of the incident. In addition to using the criteria listed by the WHO, a systemic approach looks for other signs, not to diagnose but to assess the severity of the manifestations. There are always indicators that show whether the person adapted to the abuse, was able to overcome it, or at what point their system overloaded. For that assessment, it's useful to investigate how the person describes themselves before and during the abuse, meaning: the traumatizing conditions, the ways they dealt with them, and the level of their resilience, tolerance, and subtle characteristics such as distractibility, clumsiness, and body temperature.

PERITRAUMATIC MARKERS: TEMPERAMENT AND ITS BIOLOGY

Constant traumatization (besides the tragic events like genocide listed by the WHO) is handled differently by different people depending on age, circumstances, resources, resilience, and temperament. Including *temperament* to conceptualize complex traumatization in order to separate traumatization markers from personal style is a great tool. Knowing the temperament of the person could help predict whether there was a predisposition to use certain strategies to adapt versus others. Depending on the individual's natural inclination to certain types of emotional reactions (with their specific speed and intensity), it may be possible for the person to defend themselves somehow, or they may give up without a fight. It has been calculated that 40–60% of our personality comes from our temperament (Fisher et al., 2015).

There is more than one way to define and classify temperament. My preferred one is the Fisher Temperament Inventory (FTI), a measure of personality

Table 6.4 Different temperaments according to the FTI

Dopamine	*Serotonin*	*Testosterone*	*Estrogen/Oxytocin*
Curious/energetic	Cautious/compliant	Analytical	Prosocial/empathic
Regular: would respond negatively to punishment or prolonged threat, possibly becoming rebellious and leaving; motivated to search for rewards; driven to pursue excitement.	**Regular:** prone to accept or dismiss abusive circumstances, lowering the level of priority of their own needs but using their serotonin system to regulate their mood and find solace.	**Regular:** more inclined to fight back and find reasons to stop what they don't find acceptable. Uses reasoning to cope and deal with conflict.	**Regular:** easily fall in love and even into trauma bonding; attachment is rewarding even with the cost.
Traumatized: more inclined to adapt by escaping (flight). When depleted, gets depressed.	**Traumatized:** serotonin system fails or gets spent causing medical problems, somatization, and illnesses.	**Traumatized:** emasculated or ridiculed; shifts in identity but have enough determination to leave abusive situations.	**Traumatized:** more easily fall into submit or fade. Unceasingly search for connection; bear abuse to show/receive love

based on neurobiology that uses the idea that behavior is influenced by the dominance of a specific neurotransmitter (Fisher et al., 2015). It proposes four different types of temperament: Curious/Energetic connected to dopamine; Cautious/Social Norm Compliant to serotonin; Analytical/Toughminded to testosterone; and Prosocial/Empathetic to estrogen/oxytocin. The production of those chemicals is connected with the type of engagement the person looks for or avoids. Its criteria are shown in Table 6.4.

These different types of natural inclinations can be used to inform to what extent the abuse was agonized or handled, and what type of interventions each one requires to overcome the challenges of the survival mode. This approach explains how one of the main reasons people 'get stuck' in one survival strategy versus another is not only the *circumstances* and the adaptation but also their natural *tendencies* and *traits*. Once the temperament is spotted, and if it's coherent with the survival style adopted, then the adaptation may be treated as a strength and not as a shortcoming.

> It's not hard to spot that Michaela's temperament belongs to the cautious/social-norm-complaint type, dominated by the serotonergic system. She conformed, avoided conflict, and generated ways to adapt and comply even if that meant forgetting about her needs. Finding her temperament in this way is validating, and useful for designing interventions so that they don't go against her natural tendencies. It'd be counterproductive to expect her to set boundaries in an aggressive way, become demanding, use her logic, rebel, or other 'suggestions' that could sound against what her temperament prefers.

C-PTSD POSTTRAUMATIC MARKERS: SURVIVAL STRATEGIES

We saw in Chapter Three that when an individual develops PTSD symptoms in the days or weeks after experiencing a traumatic event, it's easier to observe how the survival mechanism shifts to becoming a strategy that then becomes dominant. When the traumatization is of the complex type that occurs during a prolonged period, it is difficult to identify whether the response to the stressors like abuse is due to temperament, if it comes from the way the ANS is adapting to the circumstances, or in what ratio they are both interacting. When there's congruence between the temperament and the dominant survival strategy, it may indicate that the person was 'loyal' to their temperament and used their resilience to adapt. If they are incongruent, there's probably a higher level of dysfunction, a lack of self, and an adaptation that goes beyond their system (social). I'm expanding here on each one to facilitate their recognition:

Lock (from freeze): if someone stays stuck in this strategy, they will be constantly ready to act or fight (sympathetic) but also expectant (dorsal vagus parasympathetic) often of something negative. Staying in this strategy consumes huge amounts of energy that makes people feel ordinarily exhausted. Since it's designed to be a preventive measure, staying in this mechanism causes indecisiveness, doubt, lack of trust, rigidity, and challenges in asking for help. For those locked in this strategy, it is difficult to experience pleasure; they are never sure, carry lots of shame, are often second-guessing, and over-identify whatever wrong is done to them but can hardly recognize or take in positive deeds done for them. They show a tendency to expect the worst as a way to be 'better' prepared.

Appease (from fawn) is characterized by keeping socially engaged (ventral vagus parasympathetic) together with a certain level of desire to fight or escape (sympathetic activation), probably ruled by estrogen and serotonin systems or a combination of both. People with a dominant 'appease' activation show signs of dependency, and use conciliation to avoid conflict but hold unspoken grudges because they feel they have to suppress their anger as a way to stay safer, especially in cases of abuse. These individuals are normally not defeated and may not meet the full criteria for C-PTSD often, but may suffer from some personality issues that can easily evolve into a personality disorder.

Assault/Aggression (from fight) is unmistakably dominated by sympathetic activation and ruled by anger and testosterone. Individuals dominated by this strategy navigate the world using physical strength, verbal abuse, and aggression to impose a type of power they may feel necessary to gain control toward reaching safety. It may be subtle or it can go all the way to antagonism and violence.

Escape (from flight) is also dominated by sympathetic activation but more clearly ruled by avoidance and dopamine. When the individual's temperament is such that anger is not a natural or preferred reaction, the person living in a hyper-active mode looks for ways to escape confrontation and responsibility in an active manner, including the regular use of substances, sex, or activities like gambling. The use of crutches not only serves to avoid but also calms down the system and helps them feel 'normal,' as in less reactive.

Submit (from tonic immobility) implies over-activation of the immobilization protections (dorsal vagus) and the production of oxytocin.

When someone is dominated by this strategy, dissociation may be present in more than one way, and individuals may become dependent, shut down, disconnected, evasive, and depressed. They may lack the energy or motivation to engage with the world in an active way. They submit easily to the demands of others, potentially identified as 'pleasers,' individuals who neglect their needs to give priority to the needs of others, constantly looking for the depleted 'love' hormone. They are great followers and can achieve great things if someone else leads.

Fade/Faint (from collapse immobility) receives several names such as faint, fail, or collapse; it is also an immobilization strategy like submit (dorsal vagus parasympathetic) but with a larger participation of the Ventrolateral Periaqueductal Gray, which plays a big role in the experience of pain. That implies that the level of dissociation is more extreme than in any other strategy since the numbing agents were more active during the struggle and continue being used to survive. These individuals are disengaged, dissociative, and may carry a hard-to-withstand sense of dissatisfaction with the depletion of serotonin. They may feel so defeated that intimacy (of all sorts) could seem unavailable, which pushes them to accept abuse without even considering it as such. It's common to see that individuals stuck in this state move from one tragedy to the next, are easily targeted for all sorts of exploitation, and readily assume the victim role.

Let's keep in mind that all the descriptions I'm including here are generalizations and move in a continuum from low to extreme. Each one of us is unique and presents a combination of factors that may contradict every other generalization. Some people hide even from themselves because they are not able to manage the shame they feel for behaving/feeling the way they do, while others develop a sense of entitlement to justify their actions. All manifestations move in a range influenced by circumstances, how each individual has learned to express themselves, how emotionality was learned (what scripts the person carries), and how much or how little their environment allows them to be themselves versus imposing specific actions and values.

Learning about the abusive relationships that Michaela suffered and how she endured them gave us enough information to predict complex traumatization. But we still need more information about her childhood and her family in order to fully conceptualize her case. That comes next.

References

Barrett, L. F. (2020). *Seven and a Half Lessons about the Brain* (pp. 136–140). Boston, MA: Houghton Mifflin Harcourt.Bowins, B. E. (2012). Therapeutic dissociation: Compartmentalization and absorption. *Counselling Psychology Quarterly*, 25(3), 307–317. https://doi.org/10.1080/09515070.2012.695278

Britannica, T. Editors of Encyclopedia (2022). Stress. *Encyclopedia Britannica*. https://www.britannica.com/science/stress-psychology-and-biology

Brown, R. (2006). Different types of "dissociation" have different psychological mechanisms. *Journal of Trauma & Dissociation: The Official Journal of the International Society for the Study of Dissociation (ISSD)*, 7, 7–28. https://doi.org/10.1300/J229v07n04_02.

Bruce, A. S., Ray, W. J., Bruce, J. M., Arnett, P. A., & Carlson, R. A. (2007). The relationship between executive functioning and dissociation. *Journal of Clinical and Experimental Neuropsychology*, 29(6), 626–633. https://doi.org/10.1080/13803390600878901

Cannon, W. B. (1932). *The Wisdom of the Body*. New York: W. W. Norton & Co.

Chrousos G. P. (1998). Stressors, stress, and neuroendocrine integration of the adaptive response. The 1997 Hans Selye Memorial Lecture. *Annals of the New York Academy of Sciences*, 851, 311–335. https://doi.org/10.1111/j.1749-6632.1998.tb09006.x

Fisher, H. E., Island, H. D., Rich, J., Marchalik, D., & Brown, L. L. (2015). Four broad temperament dimensions: Description, convergent validation correlations, and comparison with the Big Five. *Frontiers in Psychology*, 6, 1098. https://doi.org/10.3389/fpsyg.2015.01098

Fullerton, C. S., Ursano, R. J., Epstein, R. S., Crowley, B., Vance, K. L., Kao, T. C., Baum, A. (2000). Peritraumatic dissociation following motor vehicle accidents: Relationship to prior trauma and prior major depression. *The Journal of Nervous and Mental Disease*, 188(5), 267–272. https://doi.org/10.1097/00005053-200005000-00003. PMID: 10830563.

Grupe, D. W., & Nitschke, J. B. (2013). Uncertainty and anticipation in anxiety: An integrated neurobiological and psychological perspective. *Nature Reviews. Neuroscience*, 14(7), 488–501. https://doi.org/10.1038/nrn3524

Guidi, J., Lucente, M., Sonino, N., Fava, G. (2021). Allostatic load and its impact on health: A systematic review. *Psychotherapy and Psychosomatics*, 90, 11–27. https://doi.org/10.1159/000510696

Holmes, E. A., Brown, R. J., Mansell, W., Fearon, R. P., Hunter, E. C., Frasquilho, F., & Oakley, D. A. (2005). Are there two qualitatively distinct forms of dissociation? A review and some clinical implications. *Clinical Psychology Review*,

25(1), 1–23. https://doi.org/10.1016/j.cpr.2004.08.006Janet, P. (1907). *The Major Symptoms of Hysteria*. London/New York: Macmillan. Second edition with new matter: 1920. Reprint of 1920-edition: Hafner, New York, 1965. (pp. 332) Janet, P. (1 909a). Les névroses, Flammarion, Paris.

Krause-Utz, A., Frost, R., Winter, D., & Elzinga, B. M. (2017). Dissociation and alterations in brain function and structure: Implications for borderline personality disorder. *Current Psychiatry Reports*, 19(1), 6. https://doi.org/10.1007/s11920-017-0757-y

LaCroix, J., & Pratto, F. (2015). Instrumentality and the denial of personhood: The social psychology of objectifying others. *Revue internationale de psychologie sociale*, 28, 183–211.

Langton, R. (2009). *Sexual Solipsism: Philosophical Essays on Pornography and Objectification* (pp. 225–232). Oxford: Oxford University Press.

Logan, J. G., & Barksdale, D. J. (2008). Allostasis and allostatic load: Expanding the discourse on stress and cardiovascular disease. *Journal of Clinical Nursing*, 17(7b), 201–208. https://doi.org/10.1111/j.1365-2702.2008.02347.x

McEwen, B. S. (2000). Allostasis and allostatic load: Implications for neuropsychopharmacology. *Neuropsychopharmacology: Official Publication of the American College of Neuropsychopharmacology*, 22(2), 108–124. https://doi.org/10.1016/S0893-133X(99)00129-3

McEwen, B. S., & Gianaros, P. J. (2011). Stress- and allostasis-induced brain plasticity. *Annual Review of Medicine*, 62, 431–445. https://doi.org/10.1146/annurev-med-052209-100430

McGinn, C. (2008). *Mindfucking: A Critique of Mental Manipulation* (1st ed.) (pp. 15–22). Routledge. https://doi.org/10.4324/9781315711812

Nussbaum, M. (1999). *Sex and Social Justice*. (pp. 213–230). Oxford: Oxford University Press.

Pec, O., Bob, P., & Raboch, J. (2014). Dissociation in schizophrenia and borderline personality disorder. *Neuropsychiatric Disease and Treatment*, 10, 487–491. https://doi.org/10.2147/NDT.S57627

Peters, A., & McEwen, B. S. (2012). Introduction for the allostatic load; special issue. *Physiology & Behavior*, 106(1), 1–4. https://doi.org/10.1016/j.physbeh.2011.12.019

Putnam, F. W. (1989). Pierre Janet and modern views of dissociation. *Journal of Traumatic Stress*, 2, 413–429. https://doi.org/10.1002/jts.2490020406

Ramsay, D. S., & Woods, S. C. (2014). Clarifying the roles of homeostasis and allostasis in physiological regulation. *Psychological Review*, 121(2), 225–247. https://doi.org/10.1037/a0035942

Schimmenti, A., & Caretti, V. (2016). Linking the overwhelming with the unbearable: Developmental trauma, dissociation, and the disconnected self. *Psychoanalytic Psychology*, 33(1), 106–128. https://doi.org/10.1037/a0038019

Soffer-Dudek, N., & Theodor-Katz, N. (2022). Maladaptive Daydreaming: Epidemiological Data on a Newly Identified Syndrome. *Frontiers in Psychiatry*, 13, 871041. https://doi.org/10.3389/fpsyt.2022.871041

Sterling P, & Eyer J. (1988). Allostasis: A new paradigm to explain arousal pathology. S. Fisher, & J. T. Reason (Eds.), *Handbook of life stress, cognition, and health* (pp. 629–649). Chichester; New York: Wiley.

Sweet, P. L. (2019). The sociology of gaslighting. *American Sociological Review*, 84(5), 851–875. https://doi.org/10.1177/0003122419874843

Szabo, S., Yoshida, M., Filakovszky, J., & Juhasz, G. (2017). "Stress" is 80 years old: From Hans Selye Original Paper in 1936 to Recent Advances in GI Ulceration. *Current Pharmaceutical Design*, 23(27), 4029–4041. https://doi.org/10.2174/1381612823666170622110046

Van der Hart, O., & Horst, R. (1989). The dissociation theory of Pierre Janet. *Journal of Traumatic Stress*, 2, 397–412. https://doi.org/10.1007/BF00974598

World Health Organization. (2019). *ICD-11: International Classification of Diseases* (11th revision). Retrieved from https://icd.who.int/

Seven
Traumatization during Development

How is early brain development connected with dysfunction?

How to spot a traumatized child?

Can developmental arrest be reversed?

The term 'childhood trauma' has become extremely popular even though it lacks specificity. No childhood is perfect, no matter how idyllic—but even when difficult and adverse, childhood circumstances are not always traumatizing. Considering them traumatizing can distort our perception of our actual situation as well as the level of responsibility toward preserving our emotional health that we accept. Hopefully, the approach taken here could assist us in figuring out if someone's present struggles connect to damaging childhood circumstances, or not. They may be objectively damaging, but how much was inflicted by others, and how much of the struggle was prolonged by internal traumatizing agents? Finding out is key to resolving traumatization or healing the dysfunction. Accepting dysfunction in adulthood because of what parents did (or missed doing) to the child is continuing to give them the power. At some point, the adult needs to retake it and become responsible for their own well-being.

Since we just spent a full section on abuse, this chapter will focus on neglect as a traumatizing agent. Neglect leaves an invisible wound that, versus abuse, shows its effects years later. Growing up with adversity has a similar effect to being abused; the main difference is that abuse is inflicted, but growing up lacking privilege or safety is circumstantial and may not be the caregivers' direct wrongdoing. Nevertheless, it needs to be addressed and healed.

With the amount of research on child maltreatment, it has become evident and undeniable that children and adolescents experience high rates

DOI: 10.4324/9781003382478-10

of potentially traumatizing experiences at home, and that they are primed to suffer from developmental issues and irreversible alterations. Developmental Trauma Disorder (DTD) diagnosis has been offered as an option to the psychiatric community but unfortunately has not been made official yet (Spinazzola et al., 2021). Nevertheless, it has tremendous value. Identifying symptoms early on, before the damage stays as default, is close to my heart; it breaks every time parents accuse their children of being difficult or having been born problematic without seeing how they or their own struggles and circumstances may play a role in the kid's behavior. To close this gap, I'll start with a look at how a healthy brain develops as a foundation for understanding how interruptions to this development—due to lack of stimulation—can have consequences, as well as what those consequences look like.

The Babysitter: Mendo's 'Trauma'

I'm the youngest of three after Ronan, the oldest, and Mendo. If my parents are in a good mood, they would say I came six years after Mendo as a 'surprise'. When one of them is angry, I came as a 'mistake.' But being the only girl and so much younger than my brothers was worse than being thought of as a mistake. My parents made me feel like a real burden. I always had to take up as little space as possible to avoid upsetting them. From what I had gathered, I spent most of my early years in daycare or by myself. My father was working in a restaurant until 1 or 2 in the morning. My mother got a job soon after I was born to 'solve the weight' of having three children. Besides work, she dedicated a lot of time to her many friends and her appearance because "it was important for her job." So, even when her schedule was the same as my brothers' school, she didn't pick me up from daycare until hours later. But at the daycare, they loved me; they said I was a doll.

Dressing dolls

When I was little, my grandma came to visit and many times stayed over, slept in my room, and told me stories while caressing my hair or my back. She taught me how to cook, sing in Spanish, and make my t-shirts prettier with embroideries and appliqués. When I wore dresses to go to church with my abuela, just the two of us, she used to say I looked like a doll. Those were the best weekends I remember before she moved to California where one of my aunts lives. One Christmas when she wasn't with us, she sent me a doll as a gift. I never had one and I didn't know how to play with her. I didn't know how a mom plays with a daughter because my mom never played with me, so, I told her stories as my grandma did to me; I had to invent mine. My brothers played with me, though. I was their toy. They dressed me up often, especially for Halloween. I fondly remember one year when they dressed me like a ghost, all covered under a sheet. The ghost costume felt right to me; the experience of being able to see others while they couldn't see me felt…. really familiar.

My babysitters

When I was around five or six and started elementary school, my mom extended her hours at work because my brothers were old enough to babysit me. My 'babysitters' spent their afternoons playing outside with the neighbors rather than being with me. From early on, I learned how to entertain myself by drawing, daydreaming, reading, and doing homework. One time they had a soccer match and they left without preparing me dinner. I was starving! I took a package of cookies to my room with a glass of milk. I knew I wasn't supposed to eat in the bedroom, but my room was the place I felt safe. It was getting dark and the glass was still on my desk. As I rushed to the kitchen to wash it before my mom arrived, I tripped on the top stair. I think I tried harder to protect the glass than myself while rolling down. The glass broke anyway, scratching me everywhere and leaving a painful gash on my arm. I should have asked for help, but I was too afraid of being caught. I just went to my bed and pretended to be asleep. Nobody came home for hours. I learned much later that my mom was looking for Mendo and Ronan who had been in a fight with some older kids.

I had to wear a cast on my right arm for a long time. My mom was super mad at me when she saw my bloody sheets, ruined. She scolded me for being so clumsy and for disobeying her orders. She accused me of having done it on purpose to make her stay home. I was paralyzed, not knowing what to do. Still, my cast got a lot of attention at school. It was exciting how everyone wanted to draw something on it. I got a lot of pretty drawings that I wanted to protect, so I didn't shower for a couple of weeks. But then the kids were calling me 'skunky.' The nurse heard and took me to her office, and taught me how to shower without spoiling the cast. It wasn't that difficult but for whatever reason, I thought I had to keep my arm always close to my body. Everything went back to normal soon enough and kids forgot about it. My mom didn't. That month my grades went down because I couldn't do my homework and she spanked me so badly that it was hard to sit. The spanking hurt more than the fall. I think she was angry for some other reason since the spanking had never been as bad.

Even when my brothers should have been old enough to take care of me, Mendo, only a year younger than Ronan, needed more of a babysitter than me. He was the black sheep of the family "from the day he was born, and in the womb too." My grandma says that my mom had problems the whole pregnancy because she didn't want another baby. After 36 hours of labor, Mendo arrived prematurely, with some weird illness followed by a kidney infection, which kept him in the hospital for a couple of months. My mom had breastfed Ronan and planned to breastfeed Mendo, but because of the hospitalization, things got complicated. She got something called mastitis. Her milk turned rotten, and she was bedridden by the time Mendo got home from the hospital. My mom says that the infection in her breast was "more painful than giving birth and as painful as having a troubled son."

Mendo was always seen as a headache. His health was never good, and he was shorter and skinnier than most kids his age. He was always sick but was sent to school regardless because my mom didn't like to miss work. He was placed in a Special Ed classroom from kindergarten. I heard him say many times that he hated school because he was not like the other kids in his class. The other kids had more evident needs than him and he felt completely ignored by the teachers. His 'special needs' were his anger outbursts and his lack of concentration. He wasn't good at learning, couldn't control his energy, and had crazy reactions every time my mom or dad tried to discipline him. He could be scary. When he was angry he had the strength of a Viking. I remember he broke the door of his closet with his fist and headbutted a guitar. Thank God he was hardly home.

When I was around 9 or 10, things got worse. Mendo was doing poorly at school, as always, but my mom was called more often to the principal's office because he was cutting classes, bullying other kids, and making trouble in other ways I couldn't understand. I remember how much my mom hated it! Having to go to school and hear how bad her son was and receive threats about having to call the police. "As if telling me my son is messed up is going to make a difference. He's defective, what can I do? Do they expect me to keep him home just so they don't have to deal with him? Are they going to pay me my salary? As if he was the only fuckup they have to handle!" She kept nagging at my father. If I was not important before, after that I became completely inconsequential. All the attention was put on Mendo's bad behavior. Soon after I heard a horrible fight downstairs, everyone screaming, things crashing. Heard the door slam, and when I came down, Mendo had disappeared. Since I was always hiding away in my room, I don't really know what happened. Nobody told me where my brother was, or if he was coming back. I asked but everyone was mute. That's the only time in my life I've seen my father crying. I cried too. Not too long after, Ronan moved out of the house as well to go to college.

After Mendo left, I vowed to be the best-behaved daughter I could and to study as hard as possible for college exams. I was convinced that going to college would prove to my parents how much I loved them, and make them feel like they had been good parents.

Trauma Domain #7: Brain Development

Michaela didn't show clear evidence of developmental delays the way her brother Mendo did. From what his sister reports, Mendo suffered adversity from birth, most probably arresting his development. He showed less physical and mental capacity and abilities and had issues regulating his emotional reactions. Somehow all the issues present in the household were worse for him than for anyone else. In this part of the story, we can also start to see where the origin of Michaela's dissociation lies. For the full picture, let's learn more about how the brain develops or fails to do it.

Have you ever been close to a newborn? Has it not intrigued you why they are so undeveloped at the beginning, just spending several months sleeping, eating, evacuating, and oh yes, crying? Do you know why? The answer is pretty stupefying: because we are born 'too soon'—around 12 months too early—due to the lack of space in our carrier's womb (Bluestone, 2005) and because gravity pushes us to come out faster than if the uterus were hanging. And the crying? Well, because we are in pain and most of our functions hurt. Hunger, reflux, and even evacuating could feel excruciating. When we are born, we are neurologically immature and almost each one of our organs and the systems that regulate them are immature too, which means that every second, newborns' systems are struggling to keep them alive. Much of our brain's development has to happen outside our carrier in what many times is an inhospitable setting, and that's why traumatization at this phase is so consequential.

THE IMPORTANCE OF THE INITIAL YEARS

Even though the brain is capable of changing throughout the lifespan, what takes place during the first few years is what creates the foundation of what happens after (Tierney & Nelson, 2009). Before we are born, and for the first two to three years of our lives, brain development is largely gene-driven, meaning that it's already programmed. However, once the brain reaches the point where synapses are eliminated (synaptic pruning, which I'll explain soon), brain development will depend mostly on what we experience and the meaning that gets assigned to those experiences (Tierney & Nelson, 2009). Whatever we learn will stay as the basis of everything we become later. For example, the verbal sounds we hear and learn to identify will become the language we speak. You can take that literally and figuratively because it applies to everything else we absorb and repeat (until we decide to learn 'other languages' later on).

In terms of our mental health, the experiences from the first two to four years shape our perception, cognition, regulation, and emotionality which makes traumatization during those first few years so detrimental. If traumatization occurs early, the severity of the consequences is more connected to *when* it happens (and to whom) than to *the type* of traumatic occurrence or circumstances endured. In an immature system, the alterations caused by allostatic processes or the loss of internal equilibrium can have repercussions for life, medically and psychologically. It's heartbreaking to know that many of those alterations may not be able to get repaired and will cause permanent deficiencies if the development of the brain gets interrupted and surviving replaces growing. Depression, anxiety, and broken relationships are on the list of issues, and also diabetes and rheumatoid arthritis. That's why one of the main objectives of this book (and my professional career as a clinician) is to create awareness of the need not only for healing from full-blown trauma disorders but to interrupt/resolve traumatization timely to prevent suffering the consequences. The damage is correlated with how long the traumatization keeps running internally and how we become conditioned (or not) to respond. Our temperament combined with how we learn to react to stressful situations sets the way for our system to keep traumatizing itself—how long fear, defeat, and other traumatizing agents become the way we react automatically and constantly, depleting our health. When traumatization occurs in childhood, it is more difficult to have awareness of the hurt or to participate in resolving it. The brain makes certain assumptions about life that will stop the person from ever enjoying it. The adults are the ones capable of knowing how their kids are getting affected and intervening to stop the damage. When someone gets into therapy for DTD as an adult, the treatment would need to focus on catching up with the development that got interrupted when the traumatization re-routed it, affecting the natural maturation of physical, behavioral, cognitive, and emotional elements.

HOW THE BRAIN FORMS

The first year of our life is of growth. It's when our brain experiences an increase in its size, achieving 60% of the volume it will reach in adulthood. By age 5, our brain is the same size as our adult brain even though it won't achieve full maturation until our mid-twenties. Hence, those first years are crucial in terms of reaching the capacity to be fully functional and healthy for the rest of our lives, not only mentally but also physically. Our ANS's capacity to regulate begins in utero through the activity of its two branches that contributes to the development of the fetus (Cerritelli et al., 2021). Even when it has been suggested that traumatization can begin before we are born, it's not until several years of constant tension that the brain would suffer unresolvable modifications due to the reduction of many neural circuits and the alteration of their functions. Let's learn the different components that help our brain form.

Forming by Communicating between Neurons

The soft tissue that constitutes our brain includes gray and white matter, nerve cells, non-neuronal cells, and small blood vessels. Gray and white matter are made of neurons; the gray matter houses neurons' bodies and the white matter groups the neurons' axons, the long 'cable' where the electrical impulses travel away to connect with other neurons through synaptic connections. Neurons are responsible for communicating information in both chemical and electrical forms through the body. Electrical energy is generated in our brains to exchange chemicals between neurons to generate electricity. These billions of nerve impulses travel from neuron to neuron forming circuits that can process incoming information and carry out a response.

> I'm going to use an analogy between the way the brain works and spoken language to help clarify the information in this chapter. Let's picture synapses as essential for our brain communication as the alphabet is to create words.

Table 7.1 Brain waves

Name	Oscillation/Sec	Description
Delta	1 to 3–4 Hz	The slowest in frequency but carry larger amplitude (power); we experience them when we are sleeping. Unhealthy when areas of the brain function at this speed while awake
Theta	4–7 Hz	Slow connection (daydreaming, transitioning from sleeping to awake or under meditative states). Detrimental when areas of the brain lack participation in performing required tasks
Alpha	8–12 Hz	Used when relaxed, idle, and waiting for something to happen and being 'in the here and now.' Normally useful unless they stay constant and slow down some executive and motor functions.
Beta	13–38 Hz	Fast oscillations are associated with cognitive functions (concentration, assessment, calculations, energy, performance, and states of alertness). Above 20–24 Hz relate to stress, anxiety, excess energy (mania), paranoia, or states of hyper-arousal.
Gamma	40–60+ Hz	Less understood. Considered modulators of perception and states of consciousness; involved in peak performance and peak experiences; associated with higher brain functions like cognition and memory and with an improvement in working memory.

Brain Waves. The exchange of information through electrical pulses creates an oscillatory language that can be read as a rhythmic activity with a certain frequency ranging from one oscillation per second up to 100 and greater. This 'language' is called 'brain waves' and they are what makes the difference between a fast enough brain and a slow one. Speed has to do with how effectively we respond to stimuli, from running to learning. Brain waves receive names for better identification of their behavior and meaning, and are measured in hertz (oscillations per second). Table 7.1 describes them.

Brain waves represent the transmission of information from one set of neurons to another; when the same neurons connect in series, they create circuits.

Circuits. Functionally, circuits are considered *the fundamental units of our nervous system* (Martinez & Sprecher, 2020) because neurons never function in isolation. The connections that define a circuit comprise a closely packed bunch of neurons with certain processes, certain direction, and a specific function. Traumatization in childhood interrupts the formation of circuits, debilitates inborn ones, or makes them lose speed and power.

> If a synapse is a letter of the alphabet, brain waves are the sound of the letters, and circuits are the words.

Forming by Creating Circuits

The connectivity between circuits sets the tone for our mental health. When anatomical pathways, interactions, and communication between distinct units of the central nervous system (Pawela & Biswal, 2011) don't occur, there is incongruence between what we want to do and what we do. Imagine you want to forgive your offender but you feel intense hatred toward them after a simple thought of the offense. If both circuits connect, you may be able to achieve forgiveness (and coherence), but if they don't, you'll suffer polarization between the two. Traumatization causes a loss of connection between circuits and between networks. Brain connectivity is what allows us to explain how neurons and neural networks process information. Brain circuits create neural networks to make connectivity more efficient. Some neural networks are specifically built to perform a given or needed function, while others are already designed from birth. The survival mode turns off the connection among several networks losing connectivity or reinforcing some circuits that make life harder. Lack of connectivity causes dissociative experiences either by compartmentalization or by disengagement. A reduction in the number of neural networks causes issues in learning, cognitive performance, or any other function that lacks 'a program' to be performed.

> To continue building our brain language, think of connectivity as equivalent to sentences while neural networks are the grammar that makes them clear. That's why traumatized individuals can't make sense of many of their experiences. They lose coherence.

Forming by Chopping Off Useless Connections

This specific characteristic is extremely relevant to the subject matter of this chapter. At birth, our brains have around 15% more neurons than the number we have as adults. During our first seven to nine years, the connections between neurons (synapses) in a healthy brain increase to double their number, and most of the brain becomes connected (lighted up like a Christmas tree); that's why kids can learn several languages without a problem. During the following few years, the connections decrease fast all through adolescence (Feinberg, 2017) or early adulthood. That reduction in connections is due to the targeted elimination of functional synapses called *synaptic pruning* which starts as early as age 2. Do you remember that the brain is always trying to optimize space and energy consumption? Well, if certain connections (programs, functions, memories, etc.) are rarely or not used, this process will determine that those synapses are useless and, therefore, will eliminate them. This pruning optimizes the brain's energy consumption by prioritizing highly active connections or circuits, reinforcing and retaining them, and later on, myelinating them. The cost shows up when the kid is expected to perform certain tasks and stays behind because the circuits that could have assisted them were pruned.

Some of the processes of the immune system participate in the elimination of redundant or ineffective connections as if they were intruders that need to be combated. This process is key for brain development; the synapses that are eliminated may not ever be recovered (or will require a lot of effort in creating new connections through other processes that can compensate for the eliminated ones). If neurons are pruned, the circuits or networks they belonged to may get less active or disconnected. Neglect and adversity contribute largely to this process because the less engaged the kid, the more intense the pruning.

Myelination maintains the synapses that were not pruned connected, stronger, and faster. It is characterized by wrapping the axons of neurons with a highly specialized membrane called myelin—a fatty sheath and an important white matter—to insulate the neuron and make the transmission of electric current more efficient. It begins one to two months before birth and peaks within the first two years after birth but continues on subcortical and cortical structures until we get close to our third decade. Myelination is an indicator of the time it takes for the brain to mature cognitive functions. It is not absolutely required for neuronal functioning, and many axons normally remain unmyelinated throughout life by design, but most executive functions depend on myelinated neurons. Examples include many autonomic nerves, especially sympathetic ones, and more than half of the axons of the corpus callosum—the part that connects both brain hemispheres—which emphasizes its essential role in the communication between the different functions that belong to each side of the brain, and between cortical and subcortical areas. Many scans show that underdeveloped brains have a smaller volume than healthy ones.

TRAUMATIZATION DURING DEVELOPMENT: THE IRREVERSIBLE DAMAGE

Because of the enlisted characteristics of brain formation, when traumatization occurs while the brain is maturing, the brain has to assign priority to the allostatic and survival processes which compromise the processes in charge of growing. There are serious consequences at various levels.

Damage to Neurons and Brain Communication

The way neurons communicate and form circuits and networks is the foundation of how the brain performs its tasks. If myelination gets disrupted, brain connectivity is reduced, and, therefore, cognitive dysfunction, dissociated functions, reduced abilities, and failure at anticipating positive outcomes (among other issues) are probable consequences. Neuronal problems and lack of brain maturation affect all the areas mentioned in this book as trauma domains, especially because the development of the cortex gets compromised, and hence, so do executive functions. In a traumatized brain, the prefrontal cortex (PFC) slows down and communicates using low frequencies (Delta, Theta, and Alpha), while limbic areas like the insula and the amygdala work at a faster pace (High Beta) increasing reactivity and blocking many of the regulatory processes and many of the executive functions—crucial in the formation of the sense of self, learning, regulating emotional reactions, impulsivity, and a list of functions that may reach a hundred. Life can't be the same if those functions are not well developed.

Damage to Brain Structures

If there is a problem at the neuronal level, there will be problems in the structures that constitute the brain. In one way or another, some brain structures get affected by allostatic changes suffered during traumatization. The earlier the traumatization occurs, the higher the damage to brain functionality. When someone suffers from traumatization during development, almost every one of their brain structures will show some modifications; there are volume reductions in white and gray matter, particularly significant in the anterior cingulate cortex, PFC—especially the ventromedial PFC—the thalamus, hypothalamus, the insula, frontal gyrus, corpus callosum, and the amygdala (which stays hyperactive to detect the most insignificant stimulus as risk).

Having these types of alterations causes people to have difficulties making decisions for several reasons: they lack impulse control which makes them doubt their good judgment, they may have lost understanding of what others accept or disapprove of, and they could find it impossible to separate their emotionality from their actions. This happens because our brain makes decisions in one of two different ways:

1   an automatic, fast, and unconscious manner that handles several processes at the same time making associations to similar events without much care, and
2   a slow, analytical, reflective, and conscious one that takes care of only one process at a time.

When the brain is engaged in survival processes, it chooses the fast option because it may not have enough brainpower left to choose the reflective one, the one that needs the activation of the PFC. This means that the more complex processes that help someone to generate alternatives, self-reflect, empathize, etc., will not be practiced, if ever present.

Damage to Brain Chemistry

Our brain, as an electrochemical apparatus, uses two essential types of chemicals to communicate across synapses or between the brain and body: *neurotransmitters and hormones*. Neurotransmitters are produced or synthesized in the neurons, and hormones are originated by the glands. They are the chemical part of what regulates everything that is going on in our system, from our emotional states to our heart rate. With allostatic changes or after allostatic load, the production of chemicals in our system gets highly altered. Chemical alterations can distort all sorts of processes, from the perception of sensory information and memory encoding to our ability to sleep. Chronic activation of the HPA and SAM axes lowers life expectancy, decreases resilience, and is connected with many pathological processes such as chronic pain, immune, cardiovascular, and behavioral disorders, metabolic disease, depression, and other mental illnesses. It causes abnormal regulation of thyroid hormones, overproduction of norepinephrine, underproduction of serotonin, and elevated production of endogenous opioids; all of them participate in the regulation and integration of stress and fear responses.

It's interesting to notice the deregulated production of oxytocin. This hormone helps us bond and fall in love, and when there is a disruption in its production due to early traumatization, people experience problems forming personal attachments, are less selective about their needs, and may look to promiscuity as a way of producing the missing hormone.

You may remember that when there is a prolonged activation of the stress response, the stress hormones flood the system and become toxic. One of the most important chemical alterations suffered by childhood adversities and traumatic stress is long-term cortisol secretion. Cortisol influences memories of traumatic experiences—at formation or recall—by making them more prominent. In adults with a history of childhood traumatization, higher cortisol levels occur after exposure to traumatic reminders and contribute to re-traumatization. Cortisol also interferes with learning and memory, inhibits communication among neurons, lowers immune function, and may cause weight gain, high blood pressure, high cholesterol, and heart disease; insulin resistance and type 2 diabetes may also be a consequence together with Cushing's syndrome and a long list of medical issues.

Michaela had no learning disabilities, but her brother did. What she does show is emotional numbing, disconnection from pain, and a search for love and connection that may reflect changes in her chemistry. She was severely neglected emotionally, which could be guessed to be at the root of her hypo-activation. Let's learn about neglect and its consequences next.

Neglect and Adversity as External Traumatizing Agents

Some of you may have been horrified by the image of a five-year-old Michaela eating cookies as the meal of the day, her weeks without showering, or her sheets full of blood. Or maybe you were more distressed by the image of a mother scolding a girl with an unattended broken arm, or with the idea that a girl didn't know how to play with dolls. I know it horrifies me to see someone that identifies themselves as being a burden at such a young age. We are now able to understand Michaela better—her childhood story shows how a kid can experience neglect that doesn't look like the typical case of starvation or medical negligence but rather an extreme case of lack of attention to her needs. Her experience of neglect (and how it affected her) passed unnoticed. Was her experience of neglect traumatizing? Or just emotionally wounding? We saw that she qualifies for C-PTSD, but let's assess if her circumstances affected her development.

When the core human needs are not met, it's almost impossible to feel emotionally fulfilled. We need to belong, feel safe and useful to gain independence and reliance, to get satisfaction, connection, and stability. Primordially, we need to feel seen, understood, and cared for. That's why neglect is so damaging—it interrupts the possibility of meeting those needs and therefore attaining satisfaction and confidence.

It's common to find abuse and neglect packed together as one, especially in the research around PTSD. It's also common to find abuse and neglect as descriptors of 'childhood trauma,' pointed to as the factors that affect children's development. I chose to separate them because seeing them as one, ironically, neglects the neglected. Looking at neglect on its own helps us better understand the discrete consequences that it has on our nervous system.

Neglect affects our mental health differently than other types of maltreatment, and it is not necessarily inflicted together with abuse. Neglect could be seen as passive abuse though since it makes kids develop the belief they may not deserve more or better, and we know that the response of the brain to such a mental state is defeat. Neglect happens to adults too, but adults normally have a different type of relationship with neglect because they can compensate for it. Adults are capable of fulfilling some of the lacks themselves by hanging out with friends, traveling, working, shopping, etc. In an adult romantic relationship, for example, the disconnection of a neglectful partner is rarely traumatizing even when hurtful. But children, especially infants, have no way to compensate for neglect since the development of resources is cut off. Children have no other choice but to accept being ignored as if it was their fault. Let's look at traumatization during development more deeply using this point of view.

PROFILE OF NEGLECT

There are plenty of studies that confirm that life stressors can have a considerable impact on children's emotional, cognitive, social, and physical development, while at the same time, increasing the long-term risk of their mental health struggles (Glickman et al., 2021). According to data gathered by the U.S. Department of Health and Human Services, neglect is by far the most common form of child maltreatment in the US. One study found that 78.3% of child maltreatment victims suffered neglect; in 2012, over 2,200 children in the US died of abuse and neglect, with nearly 70% of those children dying because of neglect. In the US, the UK, and other developed countries, at least one in five youths experiences childhood adversities such as neglect (Elmore & Crouch, 2020). All these results come from studies that consider neglect encompassing the failure to provide for the basic needs of a minor under their care, including omission of emotional nourishment, rejection or apathy (emotional neglect), the supplying of material goods, withholding food or clothing (physical neglect), or the granting of services, depriving of education or medical attention (medical/educational neglect) to the child.

It has been found that emotional (psychological) neglect, specifically, causes poor development such as increased maladaptive behaviors, low self-esteem, low motivation, and psychopathology in adulthood (Kisely et al., 2018). The available numbers about neglect, in general, are alarming but not specific enough. It's obvious that a kid that doesn't receive enough food will be compromised, but it's not as easy to notice whether or not a child is loved. Child neglect is an act of omission, making it difficult to study or to notice the way abuse can be identified. Emotional neglect doesn't leave as many external signs—the child may not even know they are experiencing it and therefore, will not report it. As with everything else, what is considered neglect and how it affects children depend on each case. Some kids are perceived as 'neglected' because the caregiver works all day, but it's not the case if once they reunite, they receive lots of support and comfort; on the contrary, there are kids that spend the whole day with the caregiver and still are emotionally un-cared without anyone knowing. For children's development, *quality is more important than quantity*, and *connecting* is more important than *providing*. In terms of quality, some parents are great at giving the basics while neglecting the subtle needs, while others fail in providing the basics (some due to circumstances like poverty) but do offer many of the elements that help a kid feel relevant, loved, wanted, and acknowledged. *Still, is emotional neglect considered traumatic?* Let's start by investigating types of neglect and which ones could affect development.

Neglect could take many forms and can cause different levels of damage. It can be voluntary (abandonment, not accepting the role of the parent), circumstantial (poverty, too many kids at home), of omission (ignorance, illness of the caregiver), of commission (dislike of the kid, ignoring abuse), temporary (absence of care during a short period), or pervasive (addicted disconnected parent).

Physical and medical neglect are traumatizing because they put the life of the kid at risk, but emotional neglect is the type of neglect that can have a huge impact without a clear threat. Instead of suffering from allostatic changes promoted by recurrent intense stress, emotional neglect inflicts harm by promoting synaptic pruning. Note that emotional neglect in the first year of life adds to the stress of feeling abandoned, but I'll cover that in the next chapter. Here, I want to emphasize that the damage doesn't come from the overuse of the survival circuits but from the underuse of brain connectivity. Their brain areas may communicate using low frequencies, and their synapses may lack power (low voltage) which creates a whole set of challenges and insecurities that sooner or later will activate the survival circuits.

Emotional neglect is normally translated in the mind of the neglected as not being important enough or lacking value (worth)—with similar consequences to those from passive shaming. It is exercised by consistently disregarding, ignoring, or invalidating individuals' emotional needs by a significant other (Ludwig & Rostain, 2009). As a consequence, neglected kids develop difficulties understanding others' needs for love, affection, closeness, and support and may feel overwhelmed or powerless easily, incapable of meeting others' needs consistently (Ludwig & Rostain, 2009). They learn to 'speak' the language of dismissiveness, and therefore, their most viable choice may be to rely on themselves, almost feeling afraid of having needs or desires. There are cases of neglected kids that make a lot of noise or nag a lot to get attention but most shut down to play their role well (not bothering anyone). When they become adults, they may present extreme behaviors, like overextending themselves to please others, being 'loud'—in their laughs, tears, or 'fashion'—to be noticed or for sympathy, withdrawing from people, and appearing uncaring and indifferent, or becoming afraid of emotional closeness in intimate relationships (Ludwig & Rostain, 2009). Emotional neglect also impacts the development of a healthy sense of self and identity.

The individual characteristics of the child play a role, of course. We can see how some kids can't tolerate discomfort or inattention after being neglected, while others are by nature independent and can handle emotional difficulties by themselves. But yes, when a child's emotional needs are not met, that child will grow up having 'deficits' in their processes, and most importantly, they may feel insecure about who they are and what they deserve. It's common to see neglected people neglecting themselves and caring too much about others, hence, giving rise to a sense of injustice and imbalance that combine shame with suppressed anger and sadness, low self-esteem, lack of motivation/curiosity, and a long list of medical issues, from dental problems to severe chronic illnesses.

> When Mendo became a problem to his mother, Michaela was left to her own devices for food, learning, leisure, hygiene, etc., and abandoned almost daily. Feeling unimportant is hurtful, but feeling left behind and 'forgotten' adds another dimension to the neglect. Her account shows us that having her grandmother nearby when she was a baby, as well as her interaction with other people in daycare/school, allowed her to develop some resilience and agency in infancy. The extreme neglect came later, and maybe that's why her developmental issues are only of a certain type.

WHEN ADVERSITY MEANS TRAUMATIC STRESS

Adversity was not included as traumatic until a few years back. Adversity is considered a state of hardship, difficulty, or misfortune that one deals with; all the different types of abuse and neglect are now considered adverse to the healthy functioning of individuals. The Centers for Disease Control and Kaiser Permanente conducted a study on adversity during childhood in

Table 7.2 Adverse Childhood Experiences (ACEs)

1. Emotional abuse	2. Physical abuse	3. Sexual abuse
4. Emotional neglect	5. Physical/medical neglect	
6. Divorce	7. Domestic violence	8. Addiction
9. Mental illness	10. Incarceration	

the mid-1990s with a group of patients insured through Kaiser Permanente. The study—called the 'Adverse Childhood Experiences' (ACE) Study— evaluated the relationship between adult health, risk behaviors, and household dysfunction in childhood. The alarm went off when the mental health community noticed the connection between the study and traumatization during the early years of life, as they found a high correlation between adversity and abnormalities of several neurobiological systems that are implicated in the development of psychopathology. The study then became a symbol of the effects of traumatization in childhood. Basically, all the factors included in the study called 'adverse experiences' have the potential to contribute to traumatization, just not as absolute as we have been thinking. According to the study (Felitti et al., 1998), the negative effects of adversity multiply as the number of adverse circumstances increases but the study set clear parameters before something can be called adverse. An ACE was defined as undergoing, before age 18, any of the following circumstances (listed in Table 7.2) inside the house from a parent or other adult, and with *high frequency (often or very often)*.

As you can notice, the ten circumstances listed can be traumatic; the first five as child maltreatment and the following five relate to situations that can create constant stress and threat. Even though the ACE study was originally focused on the medical consequences of adversity, it discovered that the more adversity a person had experienced in childhood, the higher the medical problems, the worse the emotional struggles, and the lower the chances of survival due to the implication in the body and mind. For example, a high ACE score (4 or more) is associated with an increased risk for depression, multiple sexual partners and sexually transmitted diseases, the likelihood of attempted suicide across the lifespan, increased risk for broken bones, heart/ lung/liver disease, and multiple types of cancer. Please notice that the questionnaire asks for '*often or very often*' occurrences. Once in a while occurrences do not qualify as childhood adversity and should not be tabulated as such.

WHEN NEGLECT AND ADVERSITY BECOME TRAUMATIZING

Let me get back to *Is neglect traumatizing?* We all know neglect is hurtful, but it may be wise to hold judgment before assuming someone is traumatized from having had a neglectful upbringing, or because they report having been neglected. Emotional neglect most certainly causes developmental delays but it doesn't necessarily activate the survival circuits unless the neglect makes the kid feels at risk. The younger the child and the more severe or prolonged the neglect, the scarier the situation could feel. The perception of not having anyone around to assist them may trigger fear which most certainly initiates allostatic processes, causing delays similar to those caused by shame that could reach overload later in life. Yet, some kids don't feel afraid even when they are left alone to take care of themselves; many kids learn to manage their loneliness well, like Michaela.

An emotionally neglected kid may be easily considered traumatized based on the level of disconnection they exhibit: (a) some may be dissociated (after experiencing immobilization), while others (b) may be developmentally challenged (after an exaggerated neural pruning). Others, like Michaela—who 'escaped' to her room and her books, drawings, and dreams—(c) may use flight mechanisms to cope that may seem disconnected without being so.

There is a tendency to assume that dissociation is always a sign of autonomic dysregulation. As explained, it is not; furthermore, not everything that looks like dissociation is related to an excessive production of analgesics and lack of neural communication after the activation of survival circuits. It intrigued me for a long time to see people that seemed as having high levels of dissociation that didn't meet the criteria for a trauma disorder. Once I understood allostasis, it became clear that many individuals disengage or present dissociative symptoms without having reached allostatic load. Michaela is an example.

In terms of whether adversity is traumatizing, the first five adversities from the ACE study fall into abuse and neglect. I already explained when and how abuse and neglect can be traumatizing. The last five—parents' divorce or separation, domestic violence, addiction in the household, mental illness, or incarceration of one of the caregivers—are stressors that can make the child be and feel at risk, but not always. They may be traumatizing agents if the child is at risk or was conditioned to feel at risk, threatened, extremely insecure, or terrified. But divorce, for example, could mean recovering peace and safety, and the same goes for incarceration. DV, addiction, and mental illnesses in the household though may imply more stress in most cases.

No doubt that Michaela was seriously neglected. About the adversities at home, we know that the father had issues with the consumption of alcohol and anger, which Mendo also had. As far as we know now, besides her low self-esteem and her need to be loved, Michaela didn't show developmental issues or dysregulation as a child or a teen as Mendo did. Michaela's submissiveness may have been promoted by her temperament, by allostatic processes, or could be a marker of attachment or intergenerational trauma. We'll find out soon.

Conceptualizing Traumatization during Development

Mendo experienced traumatic events very early on: long labor, being born premature, being hospitalized at birth, etc. Due to his poor health at the beginning, and the way his mother treated him, his circumstances were unfavorable for his development. His health seemed to have improved even though his weight and height remained undeveloped, but his behavior showed a lack of emotional regulation very early. As a teenager, he had problems with impulsivity, anger, and other issues that pushed him away from his family and into extreme behaviors. Many people, including his parents, thought of his issues as genetic traits. This section will help us elucidate how that assumption may be incorrect since his behavior seems to be a clear sign of traumatization.

It has been said that members of families where children are maltreated often suffer from emotional disorders and addictions, or that they live in poverty, threatening conditions, oppression, or social isolation; lack of family cohesion in general. Some people call these unfortunate circumstances 'childhood trauma,' which could give the impression that every person without privilege would be traumatized. It's obvious that's not the case! Let's not forget that trauma refers more explicitly to the aftermath of a survival struggle and not only to misfortune, and to how the individual handles their resources during the struggle.

We saw how abuse clearly promotes fear, constant stress, and anxiety, and how its adaptive changes cause C-PTSD when the system reaches the allostatic load in adulthood. In this chapter, we are learning about brain development and neglect/adverse circumstances in childhood. Abuse during childhood has the exact same activation of survival circuits as in adulthood but the consequences are many times more detrimental because of the effect on the interruption of brain maturation. Neglect and adversity though are not as overwhelming or terror-provoking as most abuse. The lack of stimulation from neglect is detrimental because of the trimming of brain connectivity more than from the survival protections. Adverse circumstances though may put the kid on edge similar to abuse. Therefore, *the allostatic model* still applies to adversity with additional issues and deficiencies caused by the lack of connectivity after emotional neglect. Allostatic changes and/or extreme synaptic pruning in children affect brain structures' maturation and function formation independently of whether a full trauma disorder unfolds or not.

TRAUMATIZATION SYMPTOMS DURING DEVELOPMENT

Knowing about brain development is how we can best understand the high cost of its interruptions. A mature brain can respond much faster, is able to control impulsivity, and can regulate emotional responses in a way that was difficult before. It takes two and a half decades to achieve the level of maturity that gives us a sense of control over our thoughts, actions, and reactions, thanks to gaining the ability to reflect on their consequences. So, if this maturation gets hijacked by the constant activation of the stress response, interrupted by disconnected circuits, or deviated by allostatic changes, the capacity to manage impulses, mood, perception, learning, cognitive functions, etc., will decrease both in the present and in the future because the connection among areas becomes slower and deficient (or absent), and because the brain stays in a 'younger' state mentally and physiologically. This fact alone significantly affects the way one functions in society as well as how one perceives oneself. Consequences of the alterations range from developing symptoms that mirror those listed as ADHD, to physical and medical problems: from dyslexia to immune deficiency, from psoriasis to cancer, from lack of concentration to diabetes, and many more.

When a child goes through allostatic changes but doesn't reach allostatic load in childhood, their development is still compromised, only not fully. Assuming that the stressors or lack of stimulation stop at some point, many of the adaptive changes have the opportunity to revert to their original state, pruning will stop, and the development can continue its course. Neurons will branch out to create new synapses. If the brain recovers neuronal connectivity, generates enough internal resources, and receives appropriate support, the child's system could reach maturation in a timely fashion. Small disturbances can remain (low blood pressure, motor deficiencies, disorientation or clumsiness, bad memory, speech delay, insecurities, or reading problems), but normally the kid's brain learns to live with the small changes and keeps growing. More severe problems arise when the stressors or the pruning continue since there will be a point—as with complex traumatization—where the adaptive changes are too many or too constant, the lack of myelination too extreme, and hence, holding equilibrium becomes impossible. That's when the system of the child will shift into survival mode, affecting many more functions, and causing serious developmental delays and dysregulation issues similar to those covered under C-PTSD, only more acute or larger in number.

WHEN C-PTSD DIAGNOSIS GETS SHORT

Allostatic changes in childhood, plus excessive synaptic pruning, give rise to a more complex disorder than C-PTSD. Dr. Bessel Van der Kolk and his colleagues within the National Child Traumatic Stress Network came up with a diagnosis (Van der Kolk, et al., 2009) to give 'a home' (their words) to the traumatization a child experiences while developing, and offered full criteria to be used for this specific manifestation of PTSD under the name of DTD. By the way, we'd still be in the dark without Van der Kolk's contributions; most of the recent conceptualization of the trauma phenomena comes from him, his team, and those he has inspired to dig deeper and find scientifically valid results, as well as the many clinicians and thinkers he has given a forum to showcase their findings. Specifically, some members of the group have spent years doing research that demonstrates the DTD validity. DTD's symptoms. The proposed diagnosis overlap with—but extend beyond—those of PTSD; it asks for "children's exposure to a) interpersonal victimization and b) primary caregiver attachment disruption," and states that "these types of childhood adversity are more closely related to the complex symptoms involved in DTD than to PTSD" (Spinazzola et al., 2018). DTD includes the effects of attachment ruptures, which is completely understandable to be packed together. Still, in my view, the aftermath of traumatization during development and after attachment failure can be separated into two different syndromes. I dedicate the next chapter to attachment issues to show their differences. The DTD proposition had to be all-encompassing to increase the chances of making it into the DSM, but more specificity in terms of symptom clusters will always help in better designing interventions.

The proposed DTD diagnosis criteria (Ford et al., 2013) list the first criterion as

> lifetime contemporaneous exposure to both types of developmental trauma: A1. interpersonal victimization: victim of or witness to physical or sexual assault or abuse, or witness to domestic/adult intimate partner violence; and A2. primary caregiver attachment disruption: prolonged separation from or neglect or verbal/emotional abuse by a primary caregiver.

It also includes three clusters of symptoms:

• current emotion or somatic dysregulation;
• current attentional or behavioral dysregulation;
• current relational- or self-dysregulation.

You can find the full DTD criteria in Appendix C as a reference while assessing for developmental symptoms.

CONCEPTUALIZING DEVELOPMENTAL TRAUMA USING A BIO-PSYCHO-SOCIAL MODEL

Our maturation is hierarchical. Our functions grow sequentially, some having priority over others. Development takes long and happens in stages, and therefore, developmental delays can be of a different kind depending on whether traumatization is continuous (affected in every developmental stage) or temporary (only in one or two stages). When the toxic stress is short-term and is followed by periods of calmness, play, and curiosity, the child may not show signs of dysfunction even when some seeds might have been planted that could germinate years later. That's why it's a good exercise to recognize areas where the child may have suffered delays and those where the kid thrived before jumping into the catastrophizing idea that they suffer DTD because they grew up in adversity. Each developmental stage has specific milestones and tasks. Connectivity peaks in the second year of our lives and those first two to three years are crucial for most functions of the system that range from moving and talking to reasoning and regulating. To observe— and identify—whether a person has developmental issues, we could cross-check their life with the developmental milestones for each age. I'm using Erik Erikson's model (1968) for how we develop in stages influenced by biological, psychological, and social factors that provide and require different

Table 7.3 Erikson's developmental stages and issues of underdevelopment

Stage	Age	Normal Development	Developmental Issues
I. Trust versus Mistrust	0–o 1.5	motor functions, walking and communicating; learn to play, recognize objects, sort shapes and colors, and follow two-step instructions.	Brain development issues; may be clumsy, unempathetic, uncoordinated, and could develop dyslexia
II. Autonomy versus Shame/Doubt	1.5–3	learn to climb, run, pedal, express a range of emotions, learn to dress themselves, take turns, use pronouns, name familiar things, compare sizes, use imagination to fantasize, follow three-step instructions, and understand past tense and time (night/day).	language issues, difficulty forming sentences, separation anxiety, lack of interest in interactive games, poor imagination, problems playing with others, avoiding eye contact, and many problems with motor skills.
III. Autonomy versus Guilt	3–6	Use utensils, differentiate real from pretend, become social, use full sentences, learn to write, like independence, can express feelings, and can pay attention for longer.	could result in showing little interest in school or learning, withdrawn, worried or depressed, lack of engagement, show inappropriate or challenging behavior, have problems following simple directions, and may have difficulties falling or staying asleep.

(Continued)

Table 7.3 (Continued)

Stage	Age	Normal Development	Developmental Issues
IV. Industry versus Inferiority	6–12	understand the concept of numbers and math, differentiate right from left hands, develop fine motor skills (drawing), can count backward, understand fractions, create coherent narratives, develop social skills to be liked, cooperate and share, and develop agency. From 5 to 8, they have a vivid imagination; they stop being ego-centric by 7.	Lack of interest in how the world works, their appearance and physical performance may be delayed, causing embarrassment and self-consciousness. Stay behind intellectually may become evident at this age range, as well as their lack of capacity to concentrate. They may continue being egocentric and entitled.
V. Identity versus Identity Confusion	12–19	Mood varies, peers are more important than parents, they develop a strong sense of right and wrong, and develop more abstract thinking. On a quest to become independent and have their voice.	accepting parents' values without questioning show a delay in development; dependent or angry, rebellious, apathetic, isolated, disorganized, or confused; can foreclose the development of their identity and mirror the identity of someone else.

types of resources (Orenstein & Lewis, 2021). Erikson suffered several adverse circumstances as a child that affected his identity and sense of self—and influenced his interest in psychology and children's development. In his theory, he includes two opposing psychological tendencies for each stage, one positive and one negative, and the consequence of achieving or failing each stage. He proposes eight stages from birth to old age; Table 7.3 shows the first six (Orenstein & Lewis, 2021) as a framework to expand on how traumatization can affect development. Some of the milestones that are not achieved on time show later as deficiencies if they are not attended to and overcome.

THE VALUE OF SPOTTING A TRAUMATIZED CHILD EARLY

This book is about working with adults, but if we spot a kid going through traumatization early on, we can avoid a lot of pain. Kids don't ask anyone to take them to therapy. They only get there when the caregiver finds it difficult to deal with them. Also, children are not good at describing their symptoms and it's the adult's job to spot a traumatized child and to help resolve the distress they are experiencing. There are several indicators of when a child has already serious alterations in their nervous system besides the obvious extreme disengagement or hyperactivity. An important indicator is observing how the child manages their emotions. *Is the child aggressive and easily enraged? Or the opposite, very passive? Are their reactions congruent with the situation?* Here, I'm including some pointers to help you recognize children's level of traumatization:

–   **Tolerance.** The level of tolerance for their emotional reactions is a useful way to measure traumatization in children. From early on, it is possible to detect whether the kid can tolerate their emotional states. Many kids can show ups and downs in the mood without causing difficulties, while others getting angry means screaming, kicking, and breaking stuff, or they get sad and immediately lose the desire to live.
–   **Fear.** Extreme fear can be an indicator of an overactive amygdala that is looking for threats all the time. This shows when their reactions are not congruent with the level of risk—for example, they startle very easily, or their responses seem extreme.
–   **Self-soothing.** Not having the capacity to self-soothe is also observed in traumatized kids, attributed to low production of oxytocin. Oxytocin is released in response to low-intensity stimulation of the skin, like soft

touch, stroking, warmth, and suckling, and when kids lack this type of interaction with adults, they may have low production of this particular hormone, one that is so necessary to bond and feel loved. This deficit sometimes manifests as an exaggerated consumption of food, masturbation, self-cutting, or extreme ways to find alleviation for psychological pain.

– **Unexpected behavior.** The kid's system goes into immobilization often— for example, to neutralize aggression—shutting down emotionally. They may become extremely passive, disengaged, avoidant of interactions with other kids or games, and have unusual behavior in unfamiliar environments. It could also be the case that they become rageful and uncontrollable in an instant. Examples go from wetting the bed if they sleep in an unfamiliar place, eating food of only one color, to throwing inconsolable tantrums. It's common to observe learning disabilities and delayed physical development with mannerisms not comparable to kids the same age.

– **PTSD symptoms.** Children with developmental issues that suffer from a noticeably traumatizing event show PTSD symptoms right away. The DSM-5-TR includes specific PTSD criteria for children six years of age or under. The main difference is that criterion A has been modified to include exposure to

> actual or threatened death, serious injury, or sexual violation by direct experience, or by witnessing the events as they occurred to others, especially primary caregivers, and finally, by learning that the traumatic events occurred to a parent or caregiving figure.

Suffering traumatization during development could damage a child in irreparable ways, so damaging that it could reach their spirit, compromising the development not only of their brain and system but also of their capacity to love or connect.

References

Bluestone, C. D. (2005). Humans are born too soon: Impact on pediatric otolaryngology. *International Journal of Pediatric Otorhinolaryngology*, 69(1), 1–8. https://doi.org/10.1016/j.ijporl.2004.07.021

Cerritelli, F., Frasch, M. G., Antonelli, M. C., Viglione, C., Vecchi, S., Chiera, M., & Manzotti, A. (2021). A review on the vagus nerve and autonomic nervous system during fetal development: Searching for critical windows. *Frontiers in Neuroscience*, 15, 721605. https://doi.org/10.3389/fnins.2021.721605

Elmore, A. L., & Crouch, E. (2020). The association of adverse childhood experiences with anxiety and depression for children and youth, 8 to 17 years of age. *Academic Pediatrics*, 20, 600–608. https://doi.org/10.1016/j.acap.2020.02.012

Erikson, E. H. (1968). *Identity: Youth and crisis.* New York: W. W. Norton Company.

Feinberg, I. (2017). Why is synaptic pruning important for the developing brain? *Neuroscience. Scientific American.* https://doi.org/10.1038/scientific americanmind0517-75

Felitti, V. J., Anda, R. F., Nordenberg, D., Williamson, D. F., Spitz, A. M., Edwards, V., Koss, M. P., & Marks, J. S. (1998). Relationship of childhood abuse and household dysfunction to many of the leading causes of death in adults. The Adverse Childhood Experiences (ACE) Study. *American Journal of Preventive Medicine*, 14(4), 245–258. https://doi.org/10.1016/s0749-3797(98)00017-8

Ford, J. D., Grasso, D., Greene, C., Levine, J., Spinazzola, J., & Van der Kolk, B. (2013). Clinical significance of a proposed developmental trauma disorder diagnosis: Results of an international survey of clinicians. *Journal of Clinical Psychiatry*, 74(8), 841–849.

Glickman, E. A., Choi, K. W., Lussier, A. A., Smith, B. J., & Dunn, E. C. (2021). Childhood emotional neglect and adolescent depression: Assessing the protective role of peer social support in a longitudinal birth cohort. *Frontiers in Psychiatry*, 12, 681176. https://doi.org/10.3389/fpsyt.2021.681176

Kisely, S., Abajobir, A. A., Mills, R., Strathearn, L., Clavarino, A., & Najman, J. M. (2018). Child maltreatment and mental health problems in adulthood: Birth cohort study. *British Journal of Psychiatry*, 213, 698–703. https://doi.org/10.1192/bjp.2018.207

Ludwig, S., & Rostain, A. (2009). Family function and dysfunction. *Developmental-Behavioral Pediatrics.* 103–118. https://doi.org/10.1016/B978-1-4160-3370-7.00010-9

Martinez, P., & Sprecher, S.G. (2020). Of circuits and brains: The origin and diversification of neural architectures. *Frontiers in Ecology and Evolution.* 8. https://doi.org/10.3389/fevo.2020.00082

Orenstein, G. A., & Lewis, L. (2021). Eriksons stages of psychosocial development. *StatPearls* [Internet]. Treasure Island, FL: StatPearls Publishing.

Pawela, C., & Biswal, B. (2011). Brain connectivity: A new journal emerges. *Brain Connectivity*, 1(1), 1–2. https://doi.org/10.1089/brain.2011.0020

Spinazzola, J., Van der Kolk, B., & Ford, J. D. (2018). When nowhere is safe: Interpersonal trauma and attachment adversity as antecedents of posttraumatic stress disorder and developmental trauma disorder. *Journal of Traumatic Stress*, 31, 631–642. https://doi.org/10.1002/jts.22320

Spinazzola, J., Van der Kolk, B., & Ford, J. D. (2021). Developmental trauma disorder: A legacy of attachment trauma in victimized children. *Journal of Traumatic Stress*, 34(4), 711–720. https://doi.org/10.1002/jts.22697

Tierney, A. L., & Nelson, C. A., 3rd (2009). Brain development and the role of experience in the early years. *Zero to Three*, 30(2), 9–13.

Van Der Kolk, B., Ford, J. D., & Spinazzola, J. (2009). Comorbidity of developmental trauma disorder (DTD) and post-traumatic stress disorder: Findings from the DTD field trial. *European Journal of Psychotraumatology*, 10(1), 1562841. https://doi.org/10.1080/20008198.2018.1562841

Eight
Traumatization by Failing to Attach

Is 'insecure' attachment traumatizing?

What does it mean failing to attach and when is attachment traumatizing?

What's the origin of disorganized attachment?

At no point in our lives is creating a bond with another person as essential as in our first year. Without that bond, we could face 'death' not only as a feeling but as a fact. When attaching to someone fails, the baby will grow up feeling at risk and with a sense of loneliness that may be hard to explain. In this chapter, I'll share the view that there is no other psychological wound quite like the one that results from not finding reciprocity in the innate need to connect with someone reliable when we arrive into the world.

While 'attachment trauma' is a term sometimes used to refer to the rupture of the bond between two individuals like parent/child or couples, for the matter of this book, I am specific about the attachment wounds and use 'attachment traumatization' when referring to *the mental and physical deterioration suffered from not finding someone to attach to when attachment feels like a life-or-death endeavor*. Attachment traumatization can actually be described as two different possible injuries:

1 Unresolved attachment: an injury that may be equivalent to a singular, recognizable incident that happens around the moment of birth (the shock of birth, lack of connection and reciprocity in the connection, and/or rejection) potentially starting in the uterus, and
2 Attachment rupture: the injury of feeling being left alone that could be prolonged and repeated, stressing the infant due to feeling abandoned, unimportant, or alone or alone at finding solace to their needs.

DOI: 10.4324/9781003382478-11

Each one of those two can happen without the other and can hurt the infant, but when combined, they leave an indelible mark. This chapter will present the most relevant findings from attachment theory pointing to attachment difficulties but mainly focusing on unveiling on how failing to attach can lead to symptoms that are not comparable to the ones from other trauma syndromes.

The Mother: Clara's 'Trauma'

My mother, Clara, was 17 when she, my grandma, and her two sisters had to move to the States. It was a tragic move. Tragic for everything that tragic implies and tragic for what it did to my mom. It started with the death of her father. My grandfather had an important position in the government that kept him absent from domestic life. He was busy dealing with the issues that the paramilitary dominance had caused in the country, including the displacement of millions of people. After a new constitution was adopted in 1991 to make Colombia a multi-ethnic and multicultural state that provisioned rights for minority groups such as the indigenous and the Afro-Colombians, her father had to visit the outskirts of Bogota where minority groups from the countryside had occupied the land. There was a protest and the military had to intervene, causing several civilian deaths.

Her father was made responsible for the revolt. He was already a target of the paramilitary that wanted to keep the poor serving the guerrillas, a group opposed to what he was trying to achieve. Now he was a target of the government that wanted to clear their involvement by putting the blame on him for 'breaking the laws of the new constitution.' He was not only fighting for his job and his freedom but kept receiving threats of all sorts that put the whole family in crisis. My mom and sisters stopped going to school and couldn't leave the house, not even to go to the church services that meant so much to them.

Not too long after, my grandfather was assassinated one afternoon while he sat in his car waiting for a green light. I imagined what my mother felt when she saw that image of her father riddled with bullet wounds, the fear she experienced before the assassination, and the overwhelming emotions after. My grandma always talks about it in tears and trembling. Those were difficult times in Colombia. It was the same year Pablo Escobar surrendered to the authorities. The government was trying to clean up the country and some people had to pay the price for breaking the status quo. My family paid a high one.

My grandma's brother had moved to New York years back to attend engineering school and offered to help her move out of Colombia, where her life and the life of her daughters were still at risk, and her name was tainted by gossip and accusations. My uncle was doing well, but in NYC nobody has space for a woman with 3 daughters. So, they had to live in an extremely modest place. My grandma found a job as an interpreter thanks to being trilingual and enrolled my mom and sisters in the public school in the area right away. It was a big change from attending an all-girls catholic school with a uniform dress code to a liberal mixed-gender school where everyone "seemed to do whatever they wanted." I can't imagine how difficult it must have been for my mom to leave everything behind. My mom hated her new life. My grandma says that she didn't only lose her husband but also her older daughter; she said Clara became bitter and unrecognizable. Because of my grandma's job, my mom had to watch her sisters, which she accepted with fury; she rebelled against everything, including school (which she used to love) and soon started cutting classes to have adventures around the city. In one of those escapades, she met my father.

Chris was the man that showed her Manhattan's best pizza and burger places, Madison Square Garden, and Central Park. He "seduced her" and got her pregnant the first time they had sex, or that's what they say. My mom says she gave Chris her virginity because she was "in love" (she later said she meant 'attracted' joking that the only good thing about my father were his looks). My uncle had to intervene after my grandma's request, threatening Chris and demanding he marry Clara. Since Chris's mother was a devoted Catholic, she also agreed they had to marry. I wish my grandma had thought about how bad of an idea marriage was for my mom. Chris was already 30 and had not done much in his life besides changing jobs often and getting in trouble. He had never had a serious relationship but had many non-serious ones, and drank heavily. But they married anyway in a rushed visit to the city clerk's office. Chris moved in with them because my grandma had to continue working and my youngest aunt was only 14. My mom had two babies before my youngest aunt was ready to leave for college.

After her youngest sister moved out, my mom moved to their own place. It was then that my mom says that my father became an abomination: drunk every day, abusive, with frequent angry outbursts, throwing objects at her, punching walls, locking her down in the basement, and even hitting my brothers. She says she had to call 911 and had him arrested twice. Once it became unbearable and she had a steady job, she was ready to leave him when she got pregnant with me. It's my fault she had to stay, or that's what I've been told.

But staying married made her bitter and miserable, always focusing on what she didn't have or could have had instead of noticing what she had. She doesn't seem to notice how much I have loved her all my life. She only sees me as a reason behind her entrapment. It still hurts me to remember how poorly she treated me as a child, how she seemed to dislike me, telling hurtful untruths like "you have the big nose of your father's Neapolitan mother" or "you have the butt of a Cuban" making it sound like a curse to look like me. I was very ashamed of my looks for years until guys started complimenting me. I think she just wanted to look down at my father's background without realizing it hurt me. My mom sees everything about my father as bad or negative. She calls him "the Yankee" and says he is all the bad things that America has to offer.

I feel for her pain and have always tried to give her reasons to be happier and to give her a reason to be proud, but I have always failed.

That's why I worked so hard to be a good daughter, to make up for her perception of me. Until, well, some stuff happened. I know my mom would have rejected me if she knew certain things about my behavior so it was better to say nothing. She couldn't handle knowing–the disappointment would be too big, and she'd stop talking to me forever. I hope I can still make her happy. I hope she'll love me back someday.

Trauma Domain #8: Attachment

Learning about Clara gives us insight into how Michaela's and Mendo's psychological wounds and physiological injuries might be deeper than we thought. It seems as though their mother was not really into them, and worse yet, she blamed them for her misery, which is a form of passive shaming, rejection, and guilt-inducing. She was absent not only physically but emotionally, unfortunately suffering from her unresolved traumatization issues, which caused more damage to her children than she could realize. Let's see in which ways they got hurt.

Attachment is 100% connected to survival, and consequently, to traumatization. The subject of attachment has become really popular, with more written on it in the last decade than in the previous 50 years. Its trendiness can perhaps be ascribed to the 'revelation' that how we attach to our 'mother' is how we attach as adults. Needless to say, our adult relationships are at the core of our lives and our well-being. But while, yes, relationships are extremely important, attachment theory is about the bond with our caregiver and the traumatizing effect of not having it. Hence, what I'll be describing in this chapter deals with the ways in which not attaching in a constant and permanent way to one's caregiver may affect our overall mental health for the rest of our life (and not just how we relate). The attachment that concerns traumatization starts at birth—or perhaps in the uterus—and deals with having one's basic needs taken care of in order to achieve an internal sense of being safe. Not having an attachment figure we trust could be the root of all our romantic problems, the reason some of us hate our bosses, or why we can't live without our therapist, but mainly, it could be the root of having a dysregulated nervous system from the get-go. To cover attachment as a trauma domain, I will include an overview of functional attachment—and attachment styles—as a foundation for understanding what is and isn't traumatization springing from attachment issues.

WHY THE BOND BETWEEN BABY AND CARRIER/CAREGIVER IS ESSENTIAL?

The months we should have stayed in the womb—but didn't—explain not only how important the first year of brain development is, but also why not having someone taking care of the frail newborn is a matter of life or death. Our immaturity also explains why helplessness is not *learned* as it was previously thought, but *a default response* in humans. As babies, we are completely dependent on our caregivers to provide for every need we have for survival, as well as for finishing what should have happened when we were in the uterus. Simply put, we are born very fragile physically and psychologically—so we fear by default. You may find it interesting to learn that it takes more than six months for the baby to recognize its own body, and almost a year and a half to develop reflective self-awareness—as in recognizing their image in a mirror (Brownell et al., 2007)—but they recognize their main caregiver before they recognize themselves. Even though we are essentially born 'legally blind,' we can still recognize our main caregiver's face just a few days after birth. Also, the attachment figure will be helping form the baby's brain; baby's brains are like a box with goo that gets molded to whatever shape the actions and information of those around them define—principally the main caregiver (or whoever is playing the role of the reliable presence). So, you can see how important it is to understand the relationship between the baby, the bond, and the caregiver; that's what attachment studies are about. The reality is, in the world we live in now, many caregivers can't afford to accept or fulfill the job of helping the baby complete its development by staying as close to them as they were to the fetus (so: very close), and therefore, attachment issues abound.

By the way, I'm using the term carrier or caregiver instead of using 'mother' because not all babies are taken care of by a woman, by the person that gives birth, or by someone that is biologically related. Still, it's difficult to talk about attachment without a 'mother' because attachment starts before birth. A carrier is an individual that hosts the baby in their uterus for around 40 weeks. Even if that person is a surrogate 'mother' and the baby's genetic information is not the same as hers, the attachment may be the same as if they were biologically related. This is important because adoptive or foster parents—and even parents that use a surrogate carrier—might want to contemplate the attachment difficulties that the baby will go through at the moment of separation. Once the baby is born, the 'mother' becomes whoever is the principal person that provides safety and makes sure that the needs of the baby are met. It's not clear, but in circumstances where there is a surrogate carrier, it seems that the baby is able to recognize that they (the carrier and the caregiver) are not the same, which is worth considering, too, because the baby may need even more care and closeness from the caregiver to gain confidence; care of all sorts has to be in place for the baby to form a strong bond and trust in who they will identify as the attachment figure.

While attachment in our first years is very much dependent on the caregiver, attachment, in general, should not be confused with dependency. As a clinician, I have noticed that many adults that are looking for attachment figures—many times in the clinician—are looking for someone they can become *dependent on*, more than someone *dependable*. Attachment relates to *the need for connection, a link to a reliable person, and non-verbal communication that finds reciprocity and provides certainty and confidence in regular and extraordinary situations*. Dependency nullifies agency, whereas *reliability* promotes it.

WHAT HAS BEEN THEORIZED ABOUT ATTACHMENT

We know all about the connection between infants and caregivers, thanks to attachment theory which started developing in the 1950s by John Bowlby, a British psychologist, psychiatrist, and psychoanalyst who dedicated most of his life to studying the relationship between babies and mothers—perhaps because of his attachment issues due to the unavailability of his parents and the hostile nannies he had to rely on as caretakers. Many scholars have been interested and fascinated with the subject of how the mother influences the baby's brain since Bowlby's findings. Attachment theory is not only one theory since revisions and additions from different authors have been made to the original proposal but it's almost presented as a single vision.

Even when many attribute Sandor Ferenczi (1917) as a precursor of Bowlby, he has not received much credit. He was already writing about how the infant's relationship with the mother determines the formation of their personality in adult life and how the psyche develops in terms of that relationship almost 40 years before Bowlby. Melanie Klein—who was psychoanalyzed by Ferenczi for five years—became the primary figure in the development of a theory (Object Relations) that suggested that pre-verbal anxiety begins with the formation of the unconscious, resulting in the splitting of the world into good and bad based on the idealized mother (Hernandez-Halton, 2015).

John Bowlby contributed to what had been written by Klein proposing that behavioral problems, as well as mental health issues, are rooted in a problematic early childhood and a lack of trustworthy attachment figures.

His curiosity while working in a children's psychiatric unit during WWII helped him to realize that when kids were separated from their mothers, they showed different ways of reacting. Based on those observations, he created the 'strange situation' task (SSP), which became the gold standard for identifying and classifying individual differences in how secure or insecure the infant attaches to the parent (Cassidy et al., 2013). The SSP became a formal procedure when Bowly started a collaboration with Mary Ainsworth in the 1970s. Ainsworth translated Bowlby's theories from observations into a workable theory supported by a more rigorous research methodology which contributed to making the theory more scientific.

Bowlby (and several others) believed that our brain counts on an innate 'attachment system' that serves two primary functions: to protect us from potential threats of harm, and to regulate negative emotions following threatening or harmful events (Simpson & Beckes, 2017). His theory proposes that this system is a three-phase process that becomes evident when a child is separated from the caregiver: protest, despair, and avoidance/detachment. Notice how his description follows the sequence of the survival protections: protest corresponds to anger/fight, despair to either flee or submit, and detachment to dissociation during tonic and collapse immobility. This comes as no surprise if we are saying that the baby's survival depends on its proximity to the reliable attachment figure; if the mother leaves, the kid feels stressed and the survival circuits get activated. The studies show that if the caregiver comes back 'soon enough,' most kids return to baseline, while others won't recover as easily, and that if the separation is constant and/or prolonged, the kid will stay in the state of defeat that characterizes dysregulation. Bowlby basically observed that for an infant, the separation from the caregiver could be traumatizing. The stress here is not abuse, but the feeling of abandonment and the fear of being left with a stranger.

Peter Fonagy, a psychoanalyst and clinical psychologist who has occupied several key leadership positions in internationally recognized organizations, has significantly contributed to expanding attachment theory. He has theorized that the ability to make and use mental representations of their own and other people's emotional states (mentalize) and to regulate affect can determine an individual's successful development. He states that bad and insufficient parenting can leave children unable to modulate and interpret their feelings, as well as the feelings of others (Fonagy et al., 2002). His proposal on mentalization offers not only a theoretical view but also clinical applications, providing interventions to help people with attachment issues with a particular emphasis on individuals suffering from Borderline PD.

One of the main conclusions we can see from reviewing all the attachment studies has to do with the style children develop if they don't feel securely connected to the caregiver: anxious, avoidant, or disorganized. Let's look at each style individually.

ATTACHMENT STYLES: KIDS PAIN WHEN SEPARATING FROM THE CAREGIVER

Mary Ainsworth came up with a rating system based on infants' behavior during the SSP experiments. She observed three categories: secure attachment, anxious-avoidant attachment, and anxious-resistant attachment. The goal for a baby in attaching to someone is to attain enough trust in the reliability of that person to grow healthy and independent (stress-free). When a caregiver can satisfy the needs of the baby and convey (normally non-verbally) their reliability through their attention, love, and care, the baby gains enough confidence to *attach securely* to many individuals throughout their life. If the kid is not able to get that trust, they attach anyway, but *insecurely*. The main observations about the different styles can be explained as follows:

Securely attached: As infants, those with secure attachment feel free to explore and use their curiosity to engage with the world and learn from it, which foments healthy development. These infants don't cry much and are content-exploring, while the caregiver is present or absent. In a safe environment, newborns learn to tolerate hunger, loneliness, discomfort, and fatigue because they 'know' they'll be relieved. That creates trust, patience, tolerance, and resiliency.

Insecurely attached: A kid is insecurely attached when their brain anticipates that the caregiver may not be there to relieve them from pain, cold, hunger, etc.; emotional responses take over then in two ways, which are both different manifestations of fearfulness:

1   **Anxious/Ambivalent.** Making sure the caregiver responds by crying and protesting inconsolably and by grasping at the caregiver at all times, or

2   **Anxious/Avoidant/Resistant.** Avoid getting too close to evade the pain of separation by becoming angry, aloof, distant, and unresponsive to the caregiver's affection.

These styles have been proposed as constant during a person's lifespan, but later studies have largely questioned the constancy. Through my observations,

I have noticed that, yes, many people show a more predominant attachment style, but also, that kids learn to attach differently to other people who aren't the caregiver. We are always looking for people we can attach securely to. The need for attachment is hardwired and the need stays through our lives; what I mean is that we don't only attach once and our brain is always learning. We need people with whom we can feel confident and relaxed (a good provider, a trustworthy friend, a reliable partner, an honest financial advisor, etc.) with whom developing closeness won't end up hurting. Therefore, the attachment style we establish depends mostly on how we perceive the reliability of each specific individual, and once someone learns to trust a specific person, they can attach securely (at least to that person) even if they developed an insecure attachment to the main caregiver.

A third type of insecure attachment was added: disorganized attachment. Disorganized attachment shows pathology, and, therefore, needs to be treated differently. Sometime later on in the research of the SSP, Mary Main, an American psychologist and one of Ainsworth's first doctoral students from the University of California Berkeley, noticed that some babies were impossible to classify in terms of 'style' for their attachment; they had virtually no strategy of responding when their caregiver re-entered the space but instead exhibited a pattern of strange push-pull and freezing behavior. This was a very important observation for reasons that will become clear later. Main termed this behavior 'disorganized-disoriented' attachment. In relation to trauma studies, this last one is the category that shows the damage from the effects of having an unreliable caregiver.

Just as a parenthesis, I want to mention that critics of attachment theory have noted, first, that early studies lacked generalization; most of them were mainly conducted with babies and their mothers (heteronormative subjects) without observing the attachment to others around. Second, it has also been said recently that it is common to observe one attachment style toward one parent and a different one toward the other parent. Third, measures of attachment security, particularly those that observe caregiver behavior, are biased toward Western ways of thinking, letting cultural values out of the results, hence, making them incomplete. Another interesting observation is that the attachment style of many individuals doesn't depend only on the way they bond, but also on the language learned from the parents' style. I like explaining it by saying that if the primary tongue at home is English, the kid learns to speak English; if the primary style is avoidant, the baby will 'speak' avoidant. Therefore, the attachment style that someone exhibits may not be necessarily how they *attach* but how they *relate* and *how they were conditioned to respond*. For example, someone can be securely attached to their partner, but they could act avoidant when there's discordance in the relationship because that's how they learned to deal with conflict. In this way, the manner in which we attach can also be seen as an adaptation to the particular way our caregivers relate, which then becomes a scripted emotional response.

> Using Michaela's narrative, you may notice that her attachment style is not readily understood. Even though she became attached to others easily, she didn't show anxiety or avoidance of the attachment, and she clearly didn't show a pathological form of it (I'll further explain disorganized attachment later). She waited patiently for her cousin to come back, for Andreaa to return from her weekends away, for Ishmel to show up, and for Charles to text back. She exhibited anxiety when Charles broke up with her and she begged for forgiveness, but that could have been caused by her insecurities and Charles' unreliability; Charles actually seemed disorganized in his attachment, unpredictability, and flip-flopping. Still, even with all the information we have already, it's hard to say what attachment style Michaela developed in childhood. Attachment styles are less obvious than we wish.

Recent contributions by Dan Siegel, Allan Schore, and Edward Tronick to attachment theory have been exceptional. Based on neurobiology, it has been found that *not having a reliable* attachment figure affects the kid's development by using the basic premise that attachment—or lack thereof—affects how the nervous system learns to regulate itself.

BIOLOGY OF ATTACHMENT: ATTUNEMENT AND REGULATION

Under a neurobiology lens, during the first year of life (and gestation), the carrier/main-caregiver and the infant can be viewed as one biological system (Strathearn, 2011); their proximity activates neural networks that calm the nervous system promoting attunement, making its oscillations harmonic and synchronized, and stimulating the production of oxytocin and dopamine in both, causing a sense of connection, matching affect, and a sense of pleasure. The carrier's brain, just after giving birth, shows great neural plasticity in structure and function to support its new role (Kim et al., 2016). That activation is needed because one of the baby's systems that is not fully formed is the autonomic nervous system (ANS). The connection with the caregiver through eye contact, rocking, holding, verbal and non-verbal communication helps them regulate their immune functions, blood pressure, sleep, appetite, and other homeostatic processes (Schore, 2003; Siegel, 1999). It then becomes evident that the availability, consistency, and quality of the care that the baby receives is an essential component for their healthy development and resilience-building (Humphreys et al., 2022). Through the responsiveness of the caregiver, the child learns early and quickly what type of attachment-seeking behaviors is acceptable and becomes confident in their desirability, while their system learns to regulate and work harmoniously.

When the caregiver is not attuned, even when some (or many) of the basic needs of the baby get fulfilled, the baby's nervous system will still sense that it is 'alone' in its goal of learning how to stay regulated, which could overwhelm the child. Infants then will struggle with down-regulating their internal arousal to calm down and feel safe; they will be less capable of regulating their internal states and everything will feel more painful and unbearable. This implies that anxious caregivers may fail to help the baby regulate, not due to lack of love but due to their excessive worry. A 'good' caregiver is one who releases their anxiety and responds lovingly to the circumstances. The extreme version of these situations, when the caregiver has experienced unresolved traumatization and loss, resulting in disoriented, miss-attuned, and sometimes dissociated behavior toward the baby, the attachment relationship becomes imbued with traumatization and disorganization.

PATHOLOGY DUE TO ATTACHMENT FAILURE: DISORGANIZATION

When we compare ourselves with the survival capacities of other animals (often able to ambulate from the moment they are born), our disadvantages are obvious. From day 1, the way we deal with the potentially hostile world we confront is through fear. If we don't receive some signs of safety and ways to placate it, fear becomes pervasive and will define our future interactions. If our caregiver doesn't provide the conditions for our nervous system to regulate from the crib, we will grow up scared and with a system that feels unremitting rather than cyclical distressed (the main marker of traumatization and other psychological disorders). Babies that don't know how or when they will be assisted and comforted—because their caregivers shift from attending to inattentive—bounce between anxiety and avoidance as their response to the caregiver. This way to 'connect' to them was named 'disorganized attachment' (Main & Solomon, 1990). Disorganization, then, is seen as *the cost the infant has to pay for depending on a caregiver that doesn't offer predictability.*

Parents who may be unresolved with respect to their own traumatization may themselves be frightened and show behavior toward the infant that may feel frightening, unpredictable, rejecting, or absent (Duschinsky, 2018).

As you can appreciate, more than a *style*, disorganization in the attachment is a *consequence*, a detrimental one that causes a deficiency in connection, regulation, and development. Infants with disorganized attachment show signs of the *lack* of attachment not because their way to bond is disorganized but because, in their need to connect, they struggle with trying to be recipro-cated without finding solace, that is disorienting in terms of what to expect and who they are. Children with a disorganized presentation are fearful, anx-ious, and avoidant altogether, craving to attach to someone but experiencing a sense of dread, insecurity, and inadequacy that populates their emotional responses. They fear closeness because it proves dangerous, but they fear dis-tance because it's dangerous as well. In terms of trauma, this disorganization means that the infant feels at risk all the time, and we know how our system responds to that. One characteristic that is unique to the wound of not at-taching is the pervasive feeling of not being.

Rejection within the Attachment Relationship as an External Traumatizing Agent

We learned that Michaela's mother, Clara, went through a traumatiz-ing period even before her father's death, a traumatic loss that dest-abilized her life, a challenging and adverse new beginning in the US, and an unsettling marriage. The overwhelming experience before her father's assassination was likely to have set her survival protections off and running. After that, everything seemed difficult, stressful, and tax-ing. Her dissatisfaction and lack of mental space could explain why she rejected those around her and how they obstructed her from perceiv-ing the consequences her actions had on her children. Sadly, it seems evident that Mendo and Michaela were not able to feel the closeness or acceptance of their mother. Let's go into detail about the enormous consequences of feeling rejected as a child.

When talking about attachment, understanding rejection is paramount. It has been proven that we all have the specific need to be *accepted*, and that children everywhere, regardless of variations in culture, gender, age, ethnic-ity, or other conditions, need acceptance from parents and other attachment figures to grow up healthy (Rohner, 2021; Rohner et al., 2005). Most studies on rejection focus on social rejection starting in adolescence, but the rejection of the mother to the baby is not as well documented as is needed; the extent of its damage is worse than most adversity.

I don't use the word 'love' in most ambits (unless I explain it) but I feel confident saying here that *acceptance* in this context is a big component of the sentiment of love. If we don't feel accepted, we don't feel loved, no matter how much attention or material possessions we receive. Rejection is, to put it simply, the sustained sadness and devaluation of the self-concept—whether conscious or unconscious—caused by a lack of acceptance. If for an infant it is indispensable to have an attachment figure to feel safe in the world, having one that is not only unreliable but declines the responsibility of satisfying the infant's emotional needs, refuses to appreciate the value of what they bring, and instead, resents their existence, the psychological implications could be worse than those from abuse, neglect, and many other adversities together. The hurt doesn't only go into the body but it reaches the 'heart.' No device can measure that damage; a wound that may be only 'visible' to the one that knows how it feels having it, and which they will normally hide and feel ashamed of (and of themselves). In many instances, being rejected as an infant is equivalent to an internalized feeling of "it'd be better not to exist."

Once an infant suffers from rejection, and there is no one they can attach to, the chances of having developmental issues are basically guaranteed because they will experience helplessness at the outset. If there is someone, another relative or close family friend, a teacher perhaps, that makes them feel as though they matter, they will probably learn to cope with rejection in one way or another—whether it's healthy or pathological. If it's pathological, it could rapidly become social anxiety.

'Social Anxiety' is a formal disorder diagnosis within the DSM. It's reported as one of the most prevalent mental disorders (in the US); its criteria involve preoccupation or distress related to the fear and worry of being rejected. Individuals that were rejected as infants will have less tolerance to rejection later in life and may develop a variety of delays that can cause several issues, from social anxiety to the development of a personality disorder. Rejected individuals feel inadequate or not 'enough' constantly and may isolate themselves, look for reassurance, and reject others.

PHYSICAL CONSEQUENCES OF REJECTION

Do you remember that our brain produces its own opioids? Our system releases endogenous opioids to help us manage pain. Studies have found that the brain reacts to rejection in almost the exact way as it reacts to physical pain: when we feel rejected, the brain creates the same somatosensory representation, the same brain networks get activated, and similar production of opioids occurs (Kross et al., 2011). That means that the emotional pain of feeling rejected is equivalent for the brain to the physical pain of being physically injured; it also causes experiences related to several physical pain disorders such as fibromyalgia. The natural painkilling response is also similar when there is physical and emotional pain in terms of tolerance; individuals who are more sensitive to one kind of pain are also more sensitive to the other, and people with a higher threshold for pain don't need to numb their pain of rejection as others do. That's why, together with the studies of rejection, there are studies on rejection sensitivity. Rejection sensitivity has been connected to problems with attention, high distress, and maladaptive interpersonal patterns such as becoming hostile, being socially withdrawn, or over-accommodating of others.

Rejected kids' reactions don't only come from their thoughts, but from the way they perceive themselves as rejected, which participated in the formation of their self-concept and programmed their brains to anticipate what needs to be done in order to survive alone. Some kids numb the pain of rejection, which may not seem as detrimental, but remember that the constant production of opioids causes dissociation. Depending on the age when they started using numbing as a way to manage rejection, the consequences could go from mild to severe in different functions.

> Rejection would explain why Michaela was able to go to bed with a broken arm, and some of her tolerant presentation. The rejection from Clara pushed her system to live numbed to pain.

The experience of social rejection is amplified by other emotions like fear, sadness, anger, anxiety, and shame. The accumulation of these affects gives rise to a unique experience called 'social pain' and to the creation of emotional states from which we might perceive others as uncaring and hurtful. This applies to our review of attachment and rejection because the infant that is rejected may develop a very low tolerance for further rejection and may also have social phobia. Social pain is linked to anxiety, depression, and helplessness; internalized social rejection often manifests as aggression and desires for retaliation (Chester et al., 2018), and also as self-regulatory failure, i.e., emotional dysregulation. Acceptance, however, has been recognized as a regulation strategy. Acceptance promotes curiosity about emotionality as well as about the world. If the caregiver accepts the baby's emotional reactions, the baby won't see their emotions and thoughts as threatening, but rather as a transient, interesting, or at least a neutral source of information about their current state (Messina et al., 2021). Emotional acceptance is an effective way to down-regulate negative affect (Troy et al., 2018) and when accepted through the eyes of those who matter most, we learn to accept ourselves; i.e., if we accept our emotions, we will participate in the regulation of our system.

A SUMMARY OF PARENTAL ACCEPTANCE-REJECTION THEORY

Ronald P. Rohner, a psychologist, and Director of the Center for the Study of Interpersonal Acceptance and Rejection, has dedicated his life to the study of parental rejection and its effects. He started his research in the 1960s and developed a theory known as the Interpersonal Acceptance-Rejection Theory (IPARTheory). According to this theory, there is parental acceptance when a parental figure can express love, affection, and care, and provide comfort, support, and nurturance to their children, while parental rejection is seen as the absence or withdrawal of love and affection (Rohner et al., 2012). The theory assumes that rejection or acceptance could be delivered in three principal ways:

A. cold and unaffectionate,
B. hostile and aggressive, or
C. indifferent and neglecting.

It also proposed that 'undifferentiated rejection' happens when the infant has the subjective feeling that the caregiver doesn't love them or care about them without necessarily having clear indicators of A, B, or C. The theory re-postulated one of its premises in 2007 emphasizing the significance of rejection when it comes specifically from an attachment figure (Edwards & Barber, 2010). Infants may perceive significant others' affect before they can understand their behaviors but 'blame' themselves for the caregiver's animosity. The theory also claims that there are individuals that develop overall good mental health despite parental rejection and calls them 'affective copers,' a very reassuring finding. Even though IPARTheory and attachment theory evolved independently, Rohner's theory seems highly influenced by Bowlby's work (Hughes et al., 2005). IPARTheory includes the acknowledgment that acceptance and the presence of a reliable attachment figure profoundly influence a child's development over their lifespan, including personality and behavior. It also states that rejected children are likely to feel anxious and insecure which leads to other personality outcomes such as becoming hostile themselves, or other aggressive and emotionally unstable behavior in general, and dependence (or defensive-independence), unresponsiveness, substance abuse, and a negative worldview in particular. Additional studies have linked this theory to attachment theory and have found that there is a correlation between them as such: individuals with avoidance attachment style correspond to IPARTheory's affective copers, while separation anxiety corresponds to perceived parental rejection (Deveci, 2019).

AN ATTACHMENT FAILURE MARKER: REJECTION SENSITIVITY

In the aftermath of having been rejected (an external traumatizing agent) comes sensitivity to being rejected any further. Rejection sensitivity (an internal traumatizing agent) shows up as the lack of tolerance that individuals develop after experiencing rejection from caregivers (or others) for a prolonged or constant period (Pietrzak et al., 2005) which predisposes them to anxiously expect and perceive rejection, and propels an intense reaction to it (Downey & Feldman, 1996). Rejection sensitivity is found as a characteristic of several mental disorders and reflects a hyper-vigilance to cues of social rejection at the neural level as automatic activation of the survival circuits.

When someone suffers from this sensitivity—sometimes developed after being exposed to family violence, emotional neglect, punishment, and love that is conditioned—they tend to react in ways that damage significant relationships and can lead to withdrawal or aggression. The reactions triggered by their rejection sensitivity may become a self-fulfilling prophecy wherein people reject them for their behavior (Downey & Feldman, 1996). This is also connected to safety because the ventral vagus system that helps us differentiate safety from danger (neuroception) gets compromised by fearing rejection and focusing on cues that could indicate it. Social-engagement is designed to *anticipate safety*; rejection sensitivity will *anticipate rejection*, and therefore, the brain will follow those expectations, turning off the social-engagement feature, interfering with the very need to connect, and distorting the perception of social cues.

It's worth adding here that several studies assert that there is a correlation between rejection sensitivity and personality disorders (Poggi et al., 2019). For example, individuals suffering from Borderline PD often misinterpret situations because of their lack of trust and their high sensitivity to being rejected, while the same trust and rejection sensitivity explains aggressive and abusive outbursts in Narcissistic PD (Poggi et al., 2019).

WHEN REJECTION BECOMES A THREAT

Rejection has the worst consequences when it relates to attachment; it is a traumatizing agent to an infant at two different levels:

- Rejection makes the caregiver unreliable for survival and therefore causes fear of death, feelings of being a burden, or the sense that it'd be better if they didn't exist.
- Being rejected by the first person the infant needs to attach to causes the fear of not belonging, which will become a fear of always being alone, isolated, or cast out, and disorganization in the attachment.

Obviously, being rejected causes shame and guilt, which amplifies the traumatizing consequences of attachment failures or disruptions. Being abused and/or neglected can also be perceived as a lack of acceptance and love indirectly, but internalized. Traumatizing agents build on each other, making the damage more severe and straining the system longer.

The Unspoken Pain of Unresolved Attachment

According to the ACE study, Clara's kids would score at least 4 on the questionnaire (Appendix D), which reflects a considerable level of adversity—only 12.5% of the population scores 4 or above (CDC). If we add the wound of an unresolved attachment, we can understand why Mendo and Michaela struggled emotionally, even if it manifested in different ways. Michaela will continue waiting for her mother to 'love her back' using a little bit of hope as a resource, while Mendo simply left his mother behind.

Let's talk about the painful and traumatic experience of being forced into a cold and scary place without finding someone that receives us with welcoming arms. In a good pregnancy, a baby goes from the calm, comfort, and shelter offered by the womb to an animated, disturbing, and cold space. It's no doubt shocking to the baby's system, to say the least. When the pregnancy is inhospitable already, or the place that receives the baby is dismissive or aggressive, being born is hurtful. In order to understand this suffering, it's useful to distinguish between two separate areas:

Failure to attach is a connection that never happens, a bond that never forms. (I'll also refer to this as unresolved attachment.)

Attachment Rupture happens when there was an already established connection, and at some point after birth, a disruption takes place.

You might wonder, *Are ruptures as damaging as the failure to attach?* Well, they have very different consequences. Let's look at this difference more closely.

ATTACHMENT RUPTURES (DISCONTINUITY IN THE BOND)

The attachment process can become disrupted in various circumstances stemming from three main sources as listed in Table 8.1.

Table 8.1 Attachment ruptures situations

When the Caregiver...	When the Environment...	When the Baby...
is unable to attune to the baby due to unavailability through illness or extraordinary circumstances, or	promotes interpersonal stressors in the parenting relationship, or	is temperamentally sensitive to sensory changes or caregiver absences, or
becomes absent for one or more short periods (days) due to travel, hospitalizations, or unpredictable situations, or	causes the child to live in very high stress environments (entrenched poverty, violence in surrounding region) that place caregivers struggling for survival, or	has sleep problems and is hard to soothe, which disappoints or exhausts the caregiver's capacity to stay connected, or
is absorbed with other activities, doesn't give attention to the infant as they need it, or projects their unresolved trauma onto the baby, becoming punitive toward, or putting sporadic frustrations onto the baby.	means living in geographic regions where there has been political or social unrest or violence and constant displacement is required (to ensure safety).	is chronically ill and may be separated from the caregiver due to repeated or longer-term hospitalization.

It's easier to picture that *disruptions in the attachment won't affect the baby in the same way as an attachment failure* if we investigate the neuroscience behind it. Some authors assume that the baby forms an attachment before birth (Doan & Zimerman, 2003) since carrier/baby are treated by the brain as one entity, and hence, if there is a separation after being born, the rupture in the attachment is as unavoidable as cutting the umbilical cord. How fast they reconnect is key. When the separation is just temporary (incubator, mother illness, etc.), there could be some emotional pain, but those ruptures are most likely repaired, while failure to attach doesn't get repaired by the carrier by definition. If the rupture is not resolved, the baby may experience severe stress—especially if it is constant and prolonged. But the term 'disruption' signifies the possibility of reconnection. Once the bond has been developed (postpartum or in the womb), even in case of circumstantial interruptions, it is still highly probable that the infant reconnects to the caregiver and vice versa, or connects to another person that offers a similar relationship and safety (relatives, nannies, adopted parents, etc.) placating the traumatic stress. Remember that our system will always aim to recover equilibrium.

In the same way that ruptures in the therapeutic alliance between client/therapist strengthen the relationship once they're repaired, disruption in the child/caregiver attachment can offer the possibility of consolidating the bond. Miss-attunement happens to all of us because caregivers—or any other people we interact with—are not mind-readers or can't attend to us 100% of the time. But seeing an apologetic and kind stance from the caregiver and an accurate reflection of the hurt may show real affection and interest, strengthening the relationship and boosting the trust that one will not be left on their own to face the difficulties of life.

> For Mendo, the hospitalization caused a rupture, but the real damage came from the fact that once he got home, Clara was not able to make him feel accepted or wanted. He probably felt that way in the uterus, too.

Impact of Attachment Disruptions: The Pain of Not Trusting Enough

Attachment disruptions cause stress that might lead to an insecure way to attach. In those cases, the insecurity of the anxiously attached kid may become a traumatizing agent when it transforms into constant anxiety, stress, and/

or fear. The insecurity in the avoidant attachment, though, is dealt with by anger, which causes isolation and dispassion but may be more adaptive and less damaging to the infant's nervous system. Still, the insecure attachment could activate allostatic processes if the kid feels really insecure and the parents keep 'disappearing.' If other adversities add to that insecurity, the kid may even develop DTD as previously explained, or they could keep suffering allostatic changes increasing the probability of reaching overload later in life. The distress of being alone easily becomes DTD when other external traumatizing agents such as physical/sexual/emotional abuse and physical/medical neglect add to the attachment ruptures.

And yet, growing up insecurely attached can potentially leave no considerable consequences. Remember that the attachment style reflects the adaptation to the kind of relational environment a baby finds themselves in, and forms of insecurity may be adaptations for surviving in that particular environment. Constantly clinging to the caregiver is a way to avoid stress and not necessarily proof of dysregulation.

Studies on disruption and repair show that babies suffering from disruptions in the attachment bounce back in a few months and develop secure attachment after the caregiver becomes available and provides affection and attunement. There is also the possibility of developing a secure attachment to a different figure that would compensate for the previously experienced pain and provide the sense of calm and belonging that was missing, reducing the stress.

UNRESOLVED ATTACHMENT (NOBODY THERE FOR YOU)

Different circumstances (as shown in Table 8.2) can pave the way for infants to suffer from the insecurity of not feeling connected to the caregiver.

Unresolved attachment is very hard to identify because the psychological damage it causes manifests as negative symptoms (absence of normal functions). Also, dysfunction is not automatic or present in all cases; it only becomes evident when there are other stressors. Unfortunately, it establishes the foundation for dysfunction that will become evident at some point, at least to the sufferer, mainly in interpersonal relationships. Failing to attach may translate as the anticipation of isolation, rejection, and struggle that becomes the foundation of the scripts for several emotional states, such as loneliness and worthlessness. It may also be the root of many difficulties in 'connecting' with others, including one's self, dissociated identity, and lack

Table 8.2 Attachment failure scenarios

When the	Is	During	Due to
Carrier	emotionally absent	pregnancy	mental illness, or something that impedes the carrier from connecting to the fetus.
Carrier	physically absent	permanently after birth	death of the carrier, giving the baby away, or incarceration.
Carrier/ caregiver	physically unavailable	temporary	illness and hospitalization after birth.
Caregiver	emotionally unavailable	permanently	a mental condition such as a trauma disorder, a personality disorder, or psychotic states.
Carrier/ caregiver	mentally/ emotionally absent	long periods or intermittently	alcoholism, drug addiction, prioritize their life and not the baby's.
Carrier	rejects the baby	present at birth	unwanted pregnancy.
Carrier/ caregiver	emotionally unavailable	present at birth	imposed caregiving, feels trapped, blames baby.

of regulation and maturation of several internal processes. It could also manifest as an eternal need for affection and closeness that feels unresolved despite the availability of established relationships.

Physiological Consequences of Failing to Attach

According to Bowlby, the bond we create with our caregiver becomes an internal working model formed by the internalized attachment process of forming a prototype for future relationships. Still, the internal working model develops over time. What happens before the brain is able to recognize that there is an entity separated from what created it? We reviewed how, even after birth, infant and 'mother' are one biological system with shared neuronal activity. If there is no system the infant belongs to, and the neuronal activity is not shared, the process of forming a self-representation will be truncated or may be disabled. At birth, the ANS is underdeveloped, and the brain is still focused on maturing and regulating all the organs after losing the regulation given in the uterus. Failing to attach causes the interruption of specific processes which leaves the system in a vulnerable position to confront ad-verse influences. Not attaching can result in serious issues such as 'dysmatu-ration' (or staying stuck in a physiologically immature state) in one extreme, or the interruption in connectivity between the limbic system and the cortex in another, which would contribute to the failure of regulating emotional activity and internal processes, and many other functions in between.

Impact of Unresolved Attachment: Burdening Loneliness

We still lack clarity on what the exact consequences of unresolved attach-ment are since there is no homology or specificity on the research. They seem to range from a deep sense of loneliness to complete social inability. The effort of conceptualizing how failing to attach is traumatizing—and how an attachment trauma syndrome can develop—comes mostly from observa-tions and clinical evidence.

In terms of how traumatizing attachment failure is, there is more than one point of view. My conclusion is that unresolved attachment from failing to attach:

1   can leave a deep wound (in the 'heart') that stays as a psychological wound only (void or emptiness) that when dealt with avoidance more than with anxiety leaves space for regular development of most functions,
2   can stress the infant, causing allostatic changes that can become com-plex PTSD years later,
3   becomes DTD when adversity/maltreatment/disorganization are present,
4   when combined with rejection and disorganization, it could unfold as Unresolved Attachment Syndrome (I'll define it soon) that affects regu-lation and relationships.

The idea that some infants don't develop a trauma disorder after fail-ing to attach deserves some analysis because it may sound impossible. If failing to attach implies that the system doesn't learn to regulate, how could someone have normal development? If the kid stays dysregulated, there will indeed be developmental delays, but that would imply that the circumstances are stressful. Life can be acceptable if the conditions are appropriate (with the aid of internal/external resources) and if allosta-sis processes are not needed. I'm saying that the ANS may find ways to achieve regulation and continue maturing even if a couple of functions—those related to aloneness and self—may stay compromised. Everything in our system is designed to predict, adapt, and survive, and that means that the brain will do everything to keep growing. But of course, if the circumstances are not favorable, then more basic mechanisms will take over and the infant would be operating in survival mode from the beginning, high-jacking development.

Emptiness: When Loneliness is not Resolved

Even with fully functional lives, most people that didn't 'have a mother' or were 'never loved' suffer 'an absence.' It seems like there is no 'solid ground' for the self to freely develop, and therefore, the individual has difficulty 'feeling' what their place in the world is. Not being part of anyone ('no mother') may injure their connection with life, as if a candle was missing its wick; an absence of connection with a core that would have facilitated the link with one's power to emit light and warmth. I'm not saying that the baby—or later, the adult—will lack the possibility of shining; I'm saying that the inner experience will be of disconnection to their 'source,' which will trouble the person's sense of self, their capacity to understand their level of neediness and fulfillment, and their 'peace of mind.'

What I am describing is what most people call feeling empty or having a void that never gets filled up. A recent qualitative study on the subject found that emptiness is an existential feeling that influences the way the self relates interpersonally but also internally (Herron & Sani, 2022). Some people describe that inner experience as similar to the depiction of a robot with great intelligence that can reason about everything but without the capacity to feel the data they process; others have shared the analogy of eating without a sense of smell or taste, and some others, on the other side of the spectrum, describe it as unbearable anguish that propels them from one thing to the next without ever finding peace, a lack of satisfaction that never ends. That's one of the most important signs of having had the misfortune of unresolved attachment. I like calling it 'unresolved' because I want to advance the hope that it may be resolved at some point in life. I know it can be. I have witnessed and helped individuals that suffer from this issue connect with something that clears up the absence. For some people, it's God or the Universe; for some others, it's a romantic partner, while some find it in a cause, a mission, or even an imaginary figure that plays the role of the compassionate/comprehensive 'mother' they have endlessly craved. The source, in fact, is inside of us already—that source of light that can make us feel fully alive and interconnected.

Emptiness develops for other reasons too, but here I'm only including the one that comes from feeling unloved. This feeling can come and go, can become central when the person fails to find satisfaction, drive, motivation, and meaning in life, or can stay in the background as an inexplicable sadness that taints perception, temperament, and behavior intermittently. This affliction doesn't mean failure or dysfunction. Some individuals can be extremely functional and successful and still carry this debilitating and draining feeling of not having enough love from others to fill the void, only scared of never finding relief for that particular pain even when they can't recognize why or where it comes from. Many 'loving' caregivers could never be blamed by the child, and many 'lovable' children can't be recognized as sufferers of such malady. Since there is not enough research on this issue, there are almost no specific interventions for it. I use resourcing brain circuitry in different ways, one of which is to help form the neuronal connections that are missing and promote new connectivity. But it's not an easy wound to heal. It needs much love (of many types, including self-love) to reach a place of rest and the acceptance that the wound may still be subject to 'bleeding.'

Caregivers that don't attach to their infants are not hard to find, but spotting their kids proves more difficult. There are many 'mothers' that don't mean ill and don't hurt their children intentionally, but because they have not resolved their dysregulation/connectivity issues, they find themselves incapable of attuning, mentalizing, responding, or being a 'good parent.' Their kids carry the parent's pain as internalized shame and a sense of their own incompleteness.

TRAUMATIZING ATTACHMENT: FEAR CAUSING DISORGANIZATION IN THE BONDING PROCESS

Individuals that were not able to attach/connect to a caregiver and, in tandem, had to confront a scary, abusive, neglectful, or adverse caregiver/environment may also suffer from *disorganized attachment*. Since disorganization is equivalent to chaos, 'disorganized attachment' is explained as living in an internal state of confusion and disorder, which screams dysregulation. It will reflect as the disorganized way of coordinating and integrating their different mental processes. Disorganized attachment is a deficit that pushes the individual to adapt to the limited internal (and external) resources through confusion, making it almost impossible to find meaning in the relationship with their caregiver but incapable of living without them, resulting in a deficiency regulating their emotionality and unpredictable behavior. Not having access to one's 'power'—which would have provided the feeling of existing, being, and therefore significance—causes the infant to fall into deep despair and immense shame. Picture trying to soothe yourself while experiencing constant unpredictable shifts between avoiding looking for someone to meet your needs and then anxiously looking for that same thing, not being able to feel and then feeling intensely, choosing objects while craving people, wanting to be seen but preferring to be ignored, or jumping from hypo-activation to hyper-activation without understanding the reason or having the capacity to regulate the intensity of the emotional upheavals. It's mayhem.

The literature states that disorganized attachment is easier to observe among families exposed to different types of abuse, domestic violence, and family instability. In those cases, the high level of circumstantial distress in the assigned main caretaker incapacitates them to provide a peaceful and steady connection to the infant due to the lack of safety and inner cohesion they experience themselves. A terrified, neglected, dissociated, or abused caregiver becomes either (1) a caretaker only (not attached), (2) a menace instead of a provider (causing attachment ruptures and threat), or (3) a sporadic caregiver that offers moments of solace and connection (has the capacity to repair the bond).

A dysregulated caregiver that suffers from any type of trauma disorder themselves most probably lacks the capacity to attune or connect at a deep level even when they sincerely desire to do so. The unresolved attachment and disorganization then may depend on how damaged the caregiver's ANS is, and how inactive/underdeveloped their prefrontal cortex. Deficient connectivity from the PFC to the rest of the brain may imply a systemic incapacity to feel love for the child as opposed to a volitional lack of connection or rejection.

A recent understanding of what happens in the brain explains that the disorganization in the attachment is due to the creation of different circuits that don't connect under the same network; the kid has (1) circuits that produce feel-good hormones (dopamine, serotonin, and even oxytocin) when the kid is fed and attended, (2) circuits that are readily activated by stress hormones produced by the fear of rejection and abandonment that is mainly sympathetic, and (3) circuits that are formed by the release of numbing agents to keep the infant disengaged. Those circuits remain disconnected from each other in the service of adapting, which is normally conceptualized by the structural dissociation theory (Van der Hart et al., 2005) as traumatized parts (EP for emotional parts) hosted by an apparently normal part (ANP). These babies show symptoms such as rejection sensitivity, fear of abandonment, lack of sense of self, intense emotional reactivity, fragmented personality/ dissociated self, and clear dysregulation of their ANS and their emotionality. They avoid eye contact very early on, spend long periods inert, have no ability to self-soothe when uncomfortable, and can become alarmed easily, shifting back and forth between reaching out and disengaging. The lack of internal organization causes distortions in perception, and perception plays an important role in the formation of the self. As adults, they may have difficulties relating to others, experience intense emotionality (including the intense need for closeness and connection and the shame for having it) with no capacity to control it, and with the painful experience of dissatisfaction and inadequacy. These kids could easily develop a personality disorder (most probably BPD) as they grow older.

AN UNRECOGNIZED INJURY: ATTACHMENT FAILURE SYNDROME

'Attachment trauma'—even when it has become the talk of the town—is not a diagnosis and there is no such thing as an Attachment Trauma Disorder or a Posttraumatic Attachment Disorder diagnosis or criteria in the psychiatric manuals or scientific literature for a syndrome that unfolds after survival issues from the attachment. I mentioned in the previous chapter that Van der Kolk includes attachment disruptions in his DTD proposal, but that's it. Some people have said (including the DSM-5 task force) that Borderline Personality Disorder (BPD) is the diagnosis of attachment failure; however, in no way it's suggested in the DSM that BPD relates to unresolved attachment.

Still, in my mind, BPD is more connected to disorganized attachment, but unresolved attachment followed by being rejected is traumatizing in a different way; being alone with the prognostic of continuing alone is scary and defeating together. Therefore, identifying an *Attachment Failure Syndrome* (AFS) may be useful to name *the struggle of having had to survive being rejected and 'alone' as a newborn with a system that didn't find hope as a resource*. Why is it different from DTD? There are infants that are attached to their caregiver but live in scary circumstances that cause disorganization and high traumatic stress that unfolds as DTD, but there are infants that live in a safe environment and develop well yet live with an unresolved attachment and the pain of not having been accepted by the caregiver. Those kids will show a different set of symptoms specific to the attachment injury because their fears remain concealed, rapidly becoming defeat and self-devaluation. These kids shut down some emotional awareness and continue developing most functions, only carrying unrecognized emotional pain and the need to hide their assumed lack of value. When kids with AFS are also abused or put under duress, they will have symptoms of both, AFS+DTD, which we'll see in the next chapter counts as aggregated traumatization.

If it was up to me, the first criterion to assess if someone suffers from the proposed syndrome (AFS) would be *unresolved attachment plus rejection*. There is no disorganization but rejection adds an almost imperceptible sense of defeat and fear (of abandonment, of being seen, of...) plus the shame, which function as traumatizing agents that activate the survival mechanisms. The symptoms of this particular syndrome are very specific to our interaction with others, the need to be liked and accepted, and the lack of self-worth and boundaries; it's different from BPD because the symptoms are 'covert' and not as pervasive at first and may show early on as opposed to developing in late adolescence when personality forms. It could also be the case that many people diagnosed with BPD suffer from AFS instead.

References

Brownell, C. A., Zerwas, S., & Ramani, G. B. (2007). "So big": The development of body self-awareness in toddlers. *Child development*, 78(5), 1426–1440. https://doi.org/10.1111/j.1467-8624.2007.01075.x

Cassidy, J., Jones, J. D., & Shaver, P. R. (2013). Contributions of attachment theory and research: A framework for future research, translation, and policy. *Development and Psychopathology*, 25(4 Pt 2), 1415–1434. https://doi.org/10.1017/S0954579413000692

Chester, D. S., Lynam, D. R., Milich, R., & DeWall, C. N. (2018). Neural mechanisms of the rejection–aggression link. *Social Cognitive and Affective Neuroscience*, 13(5), 501–512. https://doi.org/10.1093/scan/nsy025

Deveci Şirin, H. (2019). Parental acceptance–rejection and adult separation anxiety: The mediation of adult attachment insecurity. *SAGE Open*. 9. 21582440 1988513. https://doi.org/10.1177/2158244019885138

Doan, H. M., & Zimerman, A. (2003). Conceptualizing prenatal attachment: Toward a multidimensional view. *Journal of Prenatal & Perinatal Psychology & Health*, 18(2), 109–129.

Downey, G., & Feldman, S. (1996). Implications of rejection sensitivity for intimate relationships. *Journal of Personality and Social Psychology*, 70, 1327–1343.

Duschinsky, R. (2018). Disorganization, fear and attachment: Working towards clarification. *Infant Mental Health Journal*, 39(1), 17–29. https://doi.org/10.1002/imhj.21689

Edwards, G. L., & Barber, B. L. (2010). The relationship between rejection sensitivity and compliant condom use. *Archives of Sexual Behavior*, 39(6), 1381–1388.

Fonagy, P., Gergely, G., Jurist, E., & Target, M. (2002). *Affect regulation, mentalization, and the development of the self* (pp. 145–192). New York: Other Press.

Hernandez-Halton, I. (2015). Klein, Ferenczi and the clinical diary. *American Journal of Psychoanalysis*, 75(1), 76–85. https://doi.org/10.1057/ajp.2014.56

Herron, S. J., & Sani, F. (2022). Understanding the typical presentation of emptiness: A study of lived-experience. *Journal of Mental Health*, 31(2), 188–195. https://doi.org/10.1080/09638237.2021.1922645

Hughes, M. M., Blom, M., Rohner, R. P., & Britner, P. A. (2005). Bridging parental acceptance-rejection theory and attachment theory in the preschool strange situation. *Ethos*, 33(3), 378–401. http://www.jstor.org/stable/4497900

Humphreys, K. L., King, L. S., Guyon-Harris, K. L., & Zeanah, C. H. (2022). Caregiver regulation: A modifiable target promoting resilience to early adverse experiences. *Psychological Trauma: Theory, Research, Practice, and Policy*, 14(S1), S63–S71. https://doi.org/10.1037/tra0001111

Kim, P., Strathearn, L., & Swain, J. E. (2016). The maternal brain and its plasticity in humans. *Hormones and Behavior*, 77, 113–123. https://doi.org/10.1016/j.yhbeh.2015.08.001

Kross, E., Berman, M. G., Mischel, W., Smith, E. E., & Wager, T. D. (2011). Social rejection shares somatosensory representations with physical pain. *Proceedings of the National Academy of Sciences of the United States of America*, 108(15), 6270–6275. https://doi.org/10.1073/pnas.1102693108

Main, M., & Solomon, J. (1990). Procedures for identifying infants as disorganized/disoriented during the Ainsworth Strange Situation. M. T. Greenberg, D. Cicchetti, & E. M. Cummings (Eds.), *Attachment in the preschool years: Theory, research, and intervention* (pp. 121–160). Chicago, IL: The University of Chicago Press. Chicago

Messina, I., Grecucci, A., & Viviani, R. (2021). Neurobiological models of emotion regulation: A meta-analysis of neuroimaging studies of acceptance as an emotion regulation strategy. *Social Cognitive and Affective Neuroscience*, 16(3), 257–267. https://doi.org/10.1093/scan/nsab007

Pietrzak, J., Downey, G., & Ayduk, O. (2005). Rejection sensitivity as an interpersonal vulnerability. M. W. Baldwin (Ed.), *Interpersonal cognition* (pp. 62–84). New York, NY: Guilford Press.

Poggi, A., Richetin, J., & Preti, E. (2019). Trust and rejection sensitivity in personality disorders. *Current Psychiatry Reports*, 21(8), 69. https://doi.org/10.1007/s11920-019-1059-3

Rohner, R. P. (2021). Introduction to interpersonal acceptance-rejection theory (IPARTheory) and evidence. *Online Readings in Psychology and Culture*, 6(1). https://doi.org/10.9707/ 2307–0919.1055

Rohner, R. P., Khaleque, A., & Cournoyer, D. E. (2005). Parental acceptance-rejection: Theory, methods, cross-cultural evidence, and implications. *Ethos*, 33(3), 299–334. https://doi.org/10.1525/eth.2005.33.3.299

Rohner R. P., Khaleque, A., & Cournoyer, D. E. (2012). *Introduction to parental acceptance-rejection theory, methods, evidence, and implications.* http://csiar. uconn.edu/wp-content/uploads/sites/494/2014/02/Introduction-To-Parental-Acceptance-3-27-12.pdf

Schore, A. N. (2003). *Affect regulation and the repair of the self* (pp. 33–50). W. W Norton & Co.

Siegel, D. J. (1999). *The developing mind: Toward a neurobiology of interpersonal experience* (pp. 233). New York: Guilford Press.

Simpson, J. A., & Beckes, L. (2017). Attachment theory. *Encyclopedia Britannica*. https://www.britannica.com/science/attachment-theory

Strathearn, L. (2011). Maternal neglect: Oxytocin, dopamine and the neurobiology of attachment. *Journal of Neuroendocrinology*, 23, 1054–1065.

Troy, A. S., Shallcross, A. J., Brunner, A., Friedman, R., & Jones, M. C. (2018). Cognitive reappraisal and acceptance: Effects on emotion, physiology, and perceived cognitive costs. *Emotion*, 18(1), 58–74. https://doi.org/10.1037/emo0000371

Van der Hart, O., Nijenhuis, E. R. S., & Steele, K. (2005). Dissociation: An insufficiently recognized major feature of complex posttraumatic stress disorder. *Journal of Traumatic Stress*, 18(5), 413–423. https://doi.org/10.1002/jts.20049

Nine
Societal Traumatization

What are the psychological consequences of racism and oppression?

Are they traumatizing, and if so, how?

Can we escape a trauma disorder if our parents are traumatized?

What happens when we get traumatized many times for different reasons?

We've recently seen the hard work—and the results—of the many people around the world who are bringing more awareness, justice, inclusion, and openness into our values and actions. Those applying the trauma lens in their work are joining the effort, contributing a compassionate and normalizing approach to the nuance and understanding of what being human entails, promoting a society that's more inclusive of diversity and individuality. The validation of trauma studies goes hand in hand with a more widespread understanding of the consequences of judging, ostracizing, othering, discriminating, bullying, and systemically oppressing, disenfranchising, and incarcerating people. The effects can be seen not only in individuals but in entire communities, harming society as a whole.

In this chapter, I want to talk about the damage that results from practices that societies have followed and maintained for centuries without examining their traumatizing impact. This is a heavy arena, but speaking about it openly is how we could find the way forward.

Kin: Michaela's Ancestry

My brother Ronan is the pride of the family and has always been treated better than anyone else in the house. I think it is because he got some of the red hair from my father's Irish side and the 'fine' features from

DOI: 10.4324/9781003382478-12

my mom's French grandmother. I learned implicitly that 'white' people have more privileges and opportunities when I observed that racism is exercised even inside the home.

My last name is of Spanish origin because my great-great-grandfather was Cuban, but my father doesn't speak a word of Spanish or identify with anything besides being a New Yorker. I think he rejects his Spanish heritage because people had picked on him and discriminated against him when they thought he was a Latino immigrant. He's as American as someone can be, born in America to American parents. Both his parents had European background, with two grandfathers that fought in WWII, just with a Spanish last name, which in this country makes him Hispanic, period. White and dominant people apply the "one-drop" rule to almost every ethnic group that is not Anglo-Saxon or from a certain Northern-European background. If you have one drop of blood from somewhere else, you are "other." That's probably why my mother tries so hard to talk about her European background, to avoid being treated as part of a denigrated group. Not that it makes any difference! But that's not only my mom's issue. I think it's an issue of millions of Americans that are always treated as if they were from a different species, a species that is looked down upon and treated as less deserving, no matter what.

My father talks about growing up in Manhattan's Lower East Side where people from all over lived, especially Jews and Italians. He lived in the house his mother had inherited from her Italian parents. His father was Irish from his mother's side and white American from his father; white American meaning that they came to the US so long ago that they lost track of their country of origin. Chris's family always struggled with money but had a large network of support around their church. My father used to say that at his house, bread was always short but prayers were always long.

He has one brother, my uncle Paolo. They hardly ever mentioned him but I once heard my father use a strange word when referring to him. I knew from his tone it meant my uncle was not welcome at home. When I learned that the word meant gay, I learned that ultra-religious families find it hard to accept people's individuality. How sad! I learned a little more about his family when my mom sometimes attacked my father by insulting his "drunk good for nothing parents. Did they pray between bottles or after they were wasted?" she'd say. She always said things in a way that seemed like she was blaming my father for the flaws of his family. Why was he shamed for others' flaws? I wondered.

My mom had a very different background. Her family was part of the colonizers—the 'white' people of Colombia—that treated the locals as others and always considered themselves better, showing their ridiculous imperialist heritage. I wish they had learned the lesson that class is circumstantial and not a birthright, and that race is a construct. Racism, classism, sexism, and many of those discriminatory constructs depend on situations that come and go. It should be evident to them that we humans are all the same and need to be treated with respect and dignity, but I think they carry their narratives without much processing, exactly the way I was do-ing it before college and therapy when I learned about schemas.

My therapist has explained that people tend to dissociate or compart-mentalize their biases because it's uncomfortable to face the truth. I can see it in them; my mother could be conservative when thinking about Colombia and liberal when talking about the US. My father is Republi-can because of his affiliation with the army without even thinking about how the Republicans have stopped non-whites from having opportuni-ties. My father despises Hispanics without understanding that he lives in a house full of them and that he is perceived as one. Totally dissociated! They disjoin their ideologies according to the circumstances that bet-ter serve their survival needs and default loyalties, disregarding reality. I don't know what's worse, their behavior or their lack of awareness.

I was ignorant of how racism had impacted me too until that counselor othered me in college. Her comments made me consider many of my re-lationships and my parents' situation, allowing me to see myself in a dif-ferent light. I noticed that my curves and my Spanish last name have me stereotyped as a 'typical' Hispanic. There is a tendency in America to pro-file Latin-American people as sex machines always looking to rope others into "la vida loca." I wonder if that was what Richie and Ishmel thought of me. I will never be sure but I feel like changing my last name some days and the thought of only dating non-white people crosses my mind often.

In my experience, most people with Latin-American background have their heads full of Catholic fears and old-fashioned European social judgments–different from the "spicy" ways they are portrayed. Latin America was colonized by imperialist Europeans just as the US was, and they (we?) are not the only ones. People from families with religious and conservative backgrounds—like Irish, Italian, Jewish, Polish, Indian, Korean, Iranians, you name it—suffer similar issues, especially if they come from a post-colonial society because then, they also carry many schemas about class that may never be reviewed.

It's challenging to assimilate into the "American culture" where celeb-rities are worshiped like gods, money matters sooo much, and the no-tion of freedom can mean so many different things, while we still carry old-fashioned beliefs from our families. America is a country made of im-migrants and most immigrant families keep their values and traditions for generations to preserve their identities and sense of belonging, but their descendants need to belong to America as well. It becomes challenging to belong to your 'family of origin' and to belong to America at the same time, and nobody seems to acknowledge it. It's up to each of us to deal with the struggle between betraying our family values/language/history or accepting not meeting the stereotype of what being "an American" is.

I have been very confused about who my clan is. Mendo often shares how he was bullied and called names at school for all sorts of reasons, from being 'retarded,' 'beaner,' 'midget,' or a 'narco.' So easy to use names to expel someone from the group!

What can we do if even inside the house we are marked by class and ethnicity? If we consider 'my people' to be LAM or 'Hispanics' as we are called, it'd be easy to feel like an outsider or an impostor because I don't even speak Spanish, I have never been in any Latin American country, and I can't really relate since my mom's experience of Colombia may not be objective enough. If I see myself as American, it hurts to feel rejected by Americans who will always see me as a foreigner. I don't feel Colombian, Italian, Irish, French, Cuban, or Spanish enough either. After many therapy sessions, "American" is who I feel I am. I'm not going to impose it, but I'm not going to allow anyone to impose on me who I should be or how I should box myself in a category imposed by them. Still, some days I'm not sure where I belong.

Systemic Adversity as an External Traumatizing Agent

Michaela's family members had to experience some of the consequences of living in a society that carries many biases, and biases create unnoticed emotional wounds. The biases were directly inflicted as offensive slurs, negative attitudes, profiling, or actions toward the whole family that affected each of its members.

Do you remember I said that belonging is as important a need for survival as eating? So far, we have seen the different ways that interpersonal relationships can push our system to dysfunction, culminating with disorganization in the attachment. Now, think about the consequences if, in addition to having adversity at home, the social context where the person moves around is also adverse. The damage of traumatization can escalate in ways we haven't even begun to make sense of. I'm hoping that by devoting a section to it, I can contribute to making this a more vocal aspect of trauma studies that we can maintain in our awareness at all times.

In colonizer societies, people that migrate, no matter their circumstances, are treated with disdain. The same goes for the way individuals that don't conform to the rules, norms, beliefs, or 'values' of the 'established' are treated and limited. For that reason, and because of its consequences on mental health, I'm using 'systemic adversity' (SAd) to name the treatment applied to any members of a group (family, community, or country) that show any deviation from the 'norm' imposed by the rulers and/or powerful. Systemic adversity is *an endless exposure to despair that jeopardizes the integrity and stability of large groups of people* (such as migrants but not limited to them).

When an individual is marginalized, confronting alienation every day creates a terrible hurt, a hurt that is carried unnoticed with tremendous consequences. Think of it this way: a dysfunctional home is a place where some members of the family put out their frustration, pain, hurt, and the worst of themselves on the children, the dependents, or each other. Similarly, a dysfunctional society is one where the vulnerable and unprivileged are the ones that get the worst of it. If a society adopts practices like active or passive acts of violence, rejection, oppression, disadvantage, and abuse from the 'mighty' to the disempowered, traumatization becomes systemic.

EPIGENETICS AND THE TRANSMISSION OF TRAUMA SYMPTOMS

For many decades, mental disorders were considered defects in genetic information or *part* of the individual's genetic code, and therefore, unchangeable, but it later became evident that most mental disorders were not life sentences and that they could morph and even disappear. That's why when epigenetics arose as a branch of science that studies changes in gene activity or function that can be inherited but not associated with any change in the gene itself or the DNA sequence (Moore et al., 2013), the conversation had to shift. Epigenetics explains inherited traits that are not permanent. This great discovery brought light to the fact that the sequelae of traumatization can be transmitted from one generation to the next—and the urgency to stop this transmission.

Genes are single units contained inside the nucleus of each cell that transmits hereditary information from one generation to another. Genetics focuses on changes in gene activity or function when the DNA sequence changes and the altered one gets inherited (Moore et al., 2013). But the new branch has found that there are epigenetic mechanisms that mediate the expression of the genes; even when every cell in our body contains the exact same genetic information, their expression is not simultaneous by all cell types (Moore et al., 2013). It has now been proposed that people can carry the activation of the survival mode or some of the alterations from traumatization, and even some of the allostatic changes, *from birth in their epigenetic information as 'traumatization expression.'* Epigenetics explains that exposure to toxic stress can modify DNA methylation, which may alter gene expression (Vidrascu et al., 2019), and that such a change in expression is what can be passed to future generations if the methylation persists. DNA methylation is a biological process by which methyl groups are added to the DNA molecule. Methylation's particular characteristic is that it changes the activity of a DNA segment without changing the sequence (Henneman, 2021).

The new perspective replaces the belief that the person is inherently defective because they carry unchangeable traits that cause abnormal behavior ('genetically imperfect'). The new understanding postulates that people may react in unexpected ways because their nervous system's functioning is affected by the expression of the gene that carries maladaptive brain operations: hormonal, psychophysiological, and neural mechanisms learned by the previous generations. Some studies in animals show that some of the adaptations can last several generations if they are not reversed by the porter; up to 14 generations have been tested in worms. If these theories are correct, we could say that the first adversity in the life of a child could be the consequences of the traumatization of their parents or their grandparents, maybe their great-great-great-grandparents. In terms of attachment, this could be the cause of an unformed bond, developmental issues, and a series of impediments to growing adequately. Another adversity could be being diagnosed as Bipolar or ADHD and being medicated early in life instead of identifying the issues as reversible epigenetic alterations. Medication early in life goes against normal development as well. And that's why it's so important to include these findings.

The good news is that the inherited adaptations are modifiable. Think of genes as having switches that can be turned on or off several times during our life span. The inherited 'on' switches can be inhibited in many ways, even by altering our diet. Thanks to epigenetic regulation of the glucocorticoid receptor gene, positive environmental factors can correct behavioral alterations and alleviate trauma symptoms that would otherwise stay, ruin our lives, and be transmitted to the following generation. These findings are very hopeful, especially for those where traumatization has been not only in the family but in a whole community, culture, race, society, or nation. The current social discourse on privilege could connect to this fact: it's a privilege not to fear rejection, expulsion, oppression, or alienation daily because one's parents didn't experience them. That's why it's so crucial to address the consequences of contributing to the deterioration of the mental health of our society's members, whether it's done actively by discriminating, or passively by benefiting from what privilege means and from what discrimination grants.

THE COST OF MICROAGGRESSIONS AND BEING OTHERED

Many social situations cause distress even when they may seem innocent, unintentional, and harmless. One term that can contain many types of social adversity is 'othering.' At this point, the term used to point out the consequences of othering is 'microaggressions,' but many people find the term accusatory. By our nature, we go into defensive/flight mode when we feel accused, or we go into fight mode when accusing, which may be detrimental in terms of our reactions to an interaction that needs rectification more than confrontation. Still, it's understandable that unprivileged individuals feel the need to use strong words/reactions to demand accountability for the damage inflicted by a lack of awareness and disinterest shown for centuries. Microaggressions can be of many types, from being disrespectful or impertinent toward others due to mindlessness, all the way to removing the dignity of the ones alienated by a lack of consideration and respect. People that are treated as 'other' accumulate emotional wounds that at some point can damage the autonomic nervous system (ANS) causing dysfunction not only at an individual level but also at communal or societal, provoking undesired reactions with hurtful consequences to both sides. Rejection sensitivity applies perfectly here. People that suffer from microaggressions constantly become very sensitive to continuous rejection and hurt. It not only affects the interaction but also the individual's system, like a double-edged sword. If the microaggression had consequences that caused traumatization, every microaggression will be relived by the individual again and again from generation to generation, retraumatizing them and manifesting as backlashes of previous hurts. The reaction to the next microaggression will reflect the accumulation of the hurt, but to the offender, it may seem disproportionate, which would cause further rejection and dismissiveness. Traumatization and rejection sensitivity need to be understood in order to comprehend the damage of microaggressions (on both ends).

Othering is an intersectional term that includes an ample variety of interactions that end up marginalizing and separating individuals from having access to mainstream possibilities. Othering assumes—consciously or unconsciously—that those 'other' individuals, due to their ethnic background, skin-tone, nationality, social/financial status, level of education, language, gender, size (weight and height), age, sexual orientation, disabilities, religion, etc., should not be granted the same as 'them.' Being othered may not always be traumatic but it accumulates distress due to its alienating nature, the reminder of the disadvantage, and the doubts and insecurities of the self, which can generate allostatic changes, and we know what happens when someone accumulates too many of those changes: their system overloads. As we saw, rejection and not belonging cause fear, pain, shame, and dread. Those emotions aggregate to any injuries to the person or of their community by making them feel excluded and unsafe. Othering in all its forms means rejection, abuse, and neglect; traumatizing agents that contribute to prolonging the pain and the damage.

Racism is an obvious way to alienate those who don't belong to the race of the powerful. Racism is not only othering but the intentional creation of disadvantages to those pertaining to a 'race' that is considered ineligible to have the same of what the dominant group has. I'm putting quotes around 'race' because racism is not necessarily race-based, since race is a construct created and modified by dominant groups.

We could add the objectification or devaluation of being exploited as less than human (that is implicit in racism and gender discrimination) as extreme traumatizing agents. By practicing discrimination, dominant groups in general (and colonizer/imperialistic countries in particular) ignore the needs—social neglect—of the ones that have to submit as a way to avoid facing the consequences and responsibility of abusing, having invaded, stripped away, dominated, exploited, and oppressed the original inhabitants of the dominated land. In dominating societies, oppression is practiced by placing severe restrictions on the dominated group for the advantage of a few, reducing their capacity to compete (social abuse). Oppression exercises a mental dominance that inflicts a sense of inferiority, a loss of identity, and an unspoken resentment (social mental undermining). Discriminatory and oppressive practices that prove threatening to a member of a community threaten the whole community. For instance, if a transgender individual is killed out of hatred, all the members of the transgender community will feel at risk, and their survival mechanisms will get activated, putting them on the verge of developing not only an individual but also a collective wound.

WHEN ABUSE AND NEGLECT BECOME SYSTEMIC

All these ways to practice 'otherness' become systemic and institutionalized by establishing explicit and implicit rules, laws, policies, and social practices that are detrimental to the sufferers' mental health, draining and depleting the resources and resilience of individuals and their communities. That sense of disempowerment is obviously defeating, and you know defeat is the key element to breaking the system's equilibrium and prolonging traumatization. One clear example is neglecting the health of the members of certain communities that not only lack the money or the affiliation for insurance policies but are given less priority when looking for medical assistance. It also includes allocating lower funds for education, security, hygiene, housing, and so on. Poorly educated children will have less possibility to go up the ladder for better jobs, salaries, and careers, imprinting a sense of defeat that is hard to overcome.

> I worked once with a 14-year-old Latin-American migrant that told me, "Why would I make the effort? I know I'm going to end up in jail no matter what I do." That sense of defeat is what I'm talking about.

It doesn't require much thought to understand that poverty could be an expected consequence of these practices and that it implies a traumatizing downward spiral. Low socioeconomic status has been associated with high levels of allostatic load (Gustafsson et al., 2014) and some studies prove that infants born to mothers living in poverty or areas with a high crime rate have smaller volumes of gray and white matter across the entire brain (Luby et al., 2013). Elevated stress during pregnancy also alters the development of the fetal brain, which subsequently decreases the kid's cognitive development (CNH, 2022). These adverse circumstances limit the possibilities for that child to thrive. Still, many people prefer to believe that poverty is the fault of the deprived and that society has nothing to do with it. Criminality has a similar origin. Desperate people commit desperate actions, and social adversity plus aggregated traumatization causes extreme despair, despair that prolongs dysregulation and cognitive distortions of all sorts, despair that may find drugs or substances to be the only way to placate it. When someone fears for their life or the lives/integrity of others just for their affiliation, the traumatization is constant, recurrent, pervasive, and central.

Being othered and abused/neglected—explicitly or implicitly—due to being part of an oppressed group creates distress to the individual and all the elements of the group. Depending on the group, the type of emotional injury caused by social adversity could be called social, cultural, racial, historical, or several other designations that are constantly evolving. Historical trauma, for example, appeared in the academic literature to bring attention to the consequences and repercussions—that has lasted for generations—of neglecting medical services for entire communities such as Native Americans' mental and physical health.

WHEN SYSTEMIC ADVERSITY BECOMES TRAUMATIZING

There are many areas affected when someone is exposed to systemic adversity, like identity and personality, for example; since they are highly correlated, damage to identity erodes personality and reshapes behavior. The collective-self is also affected by the categorization of the larger social framework. Identifying with one's group becomes a commitment, which may generate further rejection not of the individual necessarily but of the categorized group. This places the individual in the huge predicament of being loyal to themselves or to the group 'they belong to.' This predicament presents another challenge because there are biases against the most basic of the attachment principles; the dominant groups have spread the idea that minorities are 'more communal' and see it as a shortcoming, pushing the person to become more individualistic to avoid rejection, which, in turn, becomes rejection from the original group and not acceptance from the ruling group. Not belonging causes shame and quiet terror, rejection causes defeat, and the loss of identity debilitates and drains resilience. That's a successful formula for running out of resources, developing a trauma disorder, and delaying growth, internally and externally. Social adversity creates chaos in the psyche of the debilitated group and each of its individuals, which obviously works against achieving internal (and external) equilibrium and organization.

Mendo is a good example of how the bias of society against not only race or ethnicity, but also behavior, intellectual abilities, and even height damages a person's core. In addition to the adversity he experienced at home, he was discriminated against because he had conduct issues. He was also bullied, stereotyped, and cast out for several of his characteristics, something his father experienced too, which influenced their identity and reactivity.

Trauma Domain #9: Identity and Personality (Within the Frame of Systemic Adversity)

When the counselor in college classified her as an outsider, Michaela's identity as an American was hurt. She doubted herself and questioned whether she had been abused as a consequence of how others perceived her. Her identity as an attractive woman was also disturbed by the rape, which then made her feel like an ordinary desired object. However, Clara's identity and sense of self were shattered when she moved to the US. Her personality suffered big changes due to the effort to maintain the social recognition that she had lost, which had a negative impact on her and each member of her family.

We may not need to develop an identity to survive, but our personality is the manager of our interactions, and interactions are what sets our system into protection mode once we find those interactions (or our personality) challenging or threatening. Identity, personality, and self are interconnected but distinct. Identity refers to *how we perceive how others perceive us*, personality is *how we present ourselves to be perceived*, and self is *how we perceive ourselves*. Personality is stronger and well-integrated when identity is congruent with one's sense of self. Identity and personality are essential parts of the work when resolving traumatization. They have been left out of treatment because they are assumed as traits of 'who the person is,' considering flaws as inherited, or ignoring them as irrelevant. When personality is seen as dysfunctional, it may get attributed to a personality disorder, which in itself is rejecting and judgmental. Traumatization affects behavior and creates negative thoughts about oneself and the world, altering self-identification and pushing the traumatized individual to either create personas to adapt to the world they have to navigate or to modify their behavior aiming for belonging and acceptance.

THE EFFECTS OF TRAUMATIZATION ON OUR IDENTITY

Identity formation requires a conscious process of questioning one's purpose, values, feelings, thoughts, and behaviors. It takes years—almost as many as our brain takes to mature—to form an identity even for those that encounter no challenges. It includes questioning the way we relate to those that may—or may not—share similar habits to the ones we share with the group we identify with (Merry, 2010). Once those (and many other) questions are worked out, identity becomes more coherent with behavior and personality. But when society influences our identity (with categories, for instance), it's harder to form it.

Categorization affects identity in more ways than we think. When someone belongs to a group of oppressed or discriminated individuals who are used to having assigned an individual identity through dismissive treatment and the imposition of names that collectively dictate how one should be identified, the formation of that person's identity gets severed. It develops not as the individual sees themselves but as the dominant group wants them to see themselves. Research has found that injuries to identity and self-worth are key markers of mental disorders. Categories have been one way that those who hold power officially, or through simply belonging to dominant groups, oppress others by creating and marking limits. Carrying the hopelessness implicit in the identity category harms self-esteem, agency, and connection to the individual and the collective. It also reinforces the need to create a hollow-self that will try to solve the conflict of not being accepted by cre-ating a fake or on-the-surface personality, which hurts the identity further.

Identity is also related to the collective-self. Almost all approaches in psychi-atry and clinical psychology view individuals' mental health as at least partly influenced by adequate identity development, positive self-conceptions, high self-esteem, and/or maintaining valued social identities. This speaks of the fact that identity is formed in part of how we view ourselves, which is reflected (and affected by) the way others see us; identity formation includes the way we feel about who we are according to the way we learn to identify our char-acteristics among a group of people we share values and practices with. If the collective identity is damaged, the collective-self will be damaged as well. Take the example of immigration or refugee status. The person has not only to endure the difficulties of leaving everything behind but the maltreatment of the place where they end up moving to, plus the fear of expulsion. One of the most extreme cases of defeat of our times is seen in refugees in Sweden. It is recognized as Resignation Syndrome where kids go into an almost cata-tonic state with almost no consciousness or mobility once they reach defeat.

A less extreme case is Michaela's mother. She had no choice but to leave everything behind and move to another country where her eth-nic background is looked down upon. She coped by living in denial, compartmentalizing reality, and radically changing her behavior. Her sense of self and identity received such a blow that her perception changed, her emotions dissociated, and her personality suffered. It seems as if she was not able to ever recover and may even meet the criteria for a personality disorder.

THE EFFECTS OF SHARING A DEFEATING NARRATIVE

Personality is supposed to stay stable over time in order to be classified as such. Since behavior is motivated and influenced by external (i.e., environ-mental) as well as internal (e.g., emotional, biological, and learned) factors, personality is expected to include an organized set of actions. When some-one suffers traumatization, there is no balance or regularity in experiences and therefore, behavior projects that way of feeling. The lack of organization affects the psychological identity which relates to self-image (one's mental model of oneself), self-esteem, agency, and individuality.

Memory represents a critical tool for shaping identity since neural connec-tions are shaped by experience. Personality, then, can be described as the tendency to use certain pathways that directly shape self-regulation and emotional responses. After traumatization, the person may center their attention on what happened to them, reconstructing 'reality' around their worst memories and missing out on the opportunity to take in new information. We then try to make sense of our experiences by narrating and re-narrating events, which facilitates identity construction when we find similar stories but keeps the survival circuits running. Traumatization modifies the narrative the person uses for self-identification, and collective traumatization changes the narrative of the collective. One feeds the other, normally for the worse.

HOW SYSTEMIC TRAUMATIZATION CAUSES LOSS OF IDENTITY AND PERSONALITY

Traumatization interrupts the self-reflective functions—the central mechanism for creating coherent narratives and connecting meaningfully to others. This leaves the individual with the belief that happiness escapes their possibilities. It is common to observe an identity shift after traumatization that is not only an outcome but a widespread survival strategy that actually affects one's capacity to bounce back to the previous state (Abernathy, 2008). Think of the terms 'rape victim' or 'DV survivor'—due to the high emotional significance and impact on one's life of having gone through traumatization, the aftermath comes to be seen as central to one's sense of identity. Emotionality and motivation get affected when people compare themselves with either everybody else or with their past selves, or with the group that rejects them. This comes with spending huge amounts of time contemplating their failures, shortcomings, and flaws, thinking about how other people perceive them, assessing their ability to perform certain tasks, and convincing themselves they lack vitality, support, direction, options, and possibilities. Their sense of who they are revolves around traumatization and the traumatization or wounds of the collective.

Traumatization also causes personality issues. Societies or communities function like parents when we consider the system that forms us. Having to navigate the world without understanding it and feeling rejected individually—and as a member of a collective—proves extremely tolling. By not resolving the basic function of creating a bond with the caregiver, and similarly, with the 'world,' many suffer from confusion. Not feeling like part of something, or not understanding why we are denied acceptance, leads to the creation of personas with better chances of being accepted, and keeps us as shielded as possible by dissociating the hurt and pretending to be someone else. All sorts of psychological issues follow.

Identity and personality are potential traumatizing agents, especially within the frame of systemic adversity, because of the conflict they create. The missing coherence between how others perceive us versus not knowing how one perceives oneself is disorienting, shaming, and anxiety-provoking—traumatizing agents themselves. Personality, consequently, becomes affected by trying to compensate for the lack of certainty of what someone's role is, or where they fit in.

Aggregated Traumatization

Advocating for the rights of minority groups in Colombia precipitated the assassination of Clara's father. He was an advocate and active participant in the fight to bring equilibrium to a system that had lost it, but when there is chaos, there is confusion, and erratic behavior can jeopardize stability further. Social injustice always carries pain and fear.

Aggregated traumatization can be seen as a vicious loop of dysfunction and dysregulation that originates from more than one factor—predisposition, failed attachment, epigenetic alterations, a traumatized social system, and further participation of several traumatizing agents. The lack of equilibrium in one individual has the potential to destabilize other individuals inside and out. In the same way that our system suffers modifications when something alters its operation, families and communities are part of systems that suffer alterations when one or more of their members experience instability. So, the dysregulation and sense of defeat accumulate in the individual making it more difficult to resolve their own traumatization. It gets to a point where people stop caring about themselves while also having problems relating to others.

Imagine you step on a piece of glass and you just keep on walking without removing the shard, cleaning, or protecting your foot. Yep: messy, bloody, and painful. Now imagine if you get another cut on top, then a burn a week later without ever having healed from the previous lesions; you wish to complain but the individuals around you have broken bones and other bigger injuries, crying incessantly. No one notices your wounds and hearing others cry increases your own pain. At some point, you won't be able to identify where your hurt comes from. That's how I'd describe aggregated traumatization (where the shard may be intergenerational).

Maybe the example of the glass sounds extreme, but when the emotions and pain of others are high and constant, we then may be prompted to ignore our own emotions, and the aggregation of dysfunction will keep damaging our system without being able to know the root cause. Just think that when someone experiences shock, more than one person will tell them that everything is fine and that they should let go. That appears to be the worst advice to someone that is trying to make sense of a traumatic and overwhelming experience; the interruption of the natural flow of the emotional response causes the negative emotions to stay stuck in the system similar to food that is not digested. When the threat is not only experienced by an individual but by an entire community, it's even harder to find the space to process the hurt and find meaning. For instance, it is hard for a person that is sexually abused to find solace from a caregiver that was sexually abused themselves and never said something about it or got any support. Besides, the system can't metabolize fear when fear keeps getting activated. It'd be like trying to digest a big meal by continued eating. That's why it's challenging to help communities heal from systemic wounding that has hurt all of its members, especially if the members still carry the pain as part of an identity that has lasted generations. If the systemic wound is at the basis of someone's life, every extra adverse circumstance will aggregate the dysfunction.

PASSING THE DAMAGE OF TRAUMATIZATION TO NEW GENERATIONS

I had reservations about including the intergenerational transmission of trauma (ITT) because there is still not a clear delineation of what 'intergenerational trauma' encompasses. Some people refer to the 'transmission of trauma' to mean the learned fear and conditioned responses from the traumatization of the parents or previous generations. Some other authors are using intergenerational trauma to refer to the effects that sharing traumatic memories have on the new generations and 'installing' those memories in their descendants as if they had lived what the ancestors did. Some people even believe that those memories are not 'installed' but actually reside in the memory of the descendant as if they were their own but that can't be proven. The APa defines intergenerational trauma as the phenomenon in which the descendants of a person who has experienced a traumatic event show adverse emotional and behavioral reactions to the event that are similar to those of the person themselves but don't specify if the aversion is learned or spontaneous. Neurobiology-based literature considers intergenerational trauma as the alterations in the epigenetic information transmitted from a traumatized individual to their offspring causing the infant to show the activation of the survival mode, a dysregulated ANS (Yehuda & Lehner, 2018), and/or alterations/symptoms in their biology. For instance, in descendants of traumatized individuals, higher (or lower) levels of cortisol than normal or larger amygdala at birth have been observed. ITT may also start in the womb by transmitting the alterations that the mother is experiencing while living in a traumatizing environment.

We may be far from having scientific results reporting whether the reactions of traumatized descendants are purely epigenetic or if they come from acquired schemas and behavior. I may anticipate that it's a combination of both (nurture and nature), as can be observed in almost all of psychology's phenomena. The important point here is that when individuals suffer the consequences of traumatization without healing interventions, the sequela will be passed to their descendants and their system will be already affected from the start.

RETRAUMATIZATION: WHEN IT ISN'T THE SAME BUT STILL FEELS THE SAME

Even if it may sound outside of the social context of this chapter, I want to bring retraumatization back into focus here because its implicit characteristics are important in the process of aggregating traumatization. Since traumatization keeps us connected to the past and distorts the perception of the present, when traumatized individuals face a situation that seems *undifferentiated* from a past traumatizing experience, the brain may activate fractions of the traumatic memories together with the emotionality connected to them, causing the person to relive the traumatic situation, which reactivates the protections that traumatized them (or members of their community) previously. Using the analogy of the cut, imagine the person suffering a new cut in the same place (even if there was already a scar); it'll grow bigger, bleed profusely, and take longer to heal. This can be experienced over and over without the conscious awareness that the present pain is more connected to the previous cuts than to what's causing the cut. A microaggression is a perfect example. It hurts profoundly because of how many times and how many people have experienced the injury. The pain is not about the person committing the microaggression, but mainly about experiencing the offense again.

Reliving traumatic past experiences—whether ours or transmitted intergenerationally—brings up feelings of powerlessness; the activation will continue modifying processes because the brain predicts that the person is at risk once more. Backlashes, in the case of inherited traumatization, make it almost impossible to recognize them as part of the past. Some authors state that some of this retraumatization happens even if the traumatic events were experienced by others, whether from the same group or from ancestors. This type of retraumatization causes a set of extra symptoms—or the aggravation of previous ones. Therefore, many situations that may seem insignificant to others are perceived as insurmountable for someone that has confronted different types of traumatization and carries the traumatization of others close to them that have suffered similar situations, including the ones transmitted by previous generations. This type of activation (aggregated) keeps exacerbating symptoms and debilitating the person in many different ways: behaviors become more extreme and erratic, health deteriorates, perception and cognition have real difficulties recognizing what the meaning of life is, and motivation is lost.

WHEN AGGREGATED TRAUMATIZATION MEANS AGGREGATED DYSFUNCTION

For those born with a predisposition to get dysregulated, the traumatization suffered at the hands of traumatized parents and/or traumatizing social, systemic, or institutionalized adversity aggravates their situation. Many studies talk about the predisposition to dysregulate when there is a traumatization expression passed epigenetically from one generation to another. There is also a lot written and studied on how systemic types of oppression and discrimination affect the levels of stress and the capacity to regulate for those that live under implicit social threat or imposed defeat. The brain of those under extreme duress has its structure and biochemistry altered. Those alterations have repercussions such as 'non-approved' behavior, difficulty adapting, and a limited capacity to participate in society. On top of that, health is affected by a disease process of inflammation, imbalance in the cardiovascular system, and a compromised autoimmune system. Anger, hatred, and resentment—internal traumatizing agents—grow like weeds, infesting and tainting every experience, continuing the aggregation of traumatizing agents that cause a set of symptoms that manifest after extensive traumatization at different times in life and under different social contexts that affect every aspect of the person, internally and externally. *Aggregated traumatization signifies that the dysfunction has been part of one's life for very long, even from before one is born because it may have been carried by members of the family and/or community, and that the traumatic circumstances don't seem to cease.*

AGGREGATED TRAUMATIZATION SYNDROME: A UNIFYING DIAGNOSIS

When traumatization is aggregated, the alterations and symptoms add up in such a way that people may receive several diagnoses. To make justice to the severity of the damage caused by aggregated traumatization, I chose the name 'Aggregated Traumatization Syndrome' (AGTS) to explain the presentation of a person for whom it is almost impossible to recognize when their system shifted to survival mode because they may have had it as default since birth. By choosing such a name, I want to depict the deepest level of injury to the nervous system, body, and psyche someone can suffer from before they lose connection with reality or the connection with life. Figure 9.1 shows the loop that the system gets into when there are intergenerationally passed alterations, failed attachment, and systemic adversity before confronting the individual traumatizing agents. It's not possible to recognize the origin of the problem but the dysregulation, damage, and dysfunction keep accumulating.

All trauma disorders are adaptations for staying alive while trying to maintain the connection between mind and brain. Once the alterations reach a point where they can't keep the person 'alive,' the result is not death per se but the loss of connection with the outside world. This can lead to a lack of mental health that many times is the cause for someone's death: physically after committing suicide or reckless behavior, emotionally by complete despair, or socially by seclusion. At the extreme, some individuals continue living but only in their 'own world.' I have met several individuals stating that they are

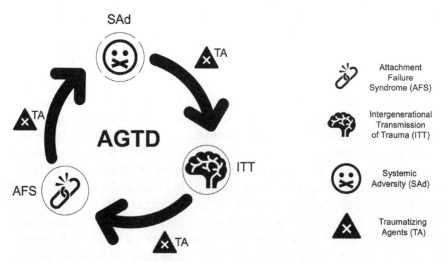

Figure 9.1 Loop of traumatization in AGTS

just waiting to die even if it takes decades, or saying that if there was a 'stop' button to end their lives, they would have pushed it already. These are not suicidal ideations per se but represent a complete loss of meaning, deep dissatisfaction, and the lack of spark to live. I have also witnessed how someone can reach the point of no return and develop psychosis that could later be diagnosed as Paranoid Personality Disorder or even Paranoid Schizophrenia. Those are extreme cases, but for most, AGTS can mean high dysfunction at every level: spending part of their lives visiting doctors due to innumerable medical issues, trying one medication after another, changing jobs or having none, hooked on substances, constantly dealing with unethical/legal issues and financial problems, finding themselves alone or on dysfunctional relationships, or incarcerated/isolated from society.

Suffering from AGTS can be so painful that people may not feel pain at all. Imagine how confusing life is for those born with a dysregulated nervous system (intergenerational), and a biological (epigenetic) sense of defeat. Think of what it'd be like if, on top of not knowing life without a dysregulated system, the person is rejected by the parent, suffers from abuse at home, and as soon as they go out, they confront systemic adversity. For someone whose perception is already affected at birth, with a predisposition to interpret everything as dangerous, regular stimuli such as the pain of hunger or tiredness could drive their tolerance off limits. The newborn may be intolerant to everything because the internal resources are already insufficient. If the caregiver can't attend to or respond to the needs of the infant, the pain will grow exponentially, likely causing many different types of dissociation that will affect development and opportunities. Most descendants of parents with AGTS suffer from attachment failure by default, followed by developmental arrest that highly affects the connection to higher-order feelings. As adults, they may find everything extremely tolling, every task impossible to perform, or a complete lack of moral compass. If additional adversity is added, life becomes an insufferable struggle all through. Under social adversity like poverty, addiction, oppression, or even accumulated resentment toward society, regulation becomes unattainable, and the need to escape (from regular things like norms, people, ideologies, etc.) becomes the only option.

The idea of having a name for aggregated traumatization is to advocate for understanding people's situations before we judge them for their limitations, behavior, or struggles. AGTS is suggested as a term that compassionately opens the possibility that the person carries a load heavier than they can bear even when what they report as heavy doesn't seem as such if seen out of context. It is also an invitation to accept some responsibility for the traumatizing experience of many of our fellow humans who have not had the opportunity to increase their chances of thriving. The concept of AGTS may incite us to actively remove our participation in social and systemic abuse and neglect, and collaborate to alleviate people's psychological pain.

An extreme example of aggregated traumatization is the one that Kalief Browder suffered from. His life was highly publicized around 2014 (Gonnerman, 2014) after the press learned that he had spent three years on Rikers Island (without committing a crime), two of which were in solitary confinement. His biological mother was addicted to crack cocaine during pregnancy and he was removed from her immediately after birth and placed in a foster home. Kalief got placed in a house where there were already many other children. Two kids were biological children of Mr. and Mrs. Browder, but they had raised—in foster care or adoption—a total of 34 kids. When Kalief left Rikers, he was 20. His case got a lot of attention and support from the media which helped him to get into community college. He tried to live the life of a young guy in the Bronx, but his struggle and the aggregation of traumatization he endured were unbearable. Two years after Rikers, he ended his life hanging from his house's window, which in my opinion is a way to end your life and also send a public message.

I only wish that the message that so many individuals 'send' when ending their lives is taken seriously and considered as a collective responsibility. If people from oppressed and discriminated communities continue adding adversity to their experience, society as a whole pays the consequences.

I have intended to show, through Michaela's family, all the layers that traumatization can leave in our body and psyche. We can't assume a person has PTSD as soon as we hear 'traumatic event' (or rape, crash, etc.) without investigating further. I've also tried to illustrate how we can't presuppose that adversity has the same impact on each person, and how 'childhood trauma' means many different things even for the children of the same mother. As in any physical injury, trauma disorders need to be attended to from the innermost to the peripheral. Otherwise, the 'infection' will continue festering on the inside and lasting healing won't be achieved.

References

Abernathy, B. E. (2008). Who am I now?: Helping trauma clients find meaning, wisdom, and a renewed sense of self. G. R. Walz, J. C. Bleuer, & R. K. Yep (Eds.), *Compelling counseling interventions: Celebrating VISTAS' fifth anniversary* (pp. 199–208). Ann Arbor, MI: Counseling Outfitters.

CNH (2022). Stress, anxiety and depression during pregnancy may hinder toddler's cognitive development. *Science Daily.* Children's National Hospital (2022, April 29).

Gonnerman, J. (2014). "Before the law." The New Yorker (6 Oct. 2014: n.pag. Web. 2 November 2015).

Gustafsson P. E., San Sebastian M., Janlert U., Theorell T., Westerlund H., Hammarström A. (2014). Life-course accumulation of neighborhood disadvantage and allostatic load: Empirical integration of three social determinants of health frameworks. *American Journal of Public Health,* 104(5), 904–910. https://doi.org/10.2105/AJPH.2013.301707. Epub 2014 Mar 13. PMID: 24625161; PMCID: PMC3987591.

Henneman, P. (2021). Advances in DNA methylation. *OBM Genetics* (ISSN 2577-5790).

Luby J., Belden A., Botteron K., et al. (2013). The effects of poverty on childhood brain development: the mediating effect of caregiving and stressful life events. *JAMA Pediatrics,* 167(12), 1135–1142. https://doi.org/10.1001/jamapediatrics.2013.3139

Merry, M. S. (2010). Volume 6. Philosophy of education. Identity. P. Peterson, E. Baker, B. McGaw (Eds.), *International encyclopedia of education* (3rd ed.) (pp. 152–156). Oxford: Elsevier.

Moore, L., Le, T., & Fan, G. (2013). DNA methylation and its basic function. *Neuropsychopharmacology,* 38, 23–38. https://doi.org/10.1038/npp.2012.112

Vidrascu, E. M., Bashore, A. C., Howard, T. D. et al. (2019). Effects of early- and mid-life stress on DNA methylation of genes associated with subclinical cardiovascular disease and cognitive impairment: A systematic review. *BMC Medical Genetics,* 20, 39. https://doi.org/10.1186/s12881-019-0764-4

Yehuda, R., & Lehrner, A. (2018). Intergenerational transmission of trauma effects: Putative role of epigenetic mechanisms. *World Psychiatry: Official Journal of the World Psychiatric Association (WPA),* 17(3), 243–257. https://doi.org/10.1002/wps.20568

Part III
Healing Traumatization

I could have decided to end this book with the last line of the previous chapter. At this point, this book has given you the information you need in order to understand the depth that traumatization can reach. You now have a range of tools to assess the damage caused to the nervous system by traumatization, and how that impacts all the system by learning about domains (emotions, memory, perception, etc.). You have also learned throughout this book how traumatization can be resolved, preventing the development of a more permanent problem and also helping eliminate any symptoms that could have appeared and stayed peri- or post-traumatization.

Still, I didn't want to end without making it more explicit that everything you've already learned is connected to healing. Traumatization is systemic; so is healing. Traumatization is multi-dimensional; so is healing. Traumatization is about survival; healing is about reprogramming the survival circuits. And while we cannot fully control whether we'll encounter traumatic circumstances, we *can* regain dominion over our minds and improve the relationship previously established with our experiences. This effort requires a high level of participation from the traumatized individual and a clinician's willingness to approach the system holistically. This is entirely possible, and hopefully easier once you finish this chapter.

DOI: 10.4324/9781003382478-13

Ten
Systemic Trauma Healing

What does systemic healing mean?

How could we structure a plan to reprogram the traumatization's alterations?

Is there a roadmap for integrating the multiple modalities available?

The list of questions about healing from traumatization could be extremely long. I could dedicate a book itself to answering them, but for now, let me share with you that to heal from all the damage inflicted by traumatization, clinicians count on multiple therapeutic interventions from a large (and growing) list of available modalities (Appendix D). There are plenty of books that describe them. What this book has already presented can be used as a foundation for understanding the client's system before a specific modality is implemented and why the modality will (or won't) work. In addition, I am implicitly proposing a shift: a shift to a more systemic mentality that prioritizes taking care of the nervous system. This mentality takes advantage of seeing the person as a unit, not focusing only on past occurrences or a couple of symptoms, but rather emphasizing the lack of coordination between the different elements that form each person's internal world. To put a complex process into simple words, this looks like helping people shift from 'survival mode' into 'living mode.' To that end, I want to share a model with you for applying more effective healing interventions, a model that adds structure to the tools you have already acquired.

A Systemic Approach to Healing Traumatization

Like a tornado that leaves everything flipped, torn, displaced, crooked, or destroyed, destabilizing cities and communities, traumatization— even from a single event—leaves a sequela of injuries, changes,

DOI: 10.4324/9781003382478-14

misplacements, alterations, and disequilibrium that devastates the body's organs and systems and the person's emotional stability. As in the case of tornadoes, there are cities with the resources to repair the damages right away, and there are others that stay engulfed in debris for long. Similarly, some people have the resources to bounce back after traumatization, while others stay devastated indefinitely. The intensity of the tornado compares not only to the intensity of the traumatic event but also to the intensity of the emotional response to it that follows. Allowing traumatizing agents to continue scaring us is equivalent to staying in the storm and continuing to live stepping on scraps of life instead of becoming proactive at rebuilding the house.

A trauma disorder can govern us at many levels and for a long period unless we start reprogramming brain circuits and rebuilding everything that became affected in its wake. Behaviorists have treated it by focusing on changes in behavior, but traumatization changes the nervous system so deeply that behavior is only a projection of the internal chaos; behavior that's a manifestation of dysregulation won't change permanently just because we want it to, and suppressing our emotional reactions can make things worse. Unfortunately, that's what happens when trying to heal traumatization by only modifying cognitions (using CBT or other 'evidence-based' modalities)—perception has been affected and cognition follows those distortions; thoughts are tainted. Emotional reactivity doesn't understand reasoning, and logic won't stop it from recurring. Cognitive restructuring needs to be done for sure, and cognitive interventions are useful and necessary at several points to reprogram scripts (to use one example), but it can't be the only approach to healing the whole system. Consider also that the part of the brain that is in charge of cognition may be working very slowly, or disconnected from other parts of the brain which may be an impediment for cognitive interventions to be successful. Other traditional forms of counseling generally miss how clients' narrations may be part of their 'trauma centrality' where memories and narratives get reshaped by the new way of feeling and seeing things. That's why claims that going in circles about negative memories increases distress are undeniable. Many traditional psychotherapies make the traumatization symptoms worsen by insisting on bringing up the depths of the darkness into the conscious and strengthening the circuits they belong to, by making interpretations of the origin of the dysfunction, or by validating a client's defeating narrative, promoting the permanence of the survival mode. Reprogramming the brain means activating new neurons and creating new paths that replace the ones that create dysfunction, not inadvertently strengthening them.

TRAUMA-FOCUSED VERSUS TRAUMA-INFORMED TREATMENT: HOW TRAUMA THERAPY WORKS

Trauma-focused is not the same as trauma-informed. Trauma-informed treatment is an academic term that appeared with the intention to point out the idea that individuals needed validation for their pain after experiencing a traumatic event. It was born after 'victims of trauma' were blamed or rejected, like a person that was doubted, accused, and interrogated immediately after a sexual assault. Trauma-focused treatment, instead, is a specialization the clinician goes through to learn how the nervous system works and how it becomes affected by shock, terror, or toxic stress, as well as how to restore the damage left after. It centers on healing the autonomic nervous system's (ANS's) dysregulation as opposed to helping the person cope with their distress. In trauma-focused treatment, the traumatized person *is an active participant in the healing* and not only a narrator of stories loaded with negativity and defeat.

Several characteristics differentiate a trauma-focused therapist from other types of clinicians that follow other methods and schools of thought:

- The neurobiological effects of traumatization create a set of symptoms that the trauma therapist includes in the conceptualization of the case and treats as components of the treatment plan. For example, traumatization manifests as a depressive mood at certain moments (and after a certain stimulus), while it manifests as anxiety at others; instead of seeing them as separate disorders, here they are seen as manifestations of the ANS's operation. In the same fashion, if the client discloses aggressivity, it's explained as part of the hyper-activation of the SNS instead of thinking of it as a flaw in the personality, a behavioral issue, or interpreting it as a hidden desire to harm the parent.
- For traumatized individuals, feeling often overrides thinking, emotions are not logical, talking about the pain and painful events is debilitating, and understanding when it started doesn't extinguish the pain. Self-reflection and inner work that promotes the activation of the PFC replace the previous interventions.
- Clients don't come to sessions to report on their week. Content is secondary and an accessory to understanding the obstacles that traumatization left. Present difficulties inform the weekly work.
- Trauma therapy focuses on affect regulation as the prerequisite for any type of meaning-making. The traumatic material and memories related to it are not addressed until the person has reached a set of regulation skills and an understanding of their system.

- The trauma-focused therapist's job is to, over time, help the client shift from the activation of the emotional brain to the activation of the neo-cortex redirecting the previous surrender to intense reactions. Through trauma work, the frontal part of the brain becomes active and strong, able to regulate the reactions and intensity of the structures of the brain that host emotional responses.
- The trauma therapist works against the stigma of seeing someone suffering from a mental health issue as defective, undesirable, and incurable by using a deep understanding of neurobiology, emotions theory, mentaliza-tion, attachment theory, and a highly compassionate comprehension of what it means to be human. Normalizing behavior is an essential com-ponent of this approach.
- The modality used to intervene is chosen at each time depending on the area that needs improvement, or the symptoms that need to be eliminated or reduced such as cognition, affect, memory, identity, agency, and mood.

WHAT SYSTEMIC HEALING INVOLVES

I had an infection on the right side of my neck that weird bacteria had made its home. The swollen lymph nodes had been growing for a year and all the antibiotics had done nothing; my fevers, pain, and other consequences in my immune system were deteriorating my health and well-being. When a doctor announced that I needed surgery to remove the accumulated pus, I looked for a different type of healing approach. I learned that allopathy—the treatment of disease by conventional means that uses drugs to minimize the effects of symptoms—was not systemic. My system was entirely affected but the doctor kept focusing on the in-fection in the neck. I found a doctor that applied systemic medicine—treatment that affects the body as a whole or that acts on a specific system, which in my case was the immune system. My infection was gone in less than two weeks! For a trauma disorder, most people think that we need to focus on traumatic memories in order to heal. Working with the memories is equivalent to removing the pus from the neck, which isn't how we resolve an infection. Treating it systemically is the solution.

By using a bio-psycho-social perspective throughout the book, I wanted you to see how maintaining constant stress and confronting jeopardizing situa-tions affect every aspect of the traumatized individual's system: their ANS, its components, and the executive functions (bio), emotionality and percep-tion (psycho), and the quality of their relationships and interactions (social). How do we apply this to treatment? For starters, it is crucial to assess all the

Traumatizing External Agents	Traumatic experience	Peritraumatic Mechanism	Traumatizing Internal Agents	Posttraumatic Strategy	Symptoms	Complexity	Domains Affected
Accident	Single traumatic event✓	Orienting ✓	Fear ✓	Befriend	**B. Intrusion** flashbacks ✓	Single	Emotion ✓
Illness			Prolonged stress		nightmares	One	
Surgery		Social Engagement✓	Anxiety		backlashes ✓	Several ✓	Dysregulation ✓
Natural Disaster	*Prolonged*			Appease	**C. Avoidance**	Complex	
Combat	from age _0?_	Fawn	Shame ✓		places ✓		Memory ✓
Physical Abuse	to age _19_		Doubt ✓		people ✓		
Emotional Abuse	Type: neglect	Freeze ✓	Guilt ✓	Lock	reminders ✓	Developmental	Perception/Cognition
Sexual Misconduct ✓			Responsibility ✓		**D. Cognition/Mood**		Self ✓
Objectification ✓	*Recurrent*	Fight	Defeat ✓		memory ✓		
Trafficking	periodicity: _random_		Identity issues ✓	Escape ✓	perception ✓	Attachment	
Rape ✓ date-rape	duration: _4 times_	Flight	Unresolved Attachment		self ✓	Unresolved	Dissociation ✓
Neglect ✓	age: _from 10 to 20_				emotions ✓	Ruptures	
Type: emotional	Type: sexual, emotional	Tonic Immobility ✓	Lonesomeness ✓	Attack	**E. Arousal/Reactivity**		Development
Adversity ✓	*Attachment*		Emptiness		irritability ✓		
Type(s): father aggression/alcohol, brother rage and conduct	Unresolved		Epigenetic info		hypervigilance ✓	Aggregated	Attachment
Attachment Issues:	Ruptures	Collapse Immobility✓	Anger/Rage	Submit	startle ✓	Intergenerational✓	
Betrayal	Type: grandmom moved away, mom absent				insomnia ✓	Cultural	Identity ✓
Abandonment	Number: 1		Resentment/ hatred		concentration ✓	Trauma of others Person(s): ___	
Rejection		Quiescent Immobility		Failed/ Disengaged ✓	Dissociation		
Social Abuse or Neglect✓					Type: detachment from pain, fantasy, isolation		
Racism							
Othering ✓				Reboot			

Figure 10.1 Michaela's trauma case conceptualization

functions that caused the loss of equilibrium. Since traumatization reprograms most of our system operations, reinforces survival circuits, and creates new automatic ones that activate undesirable or extreme reactions that the person feels unable to control, the goal of healing becomes to reduce that type of activation or replace it with the formation of circuits that activate desirable actions/feelings. The model of treatment I've been proposing in this book includes resolving fear and the additional traumatizing agents involved in order to end the struggle for survival, but also working on each one of the trauma domains, dynamically, to achieve integration and equilibrium of the whole biological system. Holistic healing includes the brain but also elements like the circadian rhythm, dental hygiene, diet, relationships—and our relationship with life and ourselves.

Many factors help us see the big picture of how the system of a client is working; to conceptualize a case, we can start by including indicators such as complexity, dominant emotions, type of situation that put the system into defense mode, survival strategies used before and after, and the emotion(s) that was elicited during the struggle. The following chart (Figure 10.1) uses Michaela's information to show how to begin conceptualizing her case before making her treatment plan.

292   Healing Traumatization

Living Mode

> Remember my analogy of how living traumatized is equivalent to living by walking on one's knees? By design, the moment that person is offered more vertical space, they will immediately go back into walking straight and on two feet. That's how our brain responds as soon as becoming more whole seems possible. By going back to being more effective and balancing into harmony as soon as *the need to force its maladaptive operation subsides,* the brain will work on resolving traumatization.

We know by now that when someone experiences traumatization and stays traumatized, it means their system shifts to operate in survival mode. But I want to make it very clear that the brain's focus is on helping us live. Surviving is merely one option for when the brain assumes we can't generate others, and lingering there is unwanted. Internal equilibrium (homeostatic or allostatic) is not only a process for avoiding death but a regulatory system built to maintain us healthy and keep us functioning optimally (Damasio, 2005). Therefore, our system is designed to have harmony in and out, giving us the possibility of a fulfilling life, engaging in learning, assimilating, investigating, discerning, and finding meaning in everything we do or experience. If you observe groups of mammals, they use their emotional brain to mingle, adapt to weather and terrain, and stay connected as a unit, and not to rehash their misfortunes.

To maintain balance and harmony, humans count on the capacity to make decisions, choices, predictions, reflections, and many more ways to participate in our system's optimal operation. The more we engage with it, the more alive and healthier our system is, and the better we function, again, in and out. In, because all our organs work in unison, and out, because our relationships, work, productivity, and collaboration would be balanced ideally as well. We feel motivated and satisfied, and our life finds meaning. But *if we fail to persist we can only subsist.* That's what mental illness is: losing connection with life itself and the vitality and enjoyment of being alive. Being mentally unwell is to stay focused on what's wrong.

LIVING MODE: MENTAL HEALTH AS A ROUTINE

We know that when we want to be healthy, we exercise, eat well, sleep enough hours, take care of our hygiene, enjoy leisure time, and have regular visits to the doctor to check that everything is working to our satisfaction.

What type of routines do we have for our mental health? How often do we check on it? Do we even know what that means?

From what I've explained so far, I want us to agree that being mentally healthy is equivalent to operating in living mode. To achieve this goal, psychotherapy should be as present in people's lives as any other health practice. For example, we brush our teeth every day and visit the dentist at least twice a year. We don't wait until our teeth are rotten to go for a visit, right? We may have also needed braces to straighten our teeth which makes us go to the dentist (orthodontist) for several years. In the same fashion, we should have a mental health daily routine, and visit our clinician at least once a month, go to therapy to 'straighten' some of our mental/emotional conflicts in intervals. That'd avoid a lot of suffering. We don't need to wait until life is unbearable to find a mental health specialist to keep our mental health in check. Maintenance builds strength, like in exercise, where progress can get lost. Let's imagine you go to the gym almost daily for a whole year and develop muscle in your arms and legs. Then you stop. Your muscles will lose strength and volume little by little unless you keep a routine to continue reinforcing what you achieved. You may not need to go daily, but if you keep exercising with a certain frequency, all the previous effort will have been worth it.

LIVING MODE: PROTECTING YOUR MIND

Our body is material, solid, and concrete, and we can find concrete ways to take care of it, but our mind and our thoughts are immaterial, and therefore, it's harder to figure out how to manage and take care of them. At least we know that thoughts and emotions correlate with brain activity. If we take care of brain activity, it could be easier to manage our thoughts and emotionality, and therefore, our actions and reactions. Brain activity could be modified if we understand what affects it. Depending on the functions that we use more often, certain brain circuits get active frequently and become stronger, consuming a large amount of the energy budget. That slows down other areas and other functions. If we participate in activating the areas that are more helpful for our well-being, we could be gaining control that otherwise seems impossible. Since most people don't think in those terms, we often do the opposite of what our brain needs. Many people, for instance, read and watch the news constantly, and for entertainment, they watch violence or shows about murderers. That'd be equivalent to eating garbage and rotten food. It feeds our brain activity with fear, anxiety, and multiple possibilities for danger.

There are simple practical formulas to help us coordinate brain and mind. Almost everything in this book has taken a neuroscientific approach to learning how the brain operates our emotionality and our mental states. Now it's time to use some of that information to figure out better ways to take care of our minds—and gain some agency in our emotional responses. Let's find out how we can discover our way to the living mode.

LIVING MODE: HEALING AGENTS

Since we conceptualize trauma disorders as the loss of internal equilibrium, and we understand that equilibrium is systemic, we need more than one healing agent to regain balance. To counterbalance the effect of each traumatizing agent, healing agents need to be both internal (like *hope*) and external (like *boundaries*). Safety or calmness help, but one often needs more. In essence, people need to develop or recover resources to override poorly modulated actions and decisions. Having resources is key to building resilience. Figure 10.2 includes several healing agents that correspond to traumatizing ones. I'll also expand on more macro and micro healing agents that are less common.

Healing Agent: External Social Systems (Collective)

At a macro level, we are part of a social system, and collective traumatization also affects each individual. The agents needed to heal a collective are social in nature, like friendship. Friends, peers, healing social networks, and the connection to a community that shares an identity can replace the internalized conflicts that arise from polarized forces that split individuals into loving and rejecting their roots and/or the group that othered, discriminated, or oppressed them. Recognizing those biases jumpstarts the process. Social injuries require social healing. Some of the healing agents that work individually could be shared with a family or community to achieve collective relief, such as the development of pride and dignity to compensate for the shame and humiliation experienced as a group and as a member of that group, with the caveat that they need to be constant, structured, and intentional.

TRAUMATIZING → HEALING	EXTERNAL	Traumatizing and Healing Agents	INTERNAL	TRAUMATIZING → HEALING
Danger/Threat → Safety, protection				Fear → Trust, knowledge
Abuse → Boundaries, self-respect				Stress → Agency, confidence
Adversity → Support, resources				Shame → Pride, self-worth
Neglect → Self-love, dignity				Defeat → Hope, optimism
Rejection → Recognition, acceptance				Hatred → Courage, compassion
Systemic Adversity → Community				Rumination → Attention, focus

Figure 10.2 Traumatizing agents and their healing agents

Healing Agent: Internal Social Systems (Human Microbiome)

We are inhabited by a multitude of organisms that make our bodies their environment. They form what is called the human microbiome—the collection of all micro-organisms living in our bodies. The microbiome includes bacteria, primitive single-celled organisms (archaea), fungi, and even some protozoans and nonliving viruses. Their genetic information (genomes) contributes to the broad picture of our genetic information. We actually carry many times more genetic information from the microbiota than from our genes. It has been discovered recently that our mental health depends in a big part on maintaining a healthy colony of these micro-organisms and that traumatization affects it. For example, over 90% of the serotonin in our body is made in our gut, and deficiencies in its production are conducive to depressive symptoms. Also, infections in the gut during pregnancy or early in life relate to anxiety-like behaviors and later impaired cognitive function. Stress seems to be a major factor in the alteration of the gut microbiota too because of its correlation with the HPA axis. The microbiome plays a role in the programming of the HPA axis early in life, and even before when the carrier transmits bacteria to the fetus. In early life, the gut microbiome shapes the nervous system and hosts immune balance. If there is a high level of stress, the gut microbiota suffers alterations that cause long-lasting immune consequences and increases the risk of developing stress-related disorders (Leclercq et al., 2016). Therefore, a balanced diet, a regular routine, dental and environmental hygiene are part of this system's healing agents.

Healing Agent: Matter and Energy Systems (Brain-Mind System)

At a macro level, I won't go beyond society, but at a micro level, I want to go farther than micro-organisms into the quantum or even into the qualia—the constitutive elements of consciousness (Koch & Hepp 2006). Even when neuroscience and physics give us a lot of answers about our mental states, we still need to understand why between two individuals under the exact same conditions, one goes down the path of suffering and the other makes the best of it. The interaction between our brain and our mind seems to be explained better by quantum physics—the branch of science that studies the behavior of matter and energy at the most fundamental level. These studies have uncovered many of the properties and behaviors of nature's building blocks.

Dan Siegel (the proponent of Interpersonal Neurobiology and one of my heroes because of his wisdom and extraordinary compassionate intelligence) defines the mind as the "emergent, self-organizing, embodied, and relational process that regulates the flow of energy and information" (Siegel, 1999). Traumatization affects relationships and the mechanisms that could assist us in embodying this *flow of energy and information*; the information gets distorted and the flow interrupted. To resolve it, we need to recover that flow inside and out. It's impossible to heal our wounds if we don't use the power of our minds and work in our relationships.

Human behavior is arbitrary and traditional methods have not been able to predict or regulate it. Quantum methods are finding ways to explain why our thoughts seem to have a life on their own and how a simple shift in attitude (and perspective) can help our system to operate better. We are still too far from a clear understanding, but if we think about the energy flow, we may develop some trust in ourselves and use our interactions in society and nature to elevate our mental health. Biofeedback, for instance, teaches us that we can control our own heart rate by changing our thoughts. Similarly, we can participate in our own systemic balancing through something like hope. Hope is a clear example of a healing agent that depends on our minds. Hope doesn't need an object and could be experienced as completely abstract. Think in the power of "I hope so" by observing your body when you say that simple phrase. We can hope without knowing what we are hoping for. Embodying the thought and allowing it to flow in your system make a difference in how your system responds. 'Experiencing' hope alleviates pain and eliminates struggle, especially when you understand how the system lost balance in the first place.

Healing Agent: Trust

Since most traumatized people lose trust and spend years 'trying to recover' it—especially if they were not able to develop trust toward the caregiver—I want to include it here as an important element to resolve and heal traumatization. Trust is dual—an experience and an attitude—that evolves from appraisal and decision-making. Trust involves a participant's stance toward the person or object that will be trusted and a willingness to do it. Once there is information about what can be trusted, and enough experiences of success while trusting, a sense of safety can be achieved and trust can become an emotional state (Lahno, 2001). Some see trust as purely instinctual, and others see it solely as a decision that a person makes, but trust has an affective component because our brain helps us determine when to trust someone. It has been proposed that we need to trust in order to connect with the one we rely on to care for us. That explains why the infant can recognize the main caregiver before they are able to recognize almost anything else. It has also been said that we need trust in order to procreate; if we didn't have a mechanism to assess who is a trustworthy candidate to mate, we would never have offspring. This explains the production of oxytocin when we need to bond.

Trust then could be seen as a protection, a natural tendency, and a necessity (McLeod, 2021). Trust induces the production of oxytocin which regulates and calms down fear by reducing the overactivation of the amygdala. It is correlated with fear in an opposite way—the more fear, the less trust and oxytocin. That's also why attachment is regulatory because trusting the caregiver induces the nervous system to regulate. Most people that suffered traumatization don't experience trust because the survival mode keeps the brain experiencing fear as a mental state, and keeps them alert at all times to find what or who is going to hurt them. That mental state may include an implicit schema that says "trusting is dangerous" and therefore, the possibility of trusting goes away, the production of oxytocin decreases, and the amygdala stays overactive. It's very difficult to stop traumatization if the decision to never trust again has been made. But deciding to trust can promote oxytocin production even if it's for minutes, then days, until the brain finds it easier to maintain a state of healing trust.

ACHIEVING LIVING MODE BY USING THE BRAIN TO CONTROL THE MIND

Most psychiatric disorders are characterized by involuntary and uncontrollable emotionality, reactions, and thoughts. One useful way to explain why we lose control is using the triune brain model presented in Chapter 2 and noticing how each specific functionality affects our well-being.

Primitive Brain Control (Dominated by Primordial Needs)

The reptilian brain is in charge of our most basic functions. If only that part of the brain were operating, we would basically spend our life the same way that iguanas do: eating, evacuating, mating, and resting/sleeping. We would not have to make big decisions or assess the consequences of our actions because we would only follow our natural pre-programmed instincts. But we humans have a different brain than them and if we renounced engaging socially or decide to live in isolation, like a snake, we would suffer. Still, giving in to predominant activation of these functions may make us feel 'lazy,' hedonistic, very interested in sex-food-leisure, and too focused on the simplistic aspects of existence, such as choosing a partner given physical attributes—wide hips (to carry more offspring), more muscles (to be better hunters)—or other decisions of the sort.

Emotional Brain Control (Dominated by Emotions)

Our mammalian brain is in charge of our interactions with others because, as mammals, we need others to survive. Most of the learning, memory, and emotions are regulated by this part of the brain. When it's more active than the other parts, we spend more time focused on relationships, fearing isolation and rejection, craving community, love, and acceptance, shifting from one emotion to another, from one tragedy to another, from one failure to the next. Life can become a constant drama in the pursuit of someone that guarantees love and emotional stability, be consumed by the wish to hurt those that hurt us, or to eliminate those that could eliminate us. Living within a kin structure, competition follows. Being part of a group is not only about hanging out or 'marriage,' but also about power, hierarchy, organization, leadership, and dominance. When we are controlled by this part of our brain, we can start wars, acting vindictive, punitive, jealous, envious, controlling, possessive, conflictive, discriminatory, and violent. This part of the brain is also about the power others have over us with their opinions or judgments. In the search for belonging, we may pretend to be someone else, always obsessing with being liked, validated, chosen, accepted, or admired, and losing the connection with our core. Being in touch with our core is essential for healing, which depends on promoting the activation of our PFC and practicing self-reflection and self-acceptance.

Cognitive Brain Control (Dominated by Cognition)

Our neocortex, the more evolved part of our brain, hosts many functions connecting and managing our primitive and mammalian functions. None of them work isolated from the others; among the functions of the neocortex is to regulate the other two layers. It also has executive functions, language, cognition, abstraction, and even empathy. The neocortex has very distinct functions in both its hemispheres. In general, being controlled by this part of the brain (more and faster activity) could mean (a) being completely engaged with our body and surroundings—as in living in the present moment in total awareness, (b) becoming extremely cognitive, trying to find the logic in everything, or (c) being very connected with the pleasure of the senses, 'in love' with the arts, for example. Being too rational is still preferable to being too emotional or being pulled by the most basic functions; balancing the three is always the goal. Whatever part of the brain consumes the brain's energy budget, it's taking that energy from the other two layers, deactivating them. The person may dismiss emotional signals and may even lose the capacity to relax, sleep, or relate when they're not in coordination. Traumatization causes the energy to be consumed by the reptilian and the limbic and neglects the neocortex.

ACHIEVING LIVING MODE BY USING THE MIND TO DIRECT THE BRAIN

Our mind has no limits. It's as expansive as the universe. If we observe our body's automatic reactions and use the power of our mind, we can override the activation of automatic circuits—whether hard-wired or created. All we need is to use some of the innate functions that assist us in connecting with our mind such as awareness, attention, openness, and autonomy (as in will-power and free-will). By being mentally present during (or immediately after) the activation of unwanted circuits—or circuits that activate unwanted actions/reactions—we can intervene, using other circuits that put in motion more desirable actions/reactions. When the brain controls our mind instead of the other way around, we are at risk of doing, feeling, thinking, or experiencing something we don't wish for. The whole issue of not being mentally well is that when we find ourselves there, we feel as though we have no control over anything. Once we do, then we recover emotional stability and we are mentally healthier. This may seem very difficult; we all struggle at trying to control our emotions and have likely tried many alternatives to find a solution. But the idea of 'controlling' our reactions is not the effective one. What we want is to minimize the automatic activation of primitive circuits by 'shaping' them—supervising, collaborating, and managing our mental resources. Let me give you an example:

> Let's imagine you have a problem and feel incapable of solving it. You lose sleep, become anxious, and feel helpless. The mental strain you experience reduces your mental space, which causes you to miss seeing the big picture, or seeing the picture at all, which eventually makes you incapable of solving anything. Your relationship with the situation may be such that it's as if you had put the picture too close to your eyes and still wanted to explain it. You won't be able to, because there is no mental space for you to see it (you become overwhelmed). Your view is narrow, blurry, and maybe distorted. You need to create mental space (moving the picture away from your face) before you can even distinguish its elements. That shift gives you perspective and feels like you can manage the details of the image, notice what's wrong, and plan the resolution.

There is no one-solution to fix-all our emotional issues, but one intervention I want to propose here is to learn how everyone can direct and manage their brain. I've been hinting at ways to do this throughout the book. The Prefrontal Cortex (PFC) is the most evolved part of our brain and the one that could help us gain jurisdiction over our more primordial tendencies. We can't instruct our reptilian brain to stop taking care of our primordial needs—that's just what it does—but we can direct our PFC to activate its regulatory functions. We can't stop experiencing hunger (primitive), but we can choose what and when to eat (awareness and autonomy). It may seem impossible to stop being scared of snakes but our PFC can assist us in understanding that there are no snakes in a tenth-floor apartment. Our PFC is the one helping us resolve the effect of the traumatizing agents. Even if we decide to let some of the other actions/reactions take place, it makes a big difference to have them with awareness and choice than having them act on their own. Anger is a great example. We could decide how to allow anger to manifest instead of experiencing anger as uncontrollable; we could verbalize what is making us react, we can assess how to solve it, we can negotiate with the person that activated the anger (and even with ourselves), and we can choose from a variety of possibilities instead of succumbing to the primitive instinct of yelling and hitting. It's not about *suppressing* or *dismissing*, it's about *addressing* and *deciding* how to express it and continuing to work with it until it unravels. It may sound unrealistic to you but I have seen it in action enough times after instructing and guiding my clients into it. Awareness and knowledge make the difference, and we have specific regions of the cortex that work together to help us become aware and capitalize on our experiences. Not by allowing the brain to learn based on adaptation, but by helping the brain to discriminate according to our cognitive assessment. Activating executive functions gives us insight; understanding the affect our system is experiencing puts the brakes on limbic emotional activation and gives us space to generate alternatives.

What makes us a unique species is our capacity to plan for the future, to have flexibility, and to learn from our mistakes. One of the main characteristics of being human is to have options and to be able to make choices. Less evolved species have no more options than to run or fight when attacked because they have almost no choice but to be targeted for predation. We are past that. Humans are extraordinary beings that have decided to use what the Earth provides to make our habitat extremely comfortable and protective, and still, we have not been able to inhabit an internal system that works in harmony. We are great at commanding armies, teams, and groups, but we neglect to work on directing our 'brain's general' to help us win our emotional battles. By reviewing our priorities during and after our emotional struggles, we'd open up the possibility of achieving accountability for our mental health (or lack thereof).

The survival mode keeps us mentally and physically unstable. To regain equilibrium, the survival mode should be replaced with other types of activation. Finding coherence between the external world and our experience of it is a good way to help our system regulate. Finding meaning in what can keep us engaged, and feeling engaged with life completes the set of tools that will bring us back into living mode.

Multi-Dimensional Dynamic Trauma Treatment

It's a rule in the psychotherapy profession not to make unrealistic promises. Managing expectations is part of the work, and a responsible trauma-focused therapist informs the client that traumatization doesn't heal in a few sessions, no matter what modality is used. Some people get into therapy looking for a quick fix after hearing in the media about a magic intervention or magic pill. Eye Movement Desensitization and Reprocessing (EMDR) suffers from that type of misinformation. Many people think that with a few sessions of this modality, their symptoms will disappear and their distress 'cured.' But processing traumatic memories (what EMDR is designed for) is only one component of the series of interventions that are included in trauma treatment. Remember that if one of the symptom clusters is not present, the PTSD diagnosis can't be given; that's how claims that one intervention 'cures' PTSD could be misleading. Yes, flashbacks can disappear—and therefore the diagnosis—but many more issues could still remain in need of attention.

ADAPTING THE PHASE-ORIENTED METHOD

Paced treatment is what has been used to heal from traumatization since Pierre Janet suggested it. Janet proposed to follow three steps: (I) assessment of symptoms and preparation for processing traumatic memories, (II) identification, exploration, and modification of traumatic memories, and (III) relapse prevention, attention to remaining symptoms, unification of the personality, and rehabilitation (Van der Hart et al., 1989). His proposition was not seriously implemented until the late 1990s by Judith Herman who adapted the model and published it in her book 'Trauma and Recovery.' Herman's model suggested: Stage I: Establishing Safety, Stage II: Remembrance and Mourning, and Stage III: Reconnection.

Herman's model developed after she treated a multitude of domestic abuse survivors and observed how similar their symptoms were to the ones reported by war veterans. That's why she introduced 'safety' as an important first step. It has become clear that *nobody can heal from traumatization if they are still under threat or at risk*. The model was well received and utilized but had gone through several modifications as authors became more interested in other aspects of trauma treatment. The names of the phases have changed as well as the emphasis of each of the phases. A group of recognized researchers led by Julian D. Ford (Ford et al., 2005) described a three-phase treatment that expanded on Janet and Herman's and became broadly used: phase 1: Alliance Formation and Stabilization, phase 2: Traumatic Memories Processing, and phase 3: Functional Reintegration.

The introduction of 'stabilization' during phase 1 has been one of the most important contributions to trauma treatment that differs from all other schools of thought. It became essential to understand that besides having a good relationship with the therapist and living in a safe environment, the person needed to acquire self-regulation skills to stabilize their nervous system before they could move into processing traumatic memories, integrating them, or finding their meaning. Still, practicing those three phases in therapy and all the new findings in neuroscience has taught me that there is a lot of room to expand the idea of phases within trauma treatment. That's why here I'm proposing an updated systemic model that proves more effective for managing the myriad of symptoms left by traumatization.

I used the three-phase trauma treatment for years (or tried to use it) and found that it was unrealistic to expect that the treatment was going to evolve linearly. My trainees found the same issue. The phases of trauma treatment work best if they are dynamic instead of linear. This implies that the therapist can use the interventions of each phase according to the needs of the client during treatment if a certain hierarchy is respected. I observed that the phases proposed by Ford et al. could get combined with Herman's model. For example, 'alliance formation and stabilization' could be divided further, leaving alliance and safety first and creating a new phase for stabilization to put more weight on it. After years of testing, I found that a hierarchical model applied dynamically works best. It uses blocks that build up the internal and external skills the person requires to become whole again. Each block can take the central stage at any point, as needed, to complete pieces of each stage. Hierarchy is respected as proposed before: *Safety* is priority #1, *Stabilization* #2, and *Repossessing* #3. Treatment then unfolds keeping in mind that the foundation of a successful treatment is built by many blocks of safety and alliance. With a solid foundation, other blocks keep adding to the different stages. Figure 10.3 shows the building blocks for each hierarchy:

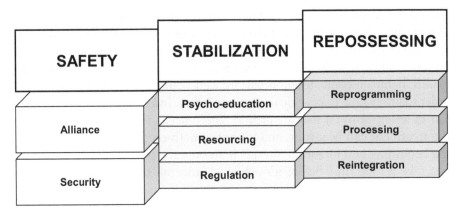

Figure 10.3 Dynamic trauma treatment hierarchy and building blocks

PHASES APPLIED DYNAMICALLY USING BUILDING BLOCKS

Safety

Alliance will always be the way to start trauma treatment (or any therapeutic relationship). Therapy of any type doesn't work if there is no rapport between the client and the therapist. Developing a certain type of connection (and trust) is the foundation of a therapeutic alliance but there is a caveat: traumatized individuals hardly trust anyone. Part of living in a state of alert is fearing others or avoiding disappointment, abuse, rejection, and judgment. It's not 'resistance'; it's conditioned fear. Therefore, helping clients develop trust in the therapist and the process is not a given, and it takes longer than we wish. Therefore, even if it's the 'first' stage in the treatment, it'd be unrealistic to think that treatment can't move on until trust is in place and the alliance is solid. So, even this phase that is perceived as essential, and many times the therapist's goal, may have to be paced and tolerated if it doesn't happen fast. Many other milestones could be achieved while trust and alliance develop. A certain set of skills are required from the therapist for this to happen: authenticity, respect, compassion, humbleness, attunement, objectivity, and '*tactful honesty.*' In trauma treatment, the therapist shares what they see (as opposed to only taking never shared notes), always delivering timely, kindly, and effectively.

Security

Since traumatized people's main issues are fear-related—such as hyper-vigilance—they suffer from all sorts of insecurities; therefore, focusing on recovering confidence is paramount. Feeling safe goes beyond the safety offered by the clinician's room. Many schools of thought don't include this step because they assume that being too nosy or getting too close to the private life of the client is not appropriate, but in terms of trauma treatment, it is unavoidable. A trauma-focused treatment requires checking on the client's health, habits, income, living situation, well-being, diet, friendships, etc., in order to know how to provide or promote safety. *Individuals can't heal from the fear of feeling at risk if they are at risk.* Safety needs to be established before the treatment can bear fruit, and it's not something that can be achieved at the beginning and forgotten after; it is an ongoing part of trauma work that can take a long time before it's achieved since all the traumatizing agents need to be addressed, one by one.

Stabilization

Since traumatization is systemic, it's often the case that processing disturbing memories also helps with calming down the nervous system, but most of the time, if the system has no coordination, accessing memories may be destabilizing. When there is a good level of emotional stability, processing emotional burdens from the past happens fast and steadily. Stabilization means that the person is able to recognize most symptoms, triggers, reactions, fears, defeating narratives, scripts, and insecurities, and to manage them so they can keep their reactions proportional to the situations they confront in their daily lives.

Psycho-education is used all through treatment but it is a good part of stabilizing traumatized people because it helps them understand themselves and normalize their experiences. It's a pretty novel practice in the therapy world. It started as a way to 'educate' family members of people suffering from schizophrenia and it has become an integral part of trauma treatment. Psycho-education implies sharing information with the client about the state of their internal system, the reasons why its functioning became modified, what it means to have brain and nervous system alterations, why they feel and experience the world the way they do, why their reactions feel uncontrollable and excessive, etc. A trauma therapist explains or demonstrates how to develop regulation skills to the point of becoming aware and tolerating their affect; they also provide a vocabulary to expand their 'emotional intelligence.' I'd dare to say that this book is, in large part, written as a psycho-education tool. Another huge benefit of psycho-education is that if both (therapist/client) have the same information, the responsibility is shared, which motivates the client to be fully committed to their recovery.

Resourcing is a great concept in psychotherapy that has not been widely documented. It has been used in modalities that leverage the connection with the body (somatic) as the focus of treatment. Pat Ogden—the creator of the

Sensorimotor Psychotherapy method—uses somatic resources as part of her interventions; Babette Rothschild expanded the concept and described how traumatized people lack resources and classified them in her book *The Body Remembers* (Rothschild, 2000). The modality that has made 'resourcing' a more used term is EMDR by including an application called Resource Development and Installation (RDI). Laurel Parnell has used it extensively in her EMDR method, arguing that before processing traumatic material, traumatized individuals need to have internal resources to assist them during the emotional valleys. Resourcing works on activating neuronal circuits that bring up ego strengths and positive affect which facilitates memory processing.

Still, the benefits of resourcing have not been addressed to the extent that resourcing deserves. In my experience, resourcing is key to reaching stability and repossessing one's life, and a great way to help traumatized individuals develop regulation, resilience, and equilibrium. It reprograms the brain the fastest, which is one of the main goals of trauma treatment. I'd have loved to expand on resourcing in this book but to convey how to help people develop internal resources, I'd need many more pages than this book can include. Look out for more information on the book's website and in my next book.

Regulation deals with the dysregulation of the ANS and emotional reactions. Regulation skills help the individual acquire enough awareness to intervene in the control of their emotionality. Regulation skills activate regulatory structures and their functions creating new connections to jumpstart the reprogramming of the brain, returning to the previous way of operating. Regulation is a part of the treatment that doesn't only happen during therapy sessions. The instructions given to self-regulate in session should be exercised the rest of the time because healing from traumatization is experiential. The client is helped to develop motivation, but the results will come from the application of the techniques explained and instructed during sessions. When the traumatized individual lacks internal and external resources, the need to use extra aids becomes necessary. I use Neurofeedback and some devices to modulate and regulate brain activity as support for treatment.

Repossessing

This phase is the main goal of the trauma treatment and it can't wait until the end of treatment to start building up pieces of the new 'you.' This phase is the one that has changed names and definitions many times since Janet, probably because many professionals have been finding out that there are many issues to be included. I'm proposing three building blocks in this phase: reprogramming, processing, and reintegration.

I chose the name 'repossession' carefully to point out the importance of 'owning' the recovery of many of the aspects of one's life that were lost when traumatization took them. Herman proposed 'Mourning,' and yes, grieving our losses is essential, but it's also important to work on rebuilding. Suffering from traumatization implies losing capacities, opportunities, and many of the things we needed to feel alright—such as agency and direction. This phase includes making the decision to take back everything that was removed. Not an easy task, but if attention refocuses on resolving the mental state of defeat, regaining confidence, enthusiasm, motivation, and joy are possible.

Reprogramming. This stage is where the individual (1) reconnects with themselves, (2) works on reactivating parts of the brain that got either shut down or disconnected, (3) rewrites their narrative and scripts, (4) becomes aware of—and owns—all the parts of the story, including reactivity or passivity, (5) develops social skills, and (6) recognizes elements that were shattered by the psychological injury. This stage is also dynamic and its building blocks can be used at any point in treatment, as soon as the client starts activating their executive functions.

Processing the traumatic memories has been the second stage of trauma treatment since Janet proposed it. Several authors have suggested additions to the stage, but have respected the importance of memories. Integration was added later as complementary to integrating the elements of the event that become decontextualized due to the fragmentation of the memory. The use of psychedelics to treat PTSD (which has been researched and is pending legalization) goes directly into integration and meaning-making, assuming that the altered mental state caused by the effect of the substance does the work of processing information and rebooting the brain. It's not conclusive yet but all the neuroscientific evidence keeps pointing out that the main reason traumatized individuals behave the way they do, or store the memories as disturbing, is due to the loss of brain connectivity, and therefore, there may be no need to continue digging into the past as the main focus of therapy if the person reconnects brain circuits.

Processing traumatic memories targets metabolizing the traumatic occurrences and reconsolidating the memories to remove the negative 'charge' left decontextualized as a consequence. Metabolizing memories assumes that they were not processed before and that they live in the brain/body, confusing the past and present. True, but not all memories from the past are unmetabolized or decontextualized in time, and therefore, not all 'painful' memories need to be reconsolidated. Sometimes it is better to allow the brain to 'delete' events that are not relevant, as it continuously does, instead of reinforcing hurts that may be forgotten if left alone. Trying to 'heal' a scar can just unnecessarily open it. *Only open wounds need to be processed.* We will always have scars, that's just part of being alive—and scratching them doesn't make them disappear.

Processing emotions is extremely important too. Part of the work targeting growth is identifying emotional states, emotional scripts, and emotionality. Once the client does, it's much easier to own behaviors, recognize the messages of the body, and reprogram reactions, developing agency and confidence.

Reintegration. Integration is the name commonly used to describe the process of incorporating pieces of the fragmented memory—or of the personality— caused by the traumatic experience into a cohesive narrative. Using neurobiology as a framework, I see reintegration as the synchronization of brain hemispheres, reactivation and connection of brain structures, formation of the sense of self, reconnection with our relationships, community, and environment, and other aspects that became disorganized, dissociated, de-skilled, fragmented, or lost. This includes developing awareness of (a) the roles we have accepted to play, (b) the strategies we adopted before, (c) the dissociated parts that became our personality, (d) the recognition of what kept promoting them, and (e) how we may have strongly identified with them to the point of not wanting to let them go.

THE SCOPE OF TRAUMA TREATMENT: A MULTI-DIMENSIONAL MODEL

Each trauma domain needs to be included in treatment. That's why in addition to dynamic, I'm calling the proposed model 'Multi-dimensional.' We need to use the building blocks dynamically but depending on the domain we are working on. Each domain needs attention; monitoring the progress made in each informs the clinician about the way the person had suffered the alterations. Each domain informs others and becomes part of the system. Sometimes one specific domain needs many sessions, while other times more than one domain can be intervened in a single session. What's important is to keep them all in mind while working on resolving traumatization and healing the system.

Figure 10.4 illustrates, as an example, how the domain 'Dysregulation' is built by the dynamic building blocks. The more complex the trauma disorder, the more domains that will be treated and the more blocks used.

The Multi-dimensional Dynamic Trauma Treatment (MDTT) is a structure from which interventions based on awareness, focus and attention, resourcing, and promotion of positive affect become intertwined with many other

Reintegration	Resourcing	Alliance	Regulation	Processing	Reprograming	Psycho-education	Processing	Regulation	Reprograming
Psycho-education	Regulation	Regulation	Security	Regulation	Resourcing	Alliance	Reprograming	Psycho-education	Regulation
Alliance	Security	Security	Alliance	Psycho-education	Resourcing	Security	Reprograming	Alliance	Resourcing
Dysregulation									

Figure 10.4 Domain 'Dysregulation' built by dynamic building blocks

modalities to pace treatment. There are many interventions for each layer of building blocks. The modalities to be used in the duration of the treatment are chosen depending on the area that needs improvement and the skills of the therapist. Some modalities are specific and some are more versatile. Neurofeedback, for example, is perhaps the most powerful tool for stabilization, but it's not designed for processing. EMDR is powerful for processing but it's not helpful at all during stabilization. That happens with other modalities too. The modalities that are required to heal traumatization can be top-down (more cognitive), or bottom-up—those that use the body as the way to recognize emotions and experiences (somatic/experiential). Some modalities are energy-oriented based on Eastern philosophies that use breathing, visualization, and meditation as a way to calm the nervous system, while others use brain stimulation to modulate neuronal activity. It is auspicious that we count on more and more ways to tackle the problems that traumatization leaves, even though it could seem confusing which one to choose. There is no one-size-fits-all. A well-formed trauma therapist knows that more than one modality is required to help the person to recover functionality and to heal emotionally and physically.

Trauma therapy is about feeling empowered in every session and feeling motivated to grow and improve. Trauma therapy is about eradicating symptoms and helping individuals to recover their whole selves and the connection with their lives and capacities. The process is intricate because traumatization creates a puzzle of a thousand pieces. If we use a puzzle as an analogy, the method I'm proposing focuses on organizing several parts of the image at a time (domains) instead of trying to go in sequence. Picture a tableau of many elements. Using the building blocks as a method would help us resolve the puzzle in clusters the way shown in Figure 10.5. This allows you to see that it's possible to picture what the full image might end up looking like because we can see more of it (we can start to make out a dog, kids, a woman, a bird, a car, etc.).

Using the sequential method would make the image look like Figure 10.6 which shows only two elements, the house and the sky, and many remaining unknowns:

Figure 10.5 Dynamic trauma treatment metaphor

Figure 10.6 Linear trauma treatment metaphor

By using building blocks, we can actively discover much more about the whole picture. And when there's greater understanding and direction, the person can heal multi-dimensionally.

References

Damasio, A. (2005). The neurobiological grounding of human values. J. P. Changeux, A. R. Damasio, W. Singer, & Y. Christen (Eds.), *Neurobiology of human values* (pp. 47–56). Berlin: Springer.

Ford, J. D., Courtois, C. A., Steele, K., Van der Hart, O. V., & Nijenhuis, E. R. (2005). Treatment of complex posttraumatic self-dysregulation. *Journal of Traumatic Stress*, 18(5), 437–447. https://doi.org/10.1002/jts.20051

Koch, C., & Hepp, K. (2006). Quantum mechanics in the brain. *Nature*, 440, 611. https://doi.org/10.1038/440611a

Lahno, B. (2001). On the emotional character of trust. *Ethical Theory and Moral Practice*, 4(2), 171–189. http://www.jstor.org/stable/27504185

Leclercq, S., Forsythe, P., & Bienenstock, J. (2016). Posttraumatic stress disorder: Does the gut microbiome hold the key? *The Canadian Journal of Psychiatry*, 61(4), 204–213. https://doi.org/10.1177/0706743716635535

McLeod, C. (2021). Trust. E. N. Zalta (Ed.), *The Stanford encyclopedia of philosophy*. https://plato.stanford.edu/archives/fall2021/entries/trust/

Rothschild, B. (2000). *The body remembers: The psychophysiology of trauma and trauma treatment* (pp. 88–90). Los Angeles, CA: W. W. Norton & Company.

Siegel, D. J. (1999). *The developing mind: Toward a neurobiology of interpersonal experience* (p. 233). New York: Guilford Press.

Van der Hart, O., Brown, P., & Van der Kolk, B. A. (1989). Pierre Janet's treatment of post-traumatic stress. *Journal of Trauma Stress*, 2, 379–395. https://doi.org/10.1007/BF00974597

Epilogue

When I was 12, my mother developed a brain tumor. The tumor was behind her eyes and in between her ears, almost exactly at the very center of her brain. Her 12-hour surgery had an audience because of how sophisticated and difficult it was at the time. The doctor had to open the skin from side to side, her skull in an area the size of a bread slice, and her cortex in a line going from her nose to her crown breaking through her frontal lobe (the orbitofrontal cortex to be exact). Everyone thought she would die.

She didn't die, but she never really came back either. The person who returned from the hospital and lived with us seemed unrelated to the woman who raised me. She became unavailable emotionally from then on. The surgery had inflicted a 'brain trauma' injuring many of her executive functions. I didn't realize this at the time, and as a teenager, I thought it was my fault.

Now that I know better, I'd say that the surgery was a crime even though it didn't kill her. Her presentation after surgery was very similar to that of a traumatized person. She was far from perfect before, but after surgery, she became extremely difficult. The surgery broke her and broke us. The rupture was not evident, not a fight or a conflict. It was just a loss of connection, traumatizing for me in one way, and for her in another. Only 30% of my mother's tumor was removed; the doctor said it could have killed her or left her as a vegetable if it touched other parts of the brain where the tumor grew. It propagated like a tree, with branches invading many other parts of her limbic and her pre-frontal cortex.

I was constantly afraid that the tumor would grow back and she would die. Fearing her was constant too. She became intolerant, frail, angry, and remarkably self-referential. Everything was about her and no one else had priority since she was fearing for her life every day. My father's health deteriorated. I became the parentified child, my little brother's tutor, my father's

DOI: 10.4324/9781003382478-15

nurse, and my mom's object; she molded me to her likes and relied on me for whatever she needed. Since it happened when I was a teen, stage 5 of my development—identity formation—was undermined. I accepted her ideas, dressed the way she wanted me to dress, and I behaved like an adult before reaching 15.

School and friends kept me engaged and thriving. I was able to enjoy life even when part of me carried pain and dread. I see now how the emotional absence of my mother drove me into a horrible marriage. Emotionally, I was weak, my self-esteem low, and my need to attach high. The emotional abuse I suffered in my marriage kept draining my spirit and mental health drop by drop. Years later, when the marriage became unbearable, my system reached the allostatic load and I collapsed. That's when joy left me. I was suffering from vasovagal syncope often and was diagnosed with several illnesses. My doctor (the one that practiced systemic medicine) explained that my system had lost synchrony. That each one of my systems was working at its own pace and had lost coordination. I even lost my period and had menopause symptoms when I was in my early forties.

How deep was my wound? Maybe some clinicians could argue I had Developmental Trauma because many indicators spoke about allostatic changes early on, or just Complex Trauma since most of the symptoms became evident once my body was not able to keep enduring emotional pain. My system was already affected by the attachment rupture and my mother's illness, but I am pretty sure I didn't meet the criteria for a posttraumatic syndrome until my marriage fell apart. I had a series of symptoms that started with my mother's surgery; my system was struggling for a long time but not to the point of losing balance. What I'm sure of is that I neglected my emotional health for years, not attending to the symptoms that were appearing and disturbing my well-being. I also know that shame was a traumatizing agent, as well as my husband's rejection. I wish I had looked for help sooner because reaching rock bottom was not fun, to say the least. I waited until the need was urgent. To recover, I ended the abuse and started working on my healing.

It took me many years though. The healing journey is demanding. It takes time to recognize what sets one's system off, identify backlashes, reprogram one's responses, trust people again, and to own one's fears and insecurities. Once I learned more about traumatization, I became concerned about my kids. Even when I loved them with my whole being, I questioned whether I had given them everything they needed, since I was hurting. At some point, I had to admit that they also needed help because my pain hurt them. This book is part of the journey I took to recognize how deep their wound was too.

If I leave you with one thing, it would be this—you can do it. Our brain never stops learning or creating new programs. With the modern scientific advances I introduced in this book, you can take back the controls and live the life you want to live. Even if you think you can't. Even if someone has told you you're broken. Even if you've tried before and failed. It's a new game now. If you heal the system, you can heal the person.

I'm rooting for you.

Appendix A
Common Sympathetic and Parasympathetic Functions

Sympathetic	Parasympathetic
Dilated pupils	Cold hands or feet
Nightmares	Constricted pupils
Physical tension	Constricts the bronchiolar diameter
Decreasing motility of the large intestine	Crying
Itchiness, pruritus	Defecation
Widening bronchial passages, dilates bronchioles (breaths easily)	Diarrhea
Inhibition of the lacrimal gland and salivation	Difficulty breathing
Poor engagement	Difficulty walking
Heart racing	Dilates blood vessels
Paling or flushing, or alternating between both	Disinhibited
Over-arousal, energized, speeded up, hyperactivity	Dizziness, nausea
Muscle tension (jaw/neck/shoulders)	Ear ringing
Perspiration	Emotional sensitivity
Tense jaw/lips, muscle spams	Increased mucous production
Anxiety, rumination	Releases epinephrine
Tachycardia, agitation, emotional reactivity	Heart-pounding
Constipation, digestion slows down or stops	Heaviness
Difficulty falling asleep	Immature, silliness
Irritable, aggressive	Low blood sugar symptoms

(*Continued*)

(Continued)

Sympathetic	Parasympathetic
Eye strain	Poor engagement
Increase peristalsis in the esophagus	Sadness
Piloerection (goosebumps)	Stimulates salivation
Inhibition of erection	Tightness in the chest/throat/neck
Loss of hearing	Urination
Loss of peripheral vision	Vasodilation (red face)
Relaxation of the bladder	Slowed heart rate
Shaking	Flatulence
Social withdrawal	Cramping, uneasy stomach
Dry mouth	Glassy eyes
Dizziness	Runny nose
Lightheadedness	Short breath
No urination	Secrete mucus
Increases orgasmic response	Immobility
Constriction of most blood vessels	Lack of deep sleep
Increases metabolic rate	Increases blood flow
Burning stomach	Decreases blood pressure
Burning in chest	Gastric juice secreted
Slows down digestion	Increases digestion
Disinhibition of spinal reflexes	Sphincter relaxed
Dilate in skeletal muscle	Bladder wall contracted
Increase in blood pressure	Increases glycogen to glucose conversion
Inhibits tumescence	Belching
Promotes emission prior to ejaculation	Increases stomach motility
	Engorges the male and female genitals

Appendix B
DSM-5-TR Posttraumatic Stress Disorder Diagnostic

Diagnostic Criteria Posttraumatic Stress Disorder in Individuals Older Than 6 Years

Note: The following criteria apply to adults, adolescents, and children older than 6 years. For children 6 years and younger, see corresponding criteria.

A. Exposure to actual or threatened death, serious injury, or sexual violence in one (or more) of the following ways:

1. Directly experiencing the traumatic event(s).
2. Witnessing, in person, the event(s) as it occurred to others.
3. Learning that the traumatic event(s) occurred to a close family member or close friend. In cases of actual or threatened death of a family member or friend, the event(s) must have been violent or accidental.
4. Experiencing repeated or extreme exposure to aversive details of the traumatic event(s) (e.g., first responders collecting human remains; police officers repeatedly exposed to details of child abuse).

Note: Criterion A4 does not apply to exposure through electronic media, television, movies, or pictures, unless this exposure is work related.

B. Presence of one (or more) of the following intrusion symptoms associated with the traumatic event(s), beginning after the traumatic event(s) occurred:

1. Recurrent, involuntary, and intrusive distressing memories of the traumatic event(s).

Note: In children older than 6 years, repetitive play may occur in which themes or aspects of the traumatic event(s) are expressed.

2. Recurrent distressing dreams in which the content and/or affect of the dream are related to the traumatic event(s).
Note: In children, there may be frightening dreams without recognizable content.

3. Dissociative reactions (e.g., flashbacks) in which the individual feels or acts as if the traumatic event(s) were recurring. (Such reactions may occur on a continuum, with the most extreme expression being a complete loss of awareness of present surroundings.)
Note: In children, trauma-specific reenactment may occur in play.

4. Intense or prolonged psychological distress at exposure to internal or external cues that symbolize or resemble an aspect of the traumatic event(s).

5. Marked physiological reactions to internal or external cues that symbolize or resemble an aspect of the traumatic event(s).

C. Persistent avoidance of stimuli associated with the traumatic event(s), beginning after the traumatic event(s) occurred, as evidenced by one or both of the following:

1. Avoidance of or efforts to avoid distressing memories, thoughts, or feelings about or closely associated with the traumatic event(s).

2. Avoidance of or efforts to avoid external reminders (people, places, conversations, activities, objects, situations) that arouse distressing memories, thoughts, or feelings about or closely associated with the traumatic event(s).

D. Negative alterations in cognitions and mood associated with the traumatic event(s), beginning or worsening after the traumatic event(s) occurred, as evidenced by two (or more) of the following:

1. Inability to remember an important aspect of the traumatic event(s) (typically due to dissociative amnesia and not to other factors such as head injury, alcohol, or drugs).

2. Persistent and exaggerated negative beliefs or expectations about oneself, others, or the world (e.g., "I am bad," "No one can be trusted," "The world is completely dangerous," "My whole nervous system is permanently ruined").

3. Persistent, distorted cognitions about the cause or consequences of the traumatic event(s) that lead the individual to blame himself/herself or others.

4. Persistent negative emotional state (e.g., fear, horror, anger, guilt, or shame).

5. Markedly diminished interest or participation in significant activities.
6. Feelings of detachment or estrangement from others.
7. Persistent inability to experience positive emotions (e.g., inability to experience happiness, satisfaction, or loving feelings).

E. Marked alterations in arousal and reactivity associated with the traumatic event(s), beginning or worsening after the traumatic event(s) occurred, as evidenced by two (or more) of the following:

1. Irritable behavior and angry outbursts (with little or no provocation) typically expressed as verbal or physical aggression toward people or objects.
2. Reckless or self-destructive behavior.
3. Hypervigilance.
4. Exaggerated startle response.
5. Problems with concentration.
6. Sleep disturbance (e.g., difficulty falling or staying asleep or restless sleep).

F. Duration of the disturbance (Criteria B, C, D, and E) is more than 1 month.
G. The disturbance causes clinically significant distress or impairment in social, occupational, or other important areas of functioning.
H. The disturbance is not attributable to the physiological effects of a substance (e.g., medication, alcohol) or another medical condition.

Specify whether:

With dissociative symptoms: The individual's symptoms meet the criteria for posttraumatic stress disorder, and in addition, in response to the stressor, the individual experiences persistent or recurrent symptoms of either of the following:

1. Depersonalization: Persistent or recurrent experiences of feeling detached from, and as if one were an outside observer of, one's mental processes or body (e.g., feeling as though one were in a dream; feeling a sense of unreality of self or body or of time moving slowly).
2. Derealization: Persistent or recurrent experiences of unreality of surroundings (e.g., the world around the individual is experienced as unreal, dreamlike, distant, or distorted).

Note: To use this subtype, the dissociative symptoms must not be attributable to the physiological effects of a substance (e.g., blackouts, behavior during alcohol intoxication) or another medical condition (e.g., complex partial seizures).

Specify if:

With delayed expression: If the full diagnostic criteria are not met until at least 6 months after the event (although the onset and expression of some symptoms may be immediate).

© American Psychiatric Association. Diagnostic and Statistical Manual of Mental Disorders: Text Revision DSM-5-TR (p. 796). Kindle Edition.

Reprinted with permission from the Diagnostic and Statistical Manual of Mental Disorders, Fifth Edition Text Revision, (Copyright ©2022). American Psychiatric Association. All Rights Reserved.

Appendix C
C-PTSD Criteria ICD-11

6B41 Complex Post-Traumatic Stress Disorder

Description

Complex Post-Traumatic Stress Disorder (Complex PTSD) is a disorder that may develop following exposure to an event or series of events of an extremely threatening or horrific nature, most commonly prolonged or repetitive events from which escape is difficult or impossible (e.g., torture, slavery, genocide campaigns, prolonged domestic violence, repeated childhood sexual or physical abuse). All diagnostic requirements for PTSD are met. In addition, Complex PTSD is characterized by severe and persistent (1) problems in affect regulation; (2) beliefs about oneself as diminished, defeated, or worthless, accompanied by feelings of shame, guilt, or failure related to the traumatic event; and (3) difficulties in sustaining relationships and in feeling close to others. These symptoms cause significant impairment in personal, family, social, educational, occupational, or other important areas of functioning.

Diagnostic Requirements

Essential (Required) Features:

- Exposure to an event or series of events of an extremely threatening or horrific nature, most commonly prolonged or repetitive events from which escape is difficult or impossible. Such events include, but are not limited to, torture, concentration camps, slavery, genocide campaigns, and other forms of organized violence, prolonged domestic violence, and repeated childhood sexual or physical abuse.

- Following the traumatic event, the development of all three core elements of Post-Traumatic Stress Disorder, lasting for at least several weeks:

    - Re-experiencing the traumatic event after the traumatic event has occurred, in which the event(s) is not just remembered but is experienced as occurring again in the here and now. This typically occurs in the form of vivid intrusive memories or images; flashbacks, which can vary from mild (there is a transient sense of the event occurring again in the present) to severe (there is a complete loss of awareness of present surroundings), or repetitive dreams or nightmares that are thematically related to the traumatic event(s). Re-experiencing is typically accompanied by strong or overwhelming emotions, such as fear or horror, and strong physical sensations. Re-experiencing in the present can also involve feelings of being overwhelmed or immersed in the same intense emotions that were experienced during the traumatic event, without a prominent cognitive aspect, and may occur in response to reminders of the event. Reflecting on or ruminating about the event(s) and remembering the feelings that one experienced at that time are not sufficient to meet the re-experiencing requirement.
    - Deliberate avoidance of reminders likely to produce re-experiencing of the traumatic event(s). This may take the form either of active internal avoidance of thoughts and memories related to the event(s), or external avoidance of people, conversations, activities, or situations reminiscent of the event(s). In extreme cases the person may change their environment (e.g., move house or change jobs) to avoid reminders.
    - Persistent perceptions of heightened current threat, for example as indicated by hypervigilance or an enhanced startle reaction to stimuli such as unexpected noises. Hypervigilant persons constantly guard themselves against danger and feel themselves or others close to them to be under immediate threat either in specific situations or more generally. They may adopt new behaviours designed to ensure safety (not sitting with ones' back to the door, repeated checking in vehicles' rear-view mirror). In Complex Post-Traumatic Stress Disorder, unlike in Post-Traumatic Stress Disorder, the startle reaction may in some cases be diminished rather than enhanced.

- Severe and pervasive problems in affect regulation. Examples include heightened emotional reactivity to minor stressors, violent outbursts, reckless or self-destructive behavior, dissociative symptoms when under stress, and emotional numbing, particularly the inability to experience pleasure or positive emotions.

- Persistent beliefs about oneself as diminished, defeated or worthless, accompanied by deep and pervasive feelings of shame, guilt or failure related to the stressor. For example, the individual may feel guilty about not having escaped from or succumbing to the adverse circumstance, or not having been able to prevent the suffering of others.
- Persistent difficulties in sustaining relationships and in feeling close to others. The person may consistently avoid, deride or have little interest in relationships and social engagement more generally. Alternatively, there may be occasional intense relationships, but the person has difficulty sustaining them.
- The disturbance results in significant impairment in personal, family, social, educational, occupational or other important areas of functioning. If functioning is maintained, it is only through significant additional effort.

Additional Clinical Features:

- Suicidal ideation and behavior, substance abuse, depressive symptoms, psychotic symptoms, and somatic complaints may be present.

Boundary with Normality (Threshold):

- A history of exposure to a stressor of extreme and prolonged or repetitive nature from which escape is difficult or impossible does not in itself indicate the presence of Complex Post-Traumatic Stress Disorder. Many people experience such stressors without developing any disorder. Rather, the presentation must meet all diagnostic requirements for the disorder.

Course Features:

- The onset of Complex Post-Traumatic Stress Disorder symptoms can occur across the lifespan, typically after exposure to chronic, repeated traumatic events and/or victimization that have continued for a period of months or years at a time.
- Symptoms of Complex Post-Traumatic Stress Disorder are generally more severe and persistent in comparison to Post-Traumatic Stress Disorder.

- Exposure to repeated traumas, especially in early development, is associated with a greater risk of developing Complex Post-Traumatic Stress Disorder rather than Post-Traumatic Stress Disorder.

© World Health Organization. (2019). *ICD-11: International classification of diseases* (11th revision). Retrieved from https://icd.who.int/

Appendix D
DTD Criteria

Criterion A: Lifetime Contemporaneous Exposure to Developmental Trauma

A1. Primary caregiving system attachment disruption: impaired caregiver, neglect, prolonged separation, verbal/emotional abuse
- most typically in conjunction with-
A2. Interpersonal victimization: physical or sexual abuse or assault, domestic/intimate partner violence

Criterion B: Affective and Somatic Dysregulation (Four Items; Three Required for DTD)

B1. Emotion dysregulation: B1a. extreme and intolerable negative affect states, OR B1b. from extreme negative affect states
B2. Somatic dysregulation: B2a. aversion to touch, OR B2b. aversion to sounds, distress/illness that cannot medically be explained or resolved
B3. Impaired awareness or dissociation of emotions or body: B3a. absence of emotion, anesthesia that cannot medically be explained or resolved
B4. Impaired capacity to describe emotions or bodily states: B4a. alexithymia OR B4b. recognize or express somatic feelings or states

Criterion C: Attentional and Behavioral Dysregulation (Five Items; Two Required for DTD)

C1. Attention bias toward or away from potential threats: C1a. threat-related rumination, OR C1b. hyper- or hypo-vigilance to actual or potential danger

C2. Impaired capacity for self-protection: C2a. extreme risk-taking, thrill-seeking or recklessness, OR C2b. intentional provocation of conflict or violence

C3. Maladaptive self-soothing

C4. Habitual (intentional or automatic) or reactive self-harm (non-suicidal self-injury)

C5. Inability to initiate or sustain goal-directed behavior

Criterion D: Self and Relational Dysregulation (Six Items; Two Required for DTD)

D1. Persistent extreme negative self-perception: self-loathing or view of self as damaged / defective

D2. Attachment insecurity and disorganization: D2a. parentified overprotection of caregivers, OR D2b. difficulty tolerating reunion after separation from primary caregivers

D3. Extreme persistent distrust, defiance or lack of reciprocity in close relationships: D3a. expectation of betrayal, OR D3b. oppositional-defiance based on expectation of coercion or exploitation

D4. Reactive physical or verbal aggression

D5. Psychological boundary deficits: D5a. inappropriate (excessive or promiscuous) intimate contact (physical or sexual), OR D5b. or excessive reliance on peers or adults for safety and reassurance

D6. Impaired capacity to regulate empathic arousal: D6a. lack of empathy for, or intolerance of, other's distress, OR D6b. excessive responsiveness to the distress of others

© 2019 Julian Ford, Joseph Spinazzola & Bessel van der Kolk

Appendix E
Adverse Childhood Experiences Questionnaire

Prior to your 18th birthday:

1. Did a parent or other adult in the household often or very often...
   Swear at you, insult you, put you down, or humiliate you? or
   Act in a way that made you afraid that you might be physically hurt?
   ○ Yes   ○ No

2. Did a parent or other adult in the household often or very often... Push,
   grab, slap, or throw something at you? or Ever hit you so hard that you
   had marks or were injured?
   ○ Yes   ○ No

3. Did an adult or person at least five years older than you ever...
   Touch or fondle you or have you touch their body in a sexual way? or
   Attempt or actually have oral or anal intercourse with you?
   ○ Yes   ○ No

4. Did you often or very often feel that ...
   No one in your family loved you or thought you were important or spe-
   cial? or
   Your family didn't look out for each other, feel close to each other, or
   support each other?
   ○ Yes   ○ No

5. Did you often or very often feel that ...
   You didn't have enough to eat, had to wear dirty clothes, and had no one
   to protect you? or Your parents were too drunk or high to take care of you
   or take you to the doctor if you needed it?
   ○ Yes   ○ No

6. Was a biological parent ever lost to you through divorced, abandonment,
   or other reason?
   ○ Yes   ○ No

7. Was your mother or stepmother:
Often or very often pushed, grabbed, slapped, or had something thrown at her? or
Sometimes, often, or very often kicked, bitten, hit with a fist, or hit with something hard? or Ever repeatedly hit over at least a few minutes or threatened with a gun or knife?
○ Yes   ○ No

8. Did you live with anyone who was a problem drinker or alcoholic or who used street drugs?
○ Yes   ○ No

9. Was a household member depressed or mentally ill? or
Did a household member attempt suicide?
○ Yes   ○ No

10. Did a household member go to prison?
○ Yes   ○ No

The Centers for Disease Control and Prevention (CDC)

Appendix F
Psychotherapy Modalities Used in Trauma Treatment

For Stabilization

- Psycho-education
  - Books, blogs, articles
  - TED talks, conferences, seminars, etc.
  - YouTube, Quora, The Mighty, apps, Podcasts, or places where you can find information that opens possibilities to understand each one's situation

- Resourcing
  - Positive Psychology
  - Buddhism and other Eastern philosophies
  - Somatic interventions (Somatic Experiencing, Sensorimotor psychotherapy, Hakomi, Gestalt, etc.)
  - Mindfulness/Awarefulness
  - Social skills training
  - The 12 Steps from Alcoholics Anonymous

- Regulation
  - Mindfulness (ACT, CFT, etc.)
  - Awarefulness
  - Cognitive Behavioral Therapy (CBT), Dialectical Behavior Therapy (DBT), Rational Emotive Behavior Therapy (REBT)
  - Yoga, Tai Chi, theater, etc.
  - Emotional Freedom Technique (EFT), tapping.
  - Hypnosis, Hakomi, Gestalt, Schema Therapy, etc.
  - Parts language (from IFS, sandbox, etc.)
  - Biofeedback (breathing, HRV)

- Neuromodulation (Entrainment, cranial electrotherapy stimulation (CES or tACT), photomodulation, transcranial magnetic stimulation (TMS), transcranial electrical stimulation, or transcranial direct current stimulation (tDCE).
- Neurofeedback

Repossessing

- Processing
  - EMDR (Eye Movement Desensitization and Reprocessing)
  - Brainspotting
  - Internal Family Systems
  - AEDP
  - Somatic Experiencing/Sensorimotor Psychotherapy
  - Mentalization
  - CBT, REBT
  - Art therapy

- Reintegration
  - Awarefulness
  - Internal Family Systems
  - CBT, REBT
  - Mentalization
  - Psychodrama
  - Pesso-Boyden System Psychomotor

- Reprogramming and growth
  - Positive Psychology
  - Awarefulness
  - Narrative Therapy
  - Social skills training
  - Grief and loss counseling
  - Spiritual practices

Glossary of Terms

(Many of the definitions of this glossary are not generic. They are specific to the scope of this book.)

Adaptation: a change (or the process of change) by which a person becomes better suited to their environment.

Adversity: difficulties; misfortune, or events that disturb the environment and the person.

Affect: manifestations of physiological changes caused by having emotional experiences that can be felt (chills, tension, tingling, etc.).

Aggregated traumatization: the accumulation of alterations in the ANS product of different types of traumatization.

Allostasis: the process by which the body responds to stressors with small physiological modifications to sustain equilibrium.

Allostatic load: the wear and tear on the allostatic processes when the system reaches the point where small changes are no longer a solution, and must shift to making more drastic modifications.

Anxiety: a stress response that becomes spontaneous and automatic due to the brain's habit of being alert and worried.

Appease: the survival strategy of pacifying or placating someone that seems threatening by assenting to their demands.

Aroused: awake and ready to interact with the world engagingly when our senses perceive our surroundings.

Attachment: to trust and connect to someone we feel affection, fondness, or sympathy for. Not to be confused with dependency.

Attachment trauma: the term used to name the hurt caused by disruptions in the bond between infant and caregiver; it also applies to the pain of not finding reciprocity in the need to attach.

Attentive immobility (orienting): a momentary state of vigilance to assess sensorial information as safe or dangerous.

Attunement: the capacity to sense the needs of others and find synchronicity with another's brain oscillations (brain waves).

Backlash: re-living a traumatic situation from the past; an emotional reaction to something or someone that behaves or reminds us of a similar loaded situation and having the emotional experience as if it was as hurtful as the original occurrence (or more).

Bio-psycho-social: an interdisciplinary model that looks at the interconnection between biology, psychology, and socio-environmental factors.

Bond: the process that causes the brain to produce oxytocin through nurturing social connections.

Brain waves: oscillations in brain activity caused by electrical impulses used to communicate between neurons.

Charge: the amount of negativity (negative valence) stored in the brain (right amygdala) connected to an emotional experience.

Clinical: relating to the observation and treatment of actual patients rather than theoretical or laboratory studies.

Clinician: a mental health professional having direct contact with and responsibility for clients, rather than being involved with theoretical or laboratory studies.

Cognition: the mental action or process of acquiring knowledge and understanding through thought, experience, and the perception of sensory information.

Compartmentalization: a brain process from which thoughts and feelings are kept separated or isolated from each other. It is suggested as one of two main dissociative processes (the other is detachment).

Complex trauma: a term used to refer to being exposed to prolonged (or constant) highly stressful situations that alter the regular operation of one's ANS.

Danger: the possibility of suffering harm or injury.

Defeat: the opposite of victory, the loss of hope and of achieving safety.

Detachment: the second branch of dissociation together with compartmentalization. It's the brain process that creates the perception of the people and things around as distorted and unreal and blurs the sense of self, numbing the person from the awareness of several elements such as emotions.

Developmental trauma: being exposed to prolonged (or constant) highly stressful situations when the brain is still developing (0–18) which interrupts the maturations of many brain functions and structures.

Diagnosis: the name given to a set of symptoms as an identifier of the nature of an illness or mental condition.

Disorder (mental): patterns of behavioral or psychological symptoms that impact multiple areas of life that create distress and dysfunction. "A syndrome characterized by clinically significant disturbance in an individual's cognition, emotion regulation, or behavior that reflects a dysfunction in the psychological, biological, or developmental processes underlying mental functioning" (DSM-5).

Dissociation: an umbrella term to refer to the disconnection, disengagement, and/or lack of continuity between thoughts, memories, surroundings, actions, time, and identity.

Distorted (perception or cognition): the twists or alterations of what's true or natural.

Dysregulation: a range of responses (emotional) that are poorly modulated and do not lie within a desirable scope of emotive responses, defined by the loss of internal equilibrium.

Emotional wound: a psychological pain left by a hurtful experience.

Emotionality: the experience of high levels of physiological changes prompted by learned and scripted mental states that propel conditioned actions.

Event (incident): an important and significant occurrence.

Fawn: a preventive mechanism that finds ways to get rid of the threat by not presenting as threatening.

Freeze: a preventive mechanism that puts the activation of fight/flight on hold until it assesses the level of risk and decides the best action.

Habitual: activation that repeats itself until it becomes a program that starts without volition or awareness.

Healing agent: a process that contains the capacity to reverse the alterations suffered by traumatization.

Homeostasis: the tendency of the human system toward a relatively stable equilibrium, especially as maintained by physiological processes.

Hyper-activation: the activation of certain structures or processes far above their regular levels.

Hyper-arousal: higher than normal activation of the sympathetic nervous system that puts the person in a state of increased responsiveness to stimuli marked by various physiological and psychological symptoms (e.g., increased levels of alertness, and elevated heart rate and respiration).

Hypo-activation: the activation of certain processes far below their regular levels.

Hypo-arousal: higher than normal activation of the parasympathetic nervous system that sets the system to be in a state of decreased responsiveness to stimuli marked by various physiological and psychological symptoms (e.g., decreased levels of awareness, physical and emotional numbness, and low heart rate and respiration).

Immobilization: a response to sudden stimuli associated with a predator or fear-conditioning as a learned response to an aversively conditioned signal where the vitals go down to a minimum.

Intergenerational trauma: the assumption that traumatization symptoms and/or alterations can be transmitted to descendants.

Lock: a survival strategy that keeps the person in a state of indecisiveness, expecting the worst, incapable of making emotional decisions, or rejecting/doubting the positives offered by others (or by life).

Mobilization: used to refer to the protective mechanisms that try to eliminate danger or threat by mobilizing (mainly by activating fight/flight).

Myelination: the process by which layers of myelin wrap around the neuronal axons and act as a layer of insulation for the transmission of electric action potentials down the neuronal axon.

Myeline: an insulating layer or sheath that forms around nerves, including those in the brain and spinal cord.

Narrative: the stories that individuals repeat constantly about their lives whether they are true/objective or only based on schemas learned from someone else or past experiences even if they no longer apply.

Natural: existing in or caused by nature as opposed to being forced by volition or decision.

Objectification: the action of degrading someone to the status of a mere object.

Pathological: involving, caused by, or of the nature of a physical or mental disease that creates dysfunction and distress.

Perception: the process of becoming aware of something through the senses.

Peritraumatic: all the responses of the ANS that occur from the moment the person is exposed to a threat to the moment the threat is gone, and before the alterations suffered become permanent.

Phenomena: "a fundamental psychological process that has theoretically-deduced antecedents and consequences and thereby helps explain human cognitions, feelings, and behaviors" (Seppo E Iso-Ahola).

Pop psychology: 'pop' comes from 'popular' and refers in psychology to the theories about mental health and behavior that are developed by popular beliefs without much foundation in science or research but that are assumed as valid.

Posttraumatic: the activity of the ANS if the person's survival mechanisms stay active and the system fails to go back to baseline after experiencing a traumatic event that is not threatening anymore.

Preventive mechanisms: hardwired mechanisms that become activated to prevent the activation of more drastic mechanisms.

Primitive: used to refer to more basic functions or processes as opposed to evolved ones. In terms of survival, primitive needs are the basic ones that humans share with all species.

Protective mechanisms: the more drastic hardwired mechanisms that get activated when threat is imminent.

Protective strategies: the habits acquired by the traumatized person to survive their circumstances.

Psychological trauma: the range of clearly differentiated observable components of suffering emotionally after experiencing an event or circumstance that causes the person to doubt their capacity to continue living as before.

Quiescent immobility: a state or period of inactivity or dormancy necessary for the system to recover some of the exhaustion experienced during the struggle for survival.

Retraumatization: the reactivation of the processes that were activated during the original traumatic experience that contributed to staying in survival mode as the default functionality. When the same fears get reactivated, it reinforces the danger that the particular event or situation presents, increasing the fear and the defeating assumptions that kept the person traumatized.

Schema: a pattern of thought or behavior that organizes categories of information and the relationships among them with the particularity of having them as assumptions that hardly change since they are rarely revised. They are assumed as certain even without logic.

Scripts (emotional): a sequence of expected behaviors or reactions connected to a given emotion acquired by personal experiences or information given by others, and accepted as real and undebatable.

Shock: an immediate response in the form of a surge of adrenaline and stress hormones after encountering a situation that seems surprising, unexpected, too much, and/or unsurmountable.

Social engagement: part of a system including a face–heart connection that enables social interactions to regulate visceral states.

Somatic: relating to the body, especially as distinct from the mind.

Survival circuits: the set of hardwired neural pathways designed to detect, respond, and thrive when confronting challenges and life-threatening situations.

Survival mechanisms: the hardwired processes designed to guarantee the survival of the species. They activate the survival circuits.

Survival mode: the altered and maladaptive way of operating automatically (using the survival circuits) and constantly after reaching a point of defeat and hopelessness in the face of adversity or assumed danger.

Survival strategies: the way the survival mechanisms are used after a trauma disorder develops regardless of confronting risk or not.

Symptom: a physical or mental manifestation that indicates that something is not working as it should, and therefore, connected to a condition of disease (present or in development).

Synapsis: the site of transmission of electric nerve impulses between two nerve cells.

Synaptic pruning: the deactivation of neurons or circuits that were not active enough during the first few years of life; they get considered useless and are eliminated to allocate more energy to those that are in use.

Syndrome: a group of symptoms that consistently occur together, or a condition characterized by a set of associated symptoms.

Systemic: relating to a system, especially as opposed to a specific and individual part; parts of a system work with each other and affect each other's functions.

Threat: a person, situation, or action likely to cause damage or inflict pain.

Tonic immobility: in humans, it's the immediate state the body falls into when the parasympathetic gets activated in an extreme way.

Trauma: refers to the effects of the activation of the innate survival circuits designed to protect the individual from the possibility of dying after a severe reaction to a threatening occurrence.

Trauma as a mental disorder: PTSD, C-PTSD, DTD, or other trauma syndromes.

Trauma as a reaction: the physiological changes that occur (and can be felt) when the survival mechanisms are activated after encountering a traumatic event.

Trauma as a response: the response of the system when confronting a threat (real or assumed), the activation of the survival mechanisms.

Trauma as an emotional wound: a prolonged hurt that causes the person to feel at risk.

Trauma as an experience: feeling terrified, overwhelmed, defeated, lost, and at risk while (or after) confronting a situation that jeopardizes the life or integrity of the individual.

Trauma as emotional distress: the set of emotional responses and emotionality the person experiences while (or after) confronting a situation that jeopardizes the life or integrity of the individual.

Trauma bonding: a psychological dependency that occurs to abused people and justifies the maltreatment by giving importance to the bond.

Trauma centrality: the role that traumatization plays in the narrative of the individual, their life, their reactions, and the sense of who they are.

Trauma disorder: the condition of living in survival mode as default after having failed to resolve traumatization, characterized by a set of symptoms according to the type of traumatic event(s), when in life they occur, and whether there were intergenerationally transmitted alterations.

Trauma domain: a specific set of processes affected by traumatization that relate to part of our mind/brain system.

Trauma lens: a perspective on how behavior is connected to neurobiology.

Trauma modality: a set of interventions with a specific approach for facing the symptoms of a trauma disorder.

Trauma phenomena: the set of theories, thesis, assumptions, studies, and interventions related to the activation of the innate survival circuits designed to protect the individual from the possibility of dying after a severe reaction to a threatening event.

Trauma studies: theories—and the research that tries to find their validity—referring to the trauma phenomena.

Trauma symptom: a manifestation of the alterations suffered after activating the survival mechanisms that didn't reverse to their original state.

Trauma therapist: a clinician that specializes in neurobiology and its effect on a person's psychology and who applies interventions to help the system go back to baseline and the person return to a functional life.

Trauma treatment: the set of interventions focused on healing trauma symptoms and resolving traumatization.

Traumatic: an event or action with the potential to jeopardize the person's life or physical/mental/relational integrity.

Traumatic memories: memories related to a traumatic event or circumstance that normally carry a loaded/charged emotional response and a negative valence.

Traumatic stress: the state of mental or emotional strain or tension resulting from adverse, demanding, and threatening circumstances.

Traumatization: the dreadful period where the individual's system tries to overcome risk or adversity to safeguard their continuous operation. Also referred to as "The struggle for survival."

Traumatized: a person that suffers from trauma disorder. The condition where the ANS shifts to operating under a new program, a maladaptive one, that keeps the body anticipating danger in a very subjective way, malfunctioning, with a lack of internal equilibrium, and focused on survival.

Traumatizing: the relationship with something traumatic when the person considers that it can kill or injure them.

Traumatizing agent: elements that induce, prolong, or exacerbate traumatization.

Umbrella term: a term used to cover a broad category of things rather than a single specific item/concept.

Valence: the intrinsic attractiveness/"good"-ness or averseness/"bad"-ness of an event, object, or situation. The 'amount' of that experience that is stored in the brain as an indicator of the importance of that emotional experience.

Index

Note: **Bold** page numbers refer to tables and *italic* page numbers refer to figures.

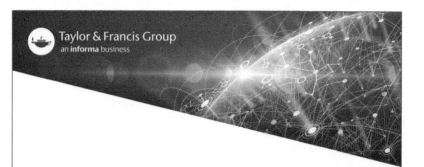